ASTROPHYSICAL DISKS

ANNALS OF THE NEW YORK ACADEMY OF SCIENCES
Volume 675

ASTROPHYSICAL DISKS

Edited by S. F. Dermott, J. H. Hunter, Jr., and R. E. Wilson

The New York Academy of Sciences
New York, New York
1992

Library of Congress Cataloging-in-Publication Data

Astrophysical disks / edited by S.F. Dermott, J.H. Hunter, Jr., and
R.E. Wilson.
    p. cm.
    Includes bibliographical references and index.
    ISBN 0-89766-739-5 (cloth).—ISBN 0-89766-740-9 (pbk.)
    1. Disks (Astrophysics)—Congresses. 2. Astronomy—Congresses.
3. Nonlinear theories—Congresses. I. Dermott, S. F. II. Hunter,
J. H. (James H.) III. Wilson, R. E. (Robert E.), 1937–
QB466.D58A78 1992
523.01—dc20   92-44412
                                           CIP

SP
Printed in the United States of America
ISBN 0-89766-739-5 (cloth)
ISBN 0-89766-740-9 (paper)
ISSN 0077-8923

ANNALS OF THE NEW YORK ACADEMY OF SCIENCES

Volume 675
December 28, 1992

ASTROPHYSICAL DISKS[a]

Editors
S. F. DERMOTT, J. H. HUNTER, JR., and R. E. WILSON

Conference Organizers
G. CONTOPOULOS, S. F. DERMOTT, J. H. HUNTER, JR., R. E. WILSON

CONTENTS

[a] The papers in this volume were presented at the Seventh Florida Workshop in Nonlinear Astronomy, entitled Astrophysical Disks, which was held on September 26–28, 1991, in Gainesville, Florida.

Financial assistance was received from:
- COLLEGE OF LIBERAL ARTS & SCIENCES, UNIVERSITY OF FLORIDA
- DIVISION OF SPONSORED RESEARCH, UNIVERSITY OF FLORIDA

Preface

S. F. DERMOTT, J. H. HUNTER, JR., AND R. E. WILSON

Department of Astronomy
University of Florida
Gainesville, Florida 32611

The Seventh Florida Workshop on Nonlinear Astronomy was held on September 26–28, 1991, in the Reitz Union building of the University of Florida. The participants had been chosen to reflect the variety of work in the field of astrophysical disks, rather than for intensive coverage of a few classes of models or observed objects. A central objective of the organizers was to have a forum in which workers in effectively disjoint areas would be stimulated by ideas and problems outside their usual experience, on which they might take an interest and make important later contributions. Topics included equilibrium gaseous disk models, dynamical gaseous models, stellar dynamics (including bars and bulges), various types of instabilities, viscosity mechanisms, magnetic effects, self-gravity, disks around black holes, disks in mass-transferring binary stars, planetary rings and other solar system structures, disk oscillations, jets and winds, spiral structure, the understanding of chaos, and observations of several kinds of disks and related objects. The sessions indeed gave the impression of strong interest across lines of previously separate modeling, and recognition of areas that now are the provinces of only a few persons, but deserve attention by many. The workshop was brightened by excellent contributions from a number of graduate students and postdocs, and the future of the field seems in capable hands.

All of this was made possible by the vision and stimulus of George Contopoulos, following in the line of annual nonlinear astronomy workshops that he organized in the mid-1980s. Willard W. Harrison, Dean of the College of Liberal Arts and Sciences, made the meeting possible by providing financial and other resources. Astronomy Department Secretary Debra A. Hunter, working beyond the call of duty, made everything flow smoothly.

NOTE: Other Florida workshops in Nonlinear Astronomy have been published by the New York Academy of Sciences. These include:

1. BUCHLER, J. R. & H. EICHHORN, Eds. 1987. Chaotic Phenomena in Astrophysics. N. Y. Acad. Sci. **497**.
2. BUCHLER, J. R., J. R. IPSER & C. A. WILLIAMS, Eds. 1988. Integrability in Dynamical Systems. N. Y. Acad. Sci. **536**.
3. BUCHLER, J. R. & S. T. GOTTESMAN, Eds. 1989. Galactic Models. N. Y. Acad. Sci. **596**.
4. BUCHLER, J. R. & S. T. GOTTESMAN, Eds. 1990. Nonlinear Astrophysical Fluid Dynamics. N. Y. Acad. Sci. **617**.
5. BUCHLER, J. R., S. L. DETWEILER & J. R. IPSER. 1991. Nonlinear Problems in Relativity and Cosmology. N. Y. Acad. Sci. **631**.

Tidal Accretion Disk Instabilities

STEPHEN H. LUBOW[a]

Space Telescope Institute
3700 San Martin Drive
Baltimore, Maryland 21218

INTRODUCTION

Accretion disks in close binary star systems exhibit a range of behavior that can be understood in terms of the action of instabilities. The basic accretion process by which disk fluid elements must lose angular momentum is usually explained in terms of an instability that is often thought to be magnetic in origin.[1,2] However, accretion disk instabilities have been very difficult to obtain theoretically and understand in any level of detail. The purpose of this paper is to describe a class of disk instabilities that is purely gas dynamic and is due to the tidal field of the companion. Such instabilities are not responsible for the basic accretion process, but may instead explain other phenomena.

Dwarf nova systems provide an excellent laboratory for understanding the physics of accretion disks. They have been extensively analyzed over the past several decades.[3] Such systems consist of a white dwarf star surrounded by an accretion disk that is fed by a low mass companion. Binary orbital periods of these systems are usually a few hours. Every few months these systems brighten suddenly by 2 to 5 magnitudes. They remain bright for a few days before settling back to their quiescent state. This event has been interpreted as an accretion disk instability in which the outburst radiation is due to the loss of mechanical energy in the disk as the material suddenly accretes.[4,5]

For some dwarf novae, there are occasional outbursts that occur with enhanced brightening—the so-called *superoutbursts*.[6-8] Superoutbursts are about one-half magnitude brighter than the usual outbursts. The brightened state lasts for a few weeks rather than days. In addition, these systems exhibit the particularly interesting phenomenon of superhumps.

Light curves of dwarf novae in quiescence often show a peaked feature, called a (normal) *hump*. The origin of this feature is well-understood.[9,10] As the low mass companion star supplies matter to the accretion disk through a gas stream, the stream impacts the disk with high velocity. The resulting radiation from this hypersonic impact produces the hump in the light curve at about the appropriate phase expected for stream–disk impact. The hump phase is locked with the period of the binary.

A *superhump* is similarly a broad peak in the light curve, but one that accompanies superoutbursts. Like the normal hump, one superhump appears in the light curve per binary orbital period. The most puzzling feature of superhumps is that they are not locked in phase with the period of the binary. Instead, they drift in phase so that their period is a few percent longer than the binary period.

[a] Current address: Institute of Astronomy, Madingley Road, Cambridge CB3 OHA, England.

1

Optical lines are often associated with the cooler, outer portions of an accretion disk. During superoutburst, such lines have been found observationally to be associated with material that undergoes noncircular motions about the white dwarf.[11,12] Of importance is that these lines are found to be phased with the superhump period, rather than the period of the binary.

Such observational results led Vogt to consider a model in which the superhumps are produced in a disk or ring of material that is eccentric and slowly precessing.[11] A slowly precessing disk can give rise to the slightly different period associated with the superhump, if one envisions the superhump as being due to a beat phenomenon of the precession with the binary orbital motion.

The major dynamical question is how such a disk can generate an eccentricity. Eccentric motions carry an excess of energy above that required for a circular orbit of the same angular momentum. Dissipational effects within the disk can be expected eventually to cause the eccentricity to decay. Simulations by Whitehurst and others indicated that a disk eccentricity growth appears to occur.[13,14] Furthermore, this growth might be associated with the 3:1 resonance, where disk matter orbits the white dwarf at three times the angular speed of the binary. Accretion disks in close binaries are generally subject to powerful tidal forces near this resonance and further out. These tidal forces can prevent disk material from ever reaching the 3:1 resonance, making eccentricity excitation there impossible. Such inhibitory effects weaken for smaller mass ratios q, defined as the mass-losing star's mass divided by the white dwarf mass. For mass ratios greater than about 0.25, periodic orbits of ballistic particles, representing disk fluid elements, intersect at smaller radii than where the 3:1 resonance occurs.[15] At such intersections a fluid disk would be strongly tidally detorqued and the region would become clear of material.[16] Therefore, an accretion disk cannot easily reach the 3:1 resonance unless the binary mass ratio is fairly extreme, less than about 0.25. Mass ratios of superhump binaries are difficult to determine observationally. Nonetheless, superhump binaries do tend to have more extreme mass ratios.[13]

ECCENTRIC INSTABILITY MECHANISMS

An analysis of the stability of periodic ballistic orbits to infinitesimal perturbations reveals that the 3:1 resonance is the innermost location at which unstable orbits can occur.[15] A small perturbation of a particle's orbit from its exactly periodic state grows exponentially in time. The particles behave chaotically and amplify noise in the disk. The $m = 3$ component of the tidal potential ϕ_3 is responsible for this resonant effect.[14] The growth rate of order $\sim q\Omega_p$ for binary mass ratio q and orbital angular speed Ω_p. Although their motion is somewhat restricted by phase space by Jacobi's theorem, these particles scatter widely in radius, clearing a circular gap about the resonance.[17] The gap size scales linearly with the binary mass ratio.

However, in a true fluid the preceding process cannot occur because these particles, which represent fluid elements, cannot cross each other. Instead, the resonant response causes stresses to be exerted in the fluid. As will be described, these stresses cause wave propagation in the disk that produces important effects. To understand such processes, we have analyzed the stability of a fluid accretion disk that in general has pressure and some viscosity.[17] The basic outline of the calculation is given here. The goal is not only to determine the growth rate, but to understand this process as an instability cycle.

To carry out such an analysis, one must first define an equilibrium disk. The equilibrium consists of tidally distorted streamlines that are spatially periodic and stationary in the frame of the binary. To understand the resonant effects at the 3:1 resonance, one need only consider the tidal effects of ϕ_3, the $m = 3$ component of the companion's potential. The equilibrium state can be represented with sufficient accuracy by analytic formulas for the tidally distorted disks. The equilibrium state is then perturbed by imposing a very small eccentricity, formally small in a dimensionless sense compared with the tidal potential. We then determine whether this perturbation will grow in time.

The perturbational equations contain many terms. To make analytic progress one must expand these perturbational equations in powers of the $m = 3$ component of the tidal field, ϕ_3. In essence, the flow variables are expanded in two small parameters: the eccentricity e and the tidal potential ϕ_3. To each order in this double expansion, one obtains an equation that can be solved analytically:

1. To order $e^1\phi_3^0$, we have time-stationary eccentric streamlines in the inertial frame whose flow angular properties vary as $\cos(\theta)$ (or sin).
2. To order $e^0\phi_3^1$, we have a tidally distorted disk with dependences that vary in angle and time as $\cos(3(\theta - \Omega_p t))$ (or sin) for binary orbital angular frequency Ω_p.
3. To order $e^1\phi_3^1$, driving terms are due to products of flow variables that arise in steps 1 and 2. They then have angle and time dependence that contains terms $\cos(2(\theta - 3\Omega_p t))$ (and sin). Tightly wrapped, trailing, acoustic waves are launched at the 3:1 resonance. These waves propagate toward the disk center.
4. To order $e^1\phi_3^2$, driving terms are due to products of flow variables that arise in steps 2 and 3. These driving terms contain contributions that vary then as $\cos(\theta)$. These terms result in a resonant fluid stress that acts to strengthen the initial eccentric perturbation of step 1. This completes the instability cycle (see FIG. 1).

The eccentricity growth rate λ for a narrow fluid ring is then found to vary as $\lambda = Aq^2\Omega_p/dr$, where constant $A \sim 2.0$, q is the binary mass ratio, and dr is the radial extent of the ring. For a broad ring or disk dr is determined by the extent of radial propagation of the wave where eccentricity is excited. This "ideal" growth rate does not depend upon details such as the gas sound speed or viscosity. However, for a broad disk there may be some dependence on these quantities if they modify the size of the region of space dr where the eccentricity is excited. In time, the eccentricity in a broad disk will propagate radially toward the disk center. Also, the disk accretion itself may cause a slow radial propagation of eccentricity. Such details are not yet well understood.

Independent of these complications, this mode-coupling model makes some definite predictions about the progress of this instability. Both the eccentricity and wave amplitude are time-growing quantities in this model. By step 3, we predict that

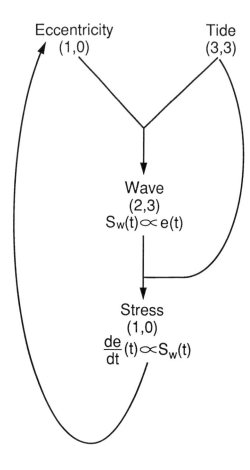

FIGURE 1. The instability cycle for eccentricity growth at the 3:1 resonance. A disturbance with periodicity $k\theta - l\Omega_p t$ is denoted by (k, l).

the wave and eccentricity should grow in proportion to each other, since the eccentricity serves as a driving term to launch the wave. That is, we predict

$$S_w(t) \propto e(t), \tag{1}$$

where S_w is a suitable measure of the strength of the resonantly excited wave. (The wave strength of a mode is defined as the radial average of the angle and time Fourier transform of the disk density in that mode.) From step 4 we predict that

$$\frac{de}{dt}(t) \propto S_w(t), \tag{2}$$

since the wave provides a stress that then causes the eccentricity changes in time. Taken together, (1) and (2) imply an exponential growth rate for both the wave and eccentricity. Since the angle and time-periodic dependences of the wave (and eccentricity) are known, Fourier methods allow a numerical test of (1) and (2) in disk simulations. Smooth particle hydrodynamic (SPH) simulations reveal a good agreement with the predictions of this mode-coupling model.[18]

The simulations show that initially both (1) and (2) hold as the eccentricity and wave grow exponentially in time (see FIG. 2). A strong resonant torque is exterted at the 3:1 resonance, which can tidally truncate the eccentric disk. At a certain point, (1) breaks down due to wave nonlinearities, while (2) continues to hold for a long time (see FIG. 3). In this stage of growth, the eccentricity increase is slower than exponential in time.

A special role is played by the elliptical motion in the near-Keplerian potential experienced by the disk. Free, eccentric motions can persist over many orbital periods in an accretion disk. These motions, which are excited near resonance, propagate very slowly in a Keplerian potential. They remain localized near the resonance, where they can act to generate an even stronger wave.

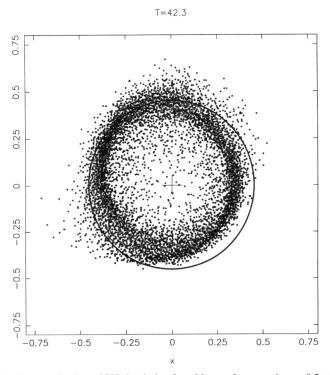

FIGURE 2. Gas annulus in an SPH simulation for a binary of mass ratio $q = 0.2$ with pure ϕ_3 tidal potential. The white dwarf primary star is centered at $x = 0, y = 0$; the low mass secondary companion is at $x = -1, y = 0$. The positions of particles in the annulus are marked by *dots*. The *circle* locates the 3:1 resonance. The simulation began with a noneccentric annulus and is shown after about seven binary orbit periods. The two-armed, trailing, inwardly propagating acoustic wave, as predicted by step 3 of the mode-coupling model, is evident, as is the eccentricity.

m=3 q=0.2

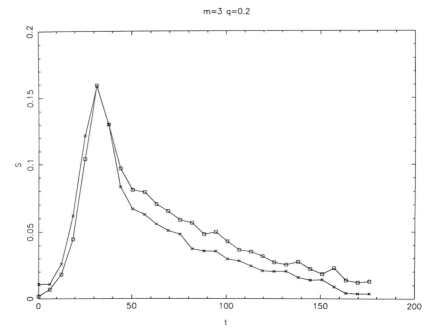

FIGURE 3. Mode strengths as a function of time in an SPH simulation for a system with $q = 0.2$. The unit of time is such that 2π corresponds to a binary orbit period. The *curve with the unfilled boxes* indicates $S_w(t)$, the wave strength of the launched acoustic wave. The *curve with the Xs* marks the numerical time derivative of the eccentricity wave strength, proportional to de/dt. Step 4 of the mode-coupling model predicts that the two curves should track each other [see (2)]. The peak marks the time at which the waves shock and nonexponential growth begins.

ORBIT CROSSINGS AND PRECESSION

The model just described is based on the perturbing effects of the $m = 3$ component of the companion's potential, ϕ_3 alone. However, the other components of the tidal potential, particularly ϕ_2, give rise to additional, nonresonant effects. The main effect is that of the orbit crossings previously described. To test the effects of orbit crossings, we have compared the results of SPH simulations in several cases. In FIGURE 4 we show the growth of the eccentric instability for a binary mass ratio of 0.1 using an SPH code with a relatively small disk viscosity $\alpha \sim 0.1$. All cases begin with the same initial state that has a small initial eccentric perturbation. As seen from the figure, case C with the full potential evolves considerably more slowly than case A, which has only ϕ_3. Furthermore, case B with tidal potential $\phi_2 + \phi_3$ evolves almost identically to the full potential model, case C. In case D, we used $2\phi_2 + \phi_3$, and find that the eccentricity decays. The vigorous, "ideal" case A cannot be realized in practice by a low viscosity disk, although the instability still proceeds. Other effects, such as an enhanced gas stream mass flux[19] or an enhanced viscosity in the outer disk[20] may allow more material to penetrate into the resonant region and approach case A. Such effects may be expected to occur naturally at superoutburst.

The most directly measurable feature of the eccentric disk model is its precession. To account for the observations of the superhump period, the disk precession must be prograde by several percent of the binary angular frequency. Some models currently exist to explain the precession.[19,21] We have recently investigated the precession using both analytic methods and SPH modeling. Both techniques indicate that the dominant effect in causing the precession is the modification of the epicyclic motion of the disk by the ϕ_0 component of the companion's potential. Other effects, such as pressure and wave stresses, can also modify the precession rate to a lesser extent. These effects can lead to a slightly changing superhump period as the instability proceeds.

The 3:1 resonance can also effect motions perpendicular to the orbit plane. Free particles at this resonance can also undergo vertical driving out of the plane. Again, these particle orbits can cross, leading to more complicated effects. However, vertical motions are less subject to orbit crossings than the horizontal motions.[22] These motions could in principle also cause some interesting effects and should be investigated further.

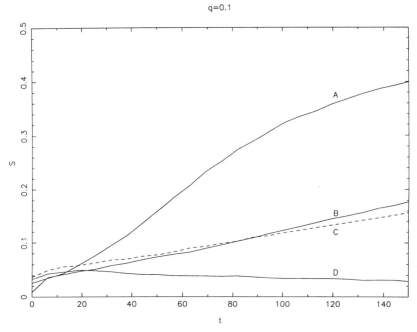

FIGURE 4. Eccentricity mode strengths as a function of time in SPH simulations for a binary with $q = 0.1$ in four cases that all begin with the same slightly eccentric disk model. The unit of time is such that 2π corresponds to a binary orbit period. Case A has only the $m = 3$ tidal component of the companion, ϕ_3; case B has tidal potential $\phi_2 + \phi_3$; case C has the full tidal potential of the companion; and case D has tidal potential $2\phi_2 + \phi_3$.

ACKNOWLEDGMENT

I thank J. Pringle for continuing discussions on this problem.

REFERENCES

1. SHAKURA, N. I. & R. A. SUNYAEV. 1973. Astron. Astrophys. **24:** 337.
2. BALBUS, S. A. & J. F. HAWLEY. 1991. Astrophys. J. **376:** 214.
3. EUROPEAN SPACE AGENCY. 1985. Recent Results on Cataclysmic Variables, SP-236.
4. OSAKI, Y. 1974. Publ. Astron. Soc. Japan **26:** 429.
5. PRINGLE, J. E. 1981. Annu. Rev. Astron. Astrophys. **19:** 137.
6. VOGT, N. 1974. Astron. Astrophys. **36:** 369.
7. WARNER, B. 1975. Mon. Not. R. Astron. Soc. **170:** 219.
8. ———. 1983. *In* Interacting Binaries, P. P. Eggleton and J. E. Pringle, Eds.: 367. NATO ASI Series.
9. SMAK, J. 1985. Acta Astron. **35:** 351.
10. HORNE, K. 1991. *In* Structure and Emission Properties of Accretion Disks, Bertout *et al.,* Eds.: 3. Editions Frontieres.
11. VOGT, N. 1982. Astrophys. J. **252:** 653.
12. HONEY, W. B., P. A. CHARLES, R. WHITEHURST, P. E. BARRETT & A. P. SMALE. 1988. Mon. Not. R. Astron. Soc. **231:** 1.
13. WHITEHURST, R. 1988. Mon. Not. R. Astron. Soc. **232:** 35.
14. HIROSE, M. & Y. OSAKI. 1990. Publ. Astron. Soc. Japan. **42:** 135.
15. PACZYNSKI, B. 1977. Astrophys. J. **216:** 822.
16. PAPALOIZOU, J. C. B. & J. E. PRINGLE. 1977. Mon. Not. R. Astron. Soc. **189:** 293.
17. LUBOW, S. H. 1991. Astrophys. J. **381:** 259.
18. ———. 1991. Astrophys. J. **381:** 268.
19. WHITEHURST, R. & A. R. KING. 1991. Mon. Not. R. Astron. Soc. **249:** 25.
20. OSAKI, Y. 1989. *In* Theory of Accretion Disks, F. Meyer *et al.,* Eds.: 183. Kluwer. Dordrect, the Netherlands.
21. ———. 1985. Astron. Astrophys. **144:** 369.
22. PACZYNSKI, B. Private communication.

Anomalous Viscosity in Accretion Disks[a]

JOHN F. HAWLEY AND STEVEN A. BALBUS

Virginia Institute for Theoretical Astronomy
Department of Astronomy
University of Virginia
P.O. Box 3818
Charlottesville, Virginia 22903

INTRODUCTION

The process of gravitationally accreting gas onto compact stars and black holes is the most likely mechanism for powering energetic systems on scales from X-ray binaries to active galactic nuclei. The infalling gas in general will have some angular momentum and will be drawn into a disk. As the gas drifts through the disk and down onto the central mass, it releases gravitational binding energy. This energy goes into heat, radiated at the disk surface. Such accretion disks have become, over the past few decades, one of the most intensively studied phenomena of high-energy astrophysics. However, despite this effort, there has been no clear answer to the central issue of accretion disk theory: How does the fluid shed its angular momentum and accrete onto the central object?

What exactly is the physical mechanism behind the dynamics of angular momentum transport? This has been a notoriously contentious issue, but one that is clearly central to an understanding of the accretion process. Because the normal collisional and radiative viscosities are woefully tiny, an oft-made assumption is that an anomalously high viscosity is generally and inevitably present in disks. What is the source of this anomalous viscosity? We can list some of its desired properties. The huge range in size and luminosity in disk accretion systems argues for a very generic mechanism. A viscosity that depends on some particular thermodynamic state of the gas or on a particular gravitational field could work in a particular type of disk, for example, quasar disks, or disks in white dwarf binaries, but some other mechanism would be required for other systems. Indeed, since disk properties vary significantly with radius, one might need several different viscous processes operating in a single disk. To be generic, the anomalous viscosity should depend primarily upon the universal property of all accretion disks, namely the shear flow, and less upon the thermodynamic state of the gas.

A plausible and suitably generic mechanism is turbulence in the disk which, if present, can produce significant angular momentum transport. This mechanism was formalized within an accretion disk model by Shakura and Sunyaev[1] who noted that one can, on dimensional grounds, construct a turbulent viscosity ν of the form $\nu = \alpha c_s H$, where c_s is the sound speed, H is the disk scale-height, and α is a parameter. Any sort of turbulence, including magnetic turbulence, can be incorporated into this

[a] This work is partially supported by National Science Foundation Grants PHY-9018251 and AST-9021348, and NASA Grants NAGW-1510 and NAGW-2376. Computations were carried out on the Cray YMP system of the National Center for Supercomputing Applications.

"α-disk" formalism.[1] For practical reasons, α is often assumed to be a constant or a simple function of radius, although there are no physical reasons for such assumptions. The difficulty with the turbulent disk picture is that despite the high Reynolds numbers expected in astrophysical disks, they are locally stable by the classical Rayleigh or Höiland criterion, which requires that angular momentum increase with radius, a condition easily satisfied by a Keplerian disk. Without some linear instability there is no assurance that a disk should be anything but laminar.

One way around the Rayleigh criterion is to look for other instabilities. For example, unstable vertical entropy gradients can develop under a variety of circumstances.[2] These convective instabilities might produce the desired transport by developing into nonaxisymmetric turbulence.[3] But this would be an intrinsically nonlinear process, and it is not clear that significant angular momentum transport *must* result from such an instability. Indeed, the linear analyses that have been done to date are not so encouraging. The difficulty with a convective instability is that it obtains its free energy not from the shear flow but from an unstable entropy gradient. In particular, a careful analysis shows that linear vertical convective instabilities transport angular momentum inward, exactly the opposite of what is desired.[4] In any case, it is far from obvious that convective instabilities are always present in disks. A detailed investigation would probably require three-dimensional numerical simulations.

If axisymmetric hydrodynamic stability prevents the development of turbulence, what alternatives are available to transport angular momentum? One possibility is spiral density waves. Although global spiral waves can in principle carry angular momentum through the disk, there are problems with this as a generic mechanism for anomalous transport. First, the waves would have to traverse considerable radial distances, and this is problematic in a thin accretion disk. Because of the density stratification in such disks, pressure waves are refracted toward the disk surface[5] where they dissipate in shocks. Second, the wave amplitudes must be fairly large if dynamically important amounts of angular momentum are to be transported. Thus, there must be some strong external driving force or an amplification mechanism. Two mechanisms that have been studied are tidal torques[6] and *nonaxisymmetric* instabilities. Tidal torques may well be important in some binary systems, but are certainly not always present. An important global nonaxisymmetric instability was first discussed by Papaloizou and Pringle.[7] Rapidly growing unstable global modes are present in thick, pressure-supported disks with constant, or nearly constant angular momentum distributions. However, the fastest growing of these modes is stable in a thin disk with a Keplerian angular momentum distribution (although there may still be weakly unstable modes). Further, these global modes depend on reflection from the radial boundaries of the disk.[8] Accretion flows can reduce the growth rates or eliminate the linear instability entirely.[9] Numerical simulations of the most promising case, the constant angular momentum torus, demonstrate that while the instability produces spiral waves, accretion flows halt amplification, and the rate of angular momentum transport remains rather low.[10]

These and other difficulties in finding a purely hydrodynamic source of anomalous viscosity have lead researchers to look further afield. There have been many ingenious suggestions for angular momentum transport mechanisms, but they often require specialized conditions or exotic physics, and, as previously remarked, one really wants a mechanism that is omnipresent. Magnetic fields, however, are both ubiquitous and capable of exerting local torques in a fluid. Disk models invoking the direct transport of angular momentum through magnetic stresses have been constructed.[11,12] In addition to their obvious appeal for angular momentum transport, magnetic models have other promising properties. For example, Galeev, Rosner, and Vaiana[13] have argued that the amplification of magnetic fields and the subsequent magnetic buoyancy instability will lead to the production of a hot, magnetized disk corona. Such a corona could account for the hard X-rays observed in compact systems such as Cyg X-1.[13] Blandford[14] has emphasized the ability of a magnetohydrodynamic (MHD) wind to extract angular momentum directly from the disk. Such winds could also lead to collimated jets.

The perceived difficulty with all of these magnetic field models is in the necessity of bringing the field strength up to "dynamically important" levels. Isolated magnetic flux cells present in the disk will be amplified by shear, but shear alone only generates toroidal field from poloidal field. A separate mechanism is needed to complete the field generation process and produce poloidal field from toroidal, and thus has lead to the search for a viable disk dynamo. Magnetic field generation is usually investigated in terms of a *kinematic* dynamo. The starting point for kinematic dynamo models is the assumption that for large values of the plasma β ($= P/[B^2/8\pi]$), that is, weak fields, the dynamical influence of the field is negligible. The magnetic field is amplified through the induction equation by the action of a suitable turbulent velocity field, and the back reaction on the fluid via Lorentz forces is ignored. Magnetic turbulence models that invoke the dynamo amplification of magnetic fields by combining convective motions with differential rotation[13,15] rely upon plausible, but perhaps somewhat *ad hoc* assumptions about the dynamics of disks (again, is convection *always* present?). The problem is that turbulent, nonaxisymmetric fluid motion is required *before* magnetic fields can become important. That, of course, is what originally was to be explained!

The traditional view regarding anomalous viscosity and the role of magnetic fields is summarized by Zeldovich, Ruzmaikin, and Sokoloff in their text *Magnetic Fields in Astrophysics:*[16]

> The transport of angular momentum (i.e., accretion) in the disk is therefore possible only through turbulence and/or magnetic fields. The presence of magnetic fields in the matter flowing out from the visible component is hardly in doubt (every star has a magnetic field), but the presence of turbulence is more questionable. It is known that a medium in nonuniform rotation (Keplerian rotation in our case) in which the angular momentum density increases outward is stable against all small perturbations.

What is particularly noteworthy in this quote is the juxtaposition of the assertion that magnetic fields *must* be present with the statement that the purely hydrodynamic Rayleigh criterion guarantees stability. Such matters need to be examined carefully.

A MAGNETOHYDRODYNAMIC INSTABILITY

To examine the stability of an accretion disk when magnetic fields are present we consider a differentially rotating disk that contains a "negligible" magnetic field, $B^2/8\pi \ll P$. At a given radius R within an accretion disk the vertical scale height H is of order the sound speed c_s divided by the angular velocity Ω. If we consider wavenumbers of order the angular velocity divided by the Alfvén speed, $k \sim \Omega/v_A$, then it is clear that

$$kH \sim \frac{\Omega}{v_A}\frac{c_s}{\Omega} = \frac{c_s}{v_A} \gg 1. \tag{1}$$

Thus the wavenumbers of interest in the weak field limit self-consistently lend themselves to a local analysis. The problem can be further simplified by working in the Boussinesq approximation to eliminate compressive disturbances.

Given these approximations, we consider a disk in a cylindrical coordinate system (R, ϕ, z), with R the perpendicular distance from the z axis. The initial velocity in the disk is given by $v = (0, R\Omega, 0)$. We assume axisymmetry (all terms are independent of the angle ϕ). We carry out the stability analysis by linearizing the full equations of ideal magnetohydrodynamics (MHD), and considering axisymmetric large-wavenumber Eulerian perturbations with space–time dependence $e^{i(K_R R + K_z z - \omega t)}$ to obtain a dispersion relation[17]

$$\frac{k^2}{k_z^2}\tilde{\omega}^4 - \left[\kappa^2 + \left(\frac{k_R}{k_z}N_z - N_R\right)^2\right]\tilde{\omega}^2 - 4\Omega^2(\mathbf{k}\cdot\mathbf{v_A})^2 = 0, \tag{2}$$

where

$$\tilde{\omega}^2 \equiv \omega^2 - (\mathbf{k}\cdot\mathbf{v_A})^2,$$

κ is the epicyclic frequency, and N_R and N_z are pieces of the Brunt–Väisälä frequency. Those readers interested in the intermediate steps should refer to Balbus and Hawley.[17]

A few points about (2) should be made. The equilibrium magnetic field enters only through the combination $\mathbf{k}\cdot\mathbf{v_A}$, and an azimuthal field makes no contribution. The time dependence of a background shearing magnetic field, so long as the field is weak, does not alter the basic exponential behavior of local waves or instabilities. In particular, toroidal fields are capable of neither stabilization nor destabilization. On the other hand, the $\mathbf{k}\cdot\mathbf{v_A}$ dependence shows plainly why weak fields cannot be neglected: they simply set the wavenumber scale for Alfvénic coupling to become important.

As the simplest example, consider an initial vertical field $\mathbf{B} = B_0\hat{z}$. By treating (2) as a quadratic in ω^2, and considering the limit $\omega^2 \to 0$, we obtain the requirement for stability

$$k_z^4 v_A^4 + k_z^2 v_A^2\left(N^2 + \frac{d\Omega^2}{d\ln R}\right) + N_z^2\frac{d\Omega^2}{d\ln R} > 0. \tag{3}$$

If we assume that the disk is buoyantly stable so that the Brunt–Väisälä frequency is real ($N^2 > 0$), then (3) can be satisfied for all wavenumbers only when

$$\frac{d\Omega^2}{dR} \geq 0. \tag{4}$$

There will always be an unstable wavelength so long as $d\Omega^2/dR < 0$. This also holds for more general field geometries, because the most unstable modes have $k_R = 0$ (see below). In other words, a Keplerian disk ($\Omega \sim R^{-3/2}$) is unstable!

While a formal linear analysis gives us general and unambiguous stability requirements, it is helpful to reexamine the instability from a more intuitive point of view. The underlying physical cause of the instability stems from the elastic nature of the magnetic field. The field couples fluid elements at different radii, while allowing joined elements some freedom to evolve independently. For simplicity consider a vertical field that has undergone a radial displacement ξ (FIG. 1). There are two forces that act on the displaced fluid element: magnetic tension and excess centrifugal force. Consider a fluid element displaced radially outward that is connected by a magnetic field line to another fluid element that is displaced radially inward. Since these elements are now at different radial locations, there will be shear between them due to differential rotation. However, the magnetic tension force between the

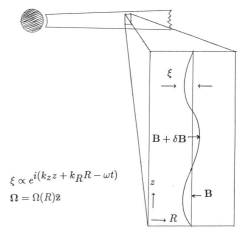

FIGURE 1. Diagram illustrating a local Lagrangian perturbation on a vertical magnetic field line inside an accretion disk.

$$\xi \propto e^{i(k_z z + k_R R - \omega t)}$$

$$\Omega = \Omega(R)\hat{z}$$

two fluid elements resists this shear, mediating a transfer of angular momentum from the inner to the outer fluid element. In the limit $\omega \to 0$ the Lagrangian perturbation of the angular velocity $\Delta\Omega$ must vanish by the law of isorotation (Ferraro's law[18]), or, due to the relative shear along the field line, the magnetic field will obviously not be time-independent. In the field-free limit it is the specific angular momentum perturbation $\Delta(R^2\Omega)$ that vanishes in the zero frequency limit—this is the crucial difference. The magnetic field transfers angular momentum from those fluid elements at smaller radii that are already deficient in this quantity, to well-endowed elements at larger radii. Hence, outwardly displaced elements with excess angular momentum will continue to move outward, and inwardly displaced elements will continue inward. Of course, if the magnetic field is strong enough, the magnetic tension force prevents the fluid elements from separating. Thus, we have a restoring magnetic tension, proportional to $-k_z^2 v_A^2 \xi$, and an excess centrifugal force, $-\xi R d\Omega^2/$

dR. The total force is

$$F = -\xi k_z^2 v_A^2 - \xi \frac{d\Omega^2}{d \ln R},$$ (5)

and stability requires a net restoring force. Hence when $d\Omega^2/d \ln R < 0$ a disk is *always unstable* at some wavelength. At a given wavelength the instability ceases only when the magnetic tension becomes strong enough to overcome the destabilizing excess centrifugal force driving a displaced fluid element. For such a strong field the mode becomes a propagating Alfvén wave.

Although the discussion to this point has centered around perturbations of an initial B_z field, there is nothing special about a particular choice of poloidal field. Since the magnetic field enters the dispersion relation only in conjunction with the wavenumber, we can scale the field strength out of the problem and cast the dispersion relation in a dimensionless form by defining $\tilde{\sigma} \equiv \tilde{\omega}/\Omega$, $\sigma \equiv \omega/\Omega$, $\mathbf{q} \equiv \mathbf{k}|\mathbf{v_A}|/\Omega$, $n \equiv N_z/\Omega$, and $\chi \equiv \kappa/\Omega$. The unstable branch of the dispersion relation has a solution

$$\sigma^2 = (\mathbf{q} \cdot \hat{\mathbf{b}})^2 \left[1 - \frac{8}{\chi^2 + (nq_R/q_z)^2 + \sqrt{(\chi^2 + (nq_R/q_z)^2)^2 + 16(q/q_z)^2(\mathbf{q} \cdot \hat{\mathbf{b}})^2}} \right].$$ (6)

The maximum growth rate occurs when

$$(\mathbf{q} \cdot \hat{\mathbf{b}})^2 = 1 - \frac{\chi^4}{16}$$ (7)

and

$$\frac{q_R}{q_z} = 0.$$

What is particularly remarkable about this dispersion relation is that not only is the maximal growth rate independent of the poloidal field strength, it is also independent of the field *orientation,* and this maximal growth rate is equal to the local Oort *A* constant,

$$|\omega| = A = -(1/2) \, d\Omega/d \ln R.$$ (8)

For a Keplerian disk the Oort *A* value is equal to $3\Omega/4$. Note that this translates to hundredfold amplification ($e^{3\pi/2}$) per 2π orbital radians, and hints at difficulties for kinematic dynamo theories.

We have investigated the generality of the dispersion relation[19] by using the Hill equations[20] to consider the disk dynamics in a rotating frame for an arbitrary local attractive force. The resulting linear dispersion relation has the same form as (2) in the absence of buoyancy terms. This indicates that the maximum growth rate is the largest possible with any local return force, which suggests this growth rate is an upper bound for *any* instability that taps into the free energy of the differential rotation of a rotationally supported accretion disk.[19]

What are the consequences of these results for the origin of anomalous viscosity in accretion disks? First it should be appreciated that angular momentum transfer is more than just a possible nonlinear consequence of this instability; *it is the root cause of the instability.* This is not a gentle transfer process—it is a genuine dynamic instability. The critical unanswered question is not whether this instability has something to do with anomalous transport. Rather, it is how does the instability saturate, and at what amplitude? In the usual disk parlance, what is the value of α? If we use simple dimensional arguments, the effective turbulent viscosity should be the characteristic wavelength of the instability times the Alfvén velocity appropriate for the saturated magnetic field amplitude. Since the characteristic wavelength is $\lambda \sim v_A/\Omega$, this gives us a viscosity $\nu \sim v_A^2/\Omega$. This linear stability limit suggests that the maximum strength a magnetic field can attain in an accretion disk is equal to that field strength for which the minimum unstable wavelength exceeds the disk scale height H. Since in an accretion disk $H \sim c_s/\Omega$, this "strong field limit" corresponds to equipartition between magnetic and thermal energy densities, or $v_A \sim c_s$. However, nonlinear effects might produce turbulent saturation at an average magnetic field strength that is smaller than equipartition. The question is, therefore: What determines the average Alfvén speed in the fully *nonlinear* accretion disk?

NUMERICAL SIMULATIONS

If we wish to understand the detailed consequences of this instability we must progress beyond the linear perturbation analysis: we must solve the complete equations of MHD, and this requires numerical methods. We have carried out an extensive series of numerical MHD simulations in accretion disk shear flows using time-explicit, operator-split finite differencing in "two and a half" dimensions—that is, we assume axisymmetry, but retain angular velocity terms. The magnetic induction equation is solved via the method of characteristic constrained transport (MOC-CT).[21,22] This technique is designed to maintain the constraint $\nabla \cdot B = 0$ while evolving Alfvén waves along characteristics. The technique has been tested on a variety of problems.[23]

Our first numerical study considered the simplified case of an isolated region of pure B_z magnetic field buried deep within an Keplerian accretion disk.[24] To simplify the problem, the initial density and pressure were constant and the boundary conditions were periodic on z and reflecting in R. The results demonstrate that the numerical simulations can reproduce the linear growth rates, and that the instability transfers considerable angular momentum. However, reflecting radial boundary conditions limit the length of time for which the simulations can be evolved. Longer and more realistic simulations are required to address the key questions of how the instability functions in a realistic accretion disk.

While we would ultimately like to carry out a full global simulation of an accretion disk, we proceed here along a more conservative course by extending the simulations of a local region in a disk through the use of periodic boundary conditions in *both* the vertical and radial directions. To be self-consistent, the computational system must be sufficiently local so that radial geometry terms in the MHD equations can be ignored. This is most easily done by considering the disk dynamics in a local corotating frame using the magnetized versions of the Hill[20] equations written in the pseudo-Cartesian coordinates $x = R - R_0, y = R_0(\phi - \Omega_0 t)$, and z. Here we will use only a two-dimensional (x, z) cross section. The Hill system is often used in the study of collisionless systems such as stellar disks.[25] In the frame corotating with the center of the grid (R_0), a Keplerian shear flow is given by $v_y = -\frac{3}{2}\Omega_0 x$. To implement the boundary conditions, we adjust the angular velocity of a fluid element, leaving one radial boundary by the difference in the Keplerian value across the grid as it is reintroduced at the other radial boundary. The dimensions of the computational box are small compared to the disk dimensions, and we ignore vertical gravitational acceleration. The density and pressure are assumed constant and chosen so that the sound speed is much less than the angular velocity $(R\Omega)_0$. This is consistent with the local approximation.

Although there are many questions a local shearing sheet system cannot address, we can nevertheless start to understand saturation mechanisms and the role the initial field geometry plays, as well as investigate purely numerical effects due to finite resolution. To these ends we have carried out a large number of simulations with various initial conditions and with grids of 64^2, 128^2, and 256^2 zones.

The first set of simulations is a straightforward extension of the earlier numerical work. The initial condition consists of a uniform B_z field onto which are added random perturbations in enthalpy at the grid-zone scale. Several initial field strengths were tried, specified by initial magnetic field energies $\beta = 1000$, 4000, and 16,000. These three simulations were evolved for five orbital periods. During the first two orbits the perturbations are small and their growth rates can be directly compared to the analytic growth rates obtained from the dispersion relation [(2)] with the Brunt–Väisälä frequency equal to zero and the epicyclic frequency set equal to its Keplerian value, Ω. The agreement between the numerical and analytic growth rates is better than one percent for the unstable wavelengths in the higher resolution simulations. The angular momentum perturbations near the end of the linear growth phase (2.5 orbits) are shown in FIGURE 2 for the three initial magnetic field energies. This comparison demonstrates that as the field strength is reduced (in this case successively by a factor of 2), the wavelength associated with the fastest growing mode is also reduced.

After the linear growth phase (at time $t = 3$ orbits) the fluid begins to move radially in response to the perturbations; fluid elements with excess angular momentum move out, those with too little angular momentum move in. Numerical field line reconnection produces mergers between fluid elements with the same sign of toroidal current; here this also means fluid elements with the same sign of angular momentum perturbation resulting in evolution toward larger length scales. What is remarkable about these initially uniform B_z models is that the final state of each simulation is the same regardless of the initial field strength. In all simulations we are left with two flow channels separated in z, one with sub-Keplerian angular momentum flowing in, the other with super-Keplerian angular momentum flowing out. FIGURE 3 shows the magnetic field lines and velocity vectors at the end of the $\beta = 4000$ simulation.

An examination of the integrated poloidal magnetic energy density versus time for these three models reveals a surprising fact: exponential field amplification occurs not only during the linear phase, but also throughout the nonlinear phase as well. The reason is that in the shearing sheet geometry there is no distinction between the linear and the exact nonlinear solutions. This was first noted in the hydrodynamic context by Goldreich and Lynden-Bell.[26] J. Goodman[27] has pointed out that the addition of the MHD terms and a vertical magnetic field to the incompressible shearing sheet equations does not alter this conclusion. The nonlin-

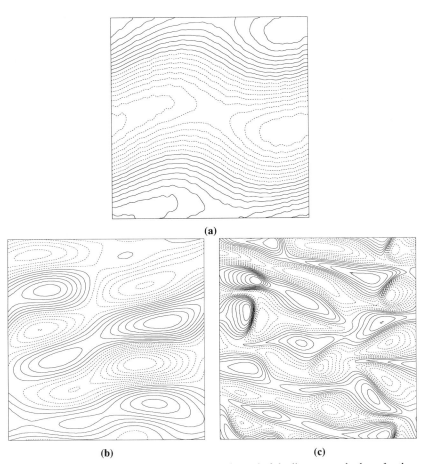

(a)

(b)   **(c)**

FIGURE 2. Angular momentum perturbations at the end of the linear growth phase for three different initial constant B_z magnetic field strengths. The three plots correspond to initial field energies (a) $\beta = 1000$, (b) $\beta = 4000$, and (c) $\beta = 16,000$. As the background field strength is reduced, the wavelength of the fastest growing mode is similarly reduced.

ear solution has the same form as the linear, with $v_z = 0$ and $B_z =$ constant, and all other variables proportional to $e^{i(k_z z - \omega t)}$. The numerical simulations evolve to this exponentially growing solution with k_z set by the periodicity length of the numerical grid.

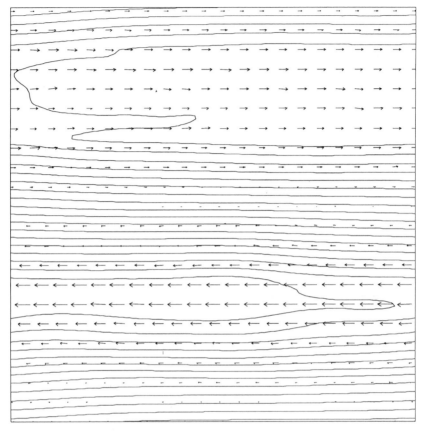

FIGURE 3. Velocity vectors (*arrows*) and magnetic field lines at 4.4 orbits in a simulation with an initial constant background B_z field. The velocities are nearly radial and have a maximum value of $0.56R\Omega$. The system has evolved into two channels, one with positive and one with negative angular momentum perturbations, flowing outward to the right and inward to the left, respectively.

As mentioned, reconnection plays a role in driving the solution toward the longest z-wavelength available in the grid. Explicit resistivity is not present in the ideal MHD equations that we solve. An implicit resistivity, hence reconnection, is nevertheless present due to numerical resolution effects. Specifically, oppositely directed magnetic fields advected into one zone will be reduced to their summed value, which results in reconnection (although without any accompanying Joule heating). The reconnection length is thereby set by the size of a grid zone. The effects of this inevitable numerical reconnection are best monitored by running a given model at multiple resolutions. In the case of the initial B_z simulations, the same result is obtained for a range of resolutions and initial field strengths, indicating that nonlinear exponential growth is the outcome for shearing sheet flows threaded by a net z-field.

Unfortunately, the reconnection associated with the numerical grid can be the significant factor in determining the nonlinear outcome of some simulations. This is most readily demonstrated by replacing the uniform B_z initial field with a B_z field that varies as the sine of the radius across the grid (so that there is zero net field initially). Again models with various initial field strengths are run at a number of grid resolutions. The linear phase proceeds in much the same manner as before, with the fastest growing wavelength modes emerging from the background within two orbits. However, the nonlinear behavior of the solutions is quite different from that observed in the uniform B_z case. There are now fluid elements with different signs of angular momentum perturbation that have the same sign of azimuthal current, and these can reconnect. Such reconnection events reduce the net poloidal motion. The result is an apparently turbulent motion in which reconnection and the instability compete for dominance. The final outcome is dependent upon resolution. This can be most easily seen by following the total magnetic field energy as a function of time, plotted in FIGURE 4 for simulations with three different resolutions. In low resolution grids reconnection dominates and the field dies out. In the highest resolution grid something close to a steady state develops; blobs of fluid with significant angular momentum form and move through the disk while other blobs' angular momentum perturbations are destroyed by reconnection. Although these simulations indicate that dissipative processes such as reconnection can limit field amplification, the level of numerical reconnection is almost certainly much greater than expected for a realistic disk plasma.

The last of the simulations we describe is the initial uniform B_R field. This case differs from the other initial poloidal field orientations in that its fastest growing mode has $q_z \rightarrow \infty$ and $q_R^2 = 15/16$ [(7)]. For all other field geometries the fastest

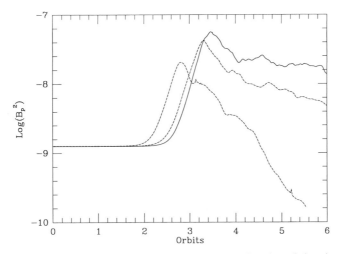

FIGURE 4. The poloidal magnetic field energy density as a function of time in orbits for simulations with three different numerical resolutions. The initial background magnetic field consists of a z-field that varies as the sine of the radius across the grid. After an initial linear growth phase, the magnetic energy falls off rapidly due to numerical reconnection for the simulation using a grid with 64 × 64 zones (*bottom dashed curve*). Doubling the resolution to 128 × 128 reduces the rate of reconnection (*middle dashed curve*). The highest resolution grid (256 × 256—*solid line*) has the least amount of energy loss due to reconnection.

growing mode has finite q_z and $q_R = 0$. The unstable modes that develop during the linear growth phase are characterized by structures that are very narrow in z, but extended in radius. As with all these simulations a comparison between the analytic and numerical growth rates finds good agreement, particularly for the fastest growing modes.

Considerable radial fluid motion begins after the unstable modes have attained nonlinear amplitudes. The total poloidal energy increases to an average value of $\beta \sim 500$, a value close to the field strength limit that would allow the shortest unstable wavelength to fit within the periodicity length of this particular numerical grid. The total poloidal field energy grows to this value regardless of the grid resolution used or the initial magnetic field strength. For these initial radial field cases the field amplitude at saturation is dependent upon the size of the computational domain: the larger the periodicity length of the grid, the stronger the saturated field. This hypothesis is tested by using a numerical grid with a larger periodicity length, and the saturated field strength is proportionally larger, as expected. Recall that larger final field energies are also accompanied by larger maximum radial velocities and angular momentum perturbations, and hence larger effective "α" values.

The numerical simulations have demonstrated two mechanisms that can cause saturation in field growth at subthermal levels: numerical reconnection in the case of zero net initial field, and the finite size of the computational domain in the case of initial radial field. However, both of these effects arise from the limitations of the numerical study and neither is important in a realistic disk. The magnetic Reynolds number due to the finite grid effects is orders of magnitude smaller than present in an accretion disk. Thus the numerical results imply that in a disk the magnetic field energy grows to equipartition. However, recall that in an accretion disk the shear flow directly generates toroidal field from poloidal. In axisymmetry this process is one way; poloidal field generates toroidal, but toroidal field can affect the disk only through magnetic pressure and buoyancy. It does not take too many orbits before the toroidal field strength becomes comparable to the thermal energy. Buoyancy instabilities are inevitable in disks with vertical stratification. Magnetic buoyancy instabilities may provide an additional limitation to the strength of the magnetic field in the disk. For example, Sakimoto and Coroniti[28] have investigated the buoyancy of isolated toroidal flux tubes and found rather stringent self-consistency limits on the magnetic field strength in disk models where the magnetic field is assumed to provide the dynamic stress. Fortunately, vertical stratification can easily be incorporated in both the local approximation and in global disk models. If we relax the assumption of axisymmetry, the toroidal field can generate poloidal, potentially creating a full MHD disk dynamo. Thus a complete investigation of the nonlinear saturation of the instability, and the possible generation of large-scale coherent fields will require a fully three-dimensional study with vertical stratification.

CONCLUSIONS

We believe that the root cause of anomalous viscosity in accretion disks is no longer unknown. The obstacle for general acceptance of turbulent disk theories has always been the lack of a clearly demonstrable and sufficiently general linear instability. We have shown that *any* weak magnetic field in a differentially rotating disk will render it dynamically unstable with an *e*-folding time of 0.2 orbital period. This is true for any field geometry: toroidal fields do *not* stabilize, and a vertical field component is not required. The only requirement, in addition to a weak magnetic field, is that the angular velocity decrease outward. That a weak vertical field can globally destabilize an incompressible fluid undergoing Couette flow was known long ago.[29,30] That the instability is both local in character and essentially independent of field geometry and magnitude apparently went unappreciated for three decades! While the precise consequences of this work for accretion disks are not yet known, it seems certain what disks are *not:* they are not laminar, hydrodynamic systems. In the absence of special structure (e.g., clumpy ballistic clouds), disks must be either fully turbulent, strongly magnetized, or both.

REFERENCES

1. SHAKURA, N. I. & R. A. SUNYAEV. 1973. Astron. Astrophys. **24:** 337–355.
2. LIN, D. N. C. & J. C. B. PAPALOIZOU. 1980. Mon. Not. R. Astron. Soc. **191:** 37–48.
3. RUDEN, S. P., J. C. B. PAPALOIZOU & D. N. C. LIN. 1988. Astrophys. J. **329:** 739–763.
4. RYU, D. & J. GOODMAN. 1992. Astrophys J. **388:** 438–450.
5. LIN, D. N. C., J. C. B. PAPALOIZOU & G. J. SAVONIJE. 1990. Astrophys. J. **364:** 326–334.
6. SPRUIT, H. C. 1989. *In* Theory of Accretion Disks, F. Meyer, W. J. Duschl, J. Frank, and E. Meyer-Hofmeister, Eds.: 325–340. Kluwer. Dordrecht, the Netherlands.
7. PAPALOIZOU, J. P. & J. PRINGLE. 1984. Mon. Not. R. Astron. Soc. **208:** 721–750.
8. NARAYAN, R., P. GOLDREICH & J. GOODMAN. 1987. Mon. Not. R. Astron. Soc. **228:** 1–41.
9. BLAES, O. 1987. Mon. Not. R. Astron. Soc. **227:** 975–992.
10. HAWLEY, J. F. 1991. Astrophys. J. **381:** 496–507.
11. EARDLEY, D. M. & A. P. LIGHTMAN. 1975. Astrophys. J. **200:** 187–203.
12. CORONITI, F. V. 1981. Astrophys. J. **244:** 587–599.
13. GALEEV, A. A., R. ROSNER & G. S. VAIANA. 1979. Astrophys. J. **229:** 318–326.
14. BLANDFORD, R. 1989. *In* Theory of Accretion Disks, F. Meyer, W. J. Duschl, J. Frank, and E. Meyer-Hofmeister. Eds.: 35–57. Kluwer. Dordrecht, the Netherlands.
15. ICHIMARU, S. 1977. Astrophys. J. **214:** 840–855.
16. ZELDOVICH, YA. B., A. A. RUZMAIDIN, & D. D. SOKOLOFF. 1983. Magnetic Fields in Astrophysics: 321. Gordon & Breach. New York.
17. BALBUS, S. A. & J. F. HAWLEY. 1991. Astrophys. J. **376:** 214–222.
18. FERRARO, V. C. A. 1937. Mon. Not. R. Astron. Soc. **97:** 458–472.
19. BALBUS, S. A. & J. F. HAWLEY. 1992. Astrophys. J. **392:** 662–666.
20. HILL, G. W. 1878. Am. J. Math. **1:** 5.
21. EVANS, C. R. & J. F. HAWLEY. 1988. Astrophys. J. **332:** 659–677.
22. STONE, J. M. & M. L. NORMAN. 1991. Astrophys. J., Suppl. **80:** 791–818.
23. STONE, J. M., J. F. HAWLEY, M. L. NORMAN & C. R. EVANS. 1991. Astrophys. J. **388:** 415–437.
24. HAWLEY, J. F. & S. A. BALBUS. 1991. Astrophys. J. **376:** 223–233.
25. TOOMRE, A. 1981. *In* The Structure and Evolution of Normal Galaxies, S. M. Fall and D. Lynden-Bell, Eds. 111–136. Cambridge University Press. Cambridge, England.
26. GOLDREICH, P. & D. LYNDEN-BELL. 1965. Mon. Not. R. Astron. Soc. **130:** 125–158.
27. GOODMAN, J. 1991. Private communication.
28. SAKIMOTO, P. J. & F. V. CORONITI. 1989. Astrophys. J. **342:** 49–63.
29. VELIKHOV, E. P. 1959. Zh. Eksp. Teor. Fiz. **36:** 1398–1404.
30. CHANDRASEKHAR, S. 1961. Hydrodynamic and Hydromagnetic Stability. Oxford University Press. New York.

Instabilities of Stellar Disks[a]

C. HUNTER

Department of Mathematics
Florida State University
Tallahassee, Florida 32306-3027
and
Sterrewacht
Huygens Laboratorium
Postbus 9513
2300 RA Leiden
The Netherlands

INTRODUCTION

This is an initial report on a planned study of the large-scale modes of oscillation, not susceptible to a local analysis, of stellar disks. The study is based on a linear stability analysis of the collisionless Boltzmann equation

$$\frac{\partial f}{\partial t} + [f, H] = 0, \tag{1}$$

for the mass distribution function f. With the motion confined to a plane for which we introduce polar coordinates (r, θ), the Hamiltonian is

$$H = \tfrac{1}{2}(v_r^2 + v_\theta^2) + \Phi(r, \theta), \tag{2}$$

where $\Phi(r, \theta)$ is the gravitational potential. We assume an axisymmetric unperturbed integrable steady state with potential $\Phi_0(r)$ for which the distribution function is

$$f = f_0(E, L), \tag{3}$$

where

$$L = rv_\theta, \qquad E = \tfrac{1}{2}v_r^2 + \frac{L^2}{2r^2} + \Phi_0(r) \tag{4}$$

are the angular momentum and energy integrals, respectively. We shall consistently use subscripts 0 and 1 for the unperturbed state and its perturbation, respectively.

The stellar orbits of the unperturbed state, which must be bound, are rosettes that typically fill an annulus

$$r_{\min} \leq r \leq r_{\max}, \tag{5}$$

[a]This work has been supported in part by National Science Foundation Grant DMS-9001404, and by a Bezoekersbeurs from NWO, the Netherlands Organization for Scientific Research.

22

between the two extreme values of r at which $v_r = 0$. The nonnegativity of v_r^2 at any specific value of r implies that only orbits for which

$$2E - 2\Phi_0(r) - \frac{L^2}{r^2} \geq 0 \tag{6}$$

pass through that value of r. These orbits can therefore have any pair of values of the integrals E and L^2 that lie in the triangle in (E, L^2)-space shown in FIGURE 1. As r varies, the varying positions of the inclined upper boundary form the envelope shown in that figure, which, with the positive L^2- and negative E-axes, circumscribes the domain of the arguments of the distribution function $f_0(E, L)$.

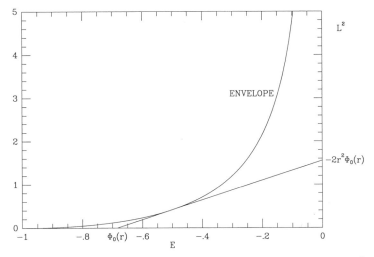

FIGURE 1. The region between the envelope and the axes is the part of (E, L^2)-space occupied by bound orbits. This figure is drawn for the case of a disk with finite total mass, so that $\Phi_0(\infty) = 0$, and with finite central potential $\Phi_0(0)$, which is used as a unit for $-E$.

Expanding the distribution function as $f = f_0 + f_1 + \cdots$ and linearizing, we obtain the equation

$$\frac{\partial f_1}{\partial t} + [f_1, H_0] = -[f_0, H_1] = -[f_0, \Phi_1] \tag{7}$$

for its perturbation that is induced by the perturbational potential Φ_1. The response is fully self-consistent if Φ_1 is also the gravitational potential of the surface density

$$\sigma_1(r, \theta, t) = \int\int f_1 \, dv_r \, dv_\theta. \tag{8}$$

METHODS FOR SOLVING THE PERTURBATION EQUATIONS

Two methods have been used successfully for solving the linearized equation (7). Vandervoort[1-3] has pioneered the use of Lagrangian methods in which one determines the perturbation to orbits in phase space, which here is the four-dimensional $(r, \theta, v_r, v_\theta)$ space. He has implemented it for some finite uniformly rotating three-dimensional stellar systems,[1,3] though ones for which the gravitational potential of the unperturbed state is quadratic in Cartesian coordinates. This quadratic form simplifies the orbits considerably.

Other workers have used a formulation due originally to Kalnajs,[4,5] and based on action-angle variables.[6] Although Kalnajs originally devised his method for stellar disks such as those considered here, he has published little in the way of results obtained using it. Now that there have been several successful applications of Kalnajs's method to higher dimensional spherically symmetric systems,[7-10] it is clear that the computations needed for disk systems are nowadays very feasible.

The actions for the unperturbed motions in the two polar coordinates are

$$J_r = \frac{1}{\pi} \int_{r_{\min}}^{r_{\max}} dr \sqrt{2E - 2\Phi_0(r) - \frac{L^2}{r^2}}, \qquad J_\theta = L. \tag{9}$$

They furnish an alternative pair of integrals of motion so that the unperturbed distribution function can be rewritten as $f_0(J_r, J_\theta)$. The unperturbed Hamiltonian can also be written as a function $H_0(J_r, J_\theta)$ of these actions. Hence when the actions and their conjugate angle variables w_r and w_θ, which form a canonical set of variables, are used to evaluate the Poisson brackets in (7), it simplifies to

$$\frac{\partial f_1}{\partial t} + \Omega_r \frac{\partial f_1}{\partial w_r} + \Omega_\theta \frac{\partial f_1}{\partial w_\theta} = \frac{\partial f_0}{\partial J_r}\frac{\partial \Phi_1}{\partial w_r} + \frac{\partial f_0}{\partial J_\theta}\frac{\partial \Phi_1}{\partial w_\theta}. \tag{10}$$

This equation introduces the two angular frequencies Ω_r and Ω_θ. They are the constant (for any unperturbed orbit) rates at which the two angle variables increase with time; that is,

$$\frac{dw_r}{dt} = \Omega_r, \qquad \frac{dw_\theta}{dt} = \Omega_\theta, \tag{11}$$

and they can be found from the unperturbed Hamiltonian as

$$\Omega_r = \frac{\partial H_0}{\partial J_r}, \qquad \Omega_\theta = \frac{\partial H_0}{\partial J_\theta}. \tag{12}$$

The reduced equation (10) is solved assuming a time dependence on $e^{-i\omega t}$ and angular dependence on $e^{im\theta}$, and then using Fourier series in the angle variables. The series needed are

$$f_1 = e^{i(mw_\theta - \omega t)} \sum_{l=-\infty}^{\infty} \hat{f}_l(J_r, J_\theta)e^{ilw_r}, \qquad \Phi_1 = e^{i(mw_\theta - \omega t)} \sum_{l=-\infty}^{\infty} \hat{\Phi}_l(J_r, J_\theta)e^{ilw_r}, \tag{13}$$

with a single w_θ-component. The relation between the two Fourier coefficients is

$$(l\Omega_r + m\Omega_\theta - \omega)\hat{f}_l = \left[l\frac{\partial f_0}{\partial J_r} + m\frac{\partial f_0}{\partial J_\theta}\right]\hat{\Phi}_l, \tag{14}$$

so that it is simple to solve for one of the Fourier expansions (13) in terms of the other. But it is less straightforward, in action-angle variables, to apply the self-consistency condition that the surface density σ_1, derived from f_1 by (8), is that responsible for the potential Φ_1, since this is a condition that is more naturally applied in physical space.

One of Kalnajs's major contributions was to show that this difficulty can be overcome by solving for f_1 in terms of Φ_1, taking the moment of this solution with some potential function $\psi_j(r)e^{i(\omega t - m\theta)}$, and then integrating over the whole of phase space. The function $\psi_j(r)$ can be a member of a real set of functions that is also used for the expansion of the potential Φ_1 in the form

$$\Phi_1(r, \theta, t) = e^{i(m\theta - \omega t)} \sum_k a_k \psi_k(r), \tag{15}$$

for some coefficients a_k. The integration over phase space is performed using position-velocity variables in one case and action-angle variables in the other. The result, using (8) and standard Fourier analysis, is

$$e^{i\omega t} \int_0^\infty \int_0^{2\pi} \sigma_1(r, \theta, t)\psi_j(r)e^{-im\theta}r \, dr \, d\theta = -\sum_k M_{jk}a_k, \tag{16}$$

where the components of the real symmetric matrix $\mathbf{M}$ are

$$M_{jk} = -(2\pi)^2 \iint dJ_r \, dJ_\theta \sum_{l=-\infty}^{\infty} \frac{[l(\partial f_0/\partial J_r) + m(\partial f_0/\partial J_\theta)]\hat{\Psi}_{j,l}\hat{\Psi}_{k,l}}{(l\Omega_r + m\Omega_\theta - \omega)}. \tag{17}$$

The matrix components,

$$\hat{\Psi}_{k,l}(J_r, J_\theta) = \frac{1}{\pi} \int_0^\pi \psi_k(r)\cos[lw_r + m(w_\theta - \theta)] \, dw_r, \tag{18}$$

are Fourier coefficients for the component potential function $\psi_k(r)e^{im\theta}$ in the two w-angle variables, and their sum,

$$\hat{\Phi}_l = \sum_k a_k \hat{\Psi}_{k,l}, \tag{19}$$

gives a Fourier coefficient of the perturbing potential Φ_1. (The simple real form of integral (18) follows from the selection of $r = r_{\min}$ as the origin of w_r for the orbit.)

To apply the self-consistency requirement, we need to know the set of density functions $\mu_j(r)e^{im\theta}$, which cause the potential functions $\psi_j(r)e^{im\theta}$. Then

$$\sigma_1(r, \theta, t) = e^{i(m\theta - \omega t)} \sum_k a_k \mu_k(r), \tag{20}$$

and the left-hand side of (16) is evaluated as another product of a known matrix with the unknown vector $\mathbf{a}$:

$$-\sum_k D_{jk}a_k, \qquad D_{jk} = -2\pi \int_0^\infty r\psi_j(r)\mu_k(r) \, dr. \tag{21}$$

Unstable modes are therefore to be found by searching for values of the frequency ω for which

$$\det\{\mathbf{M} - \mathbf{D}\} = 0, \tag{22}$$

a separate search being needed for each value of m. Some simplification, though it is minor relative to the magnitude of the problem, is achieved by using a biorthonormal set of potentials and densities; that is, functions such that

$$D_{jk} = -2\pi \int_0^\infty r\psi_j(r)\mu_k(r)\,dr = G\delta_{jk}, \tag{23}$$

where G is the gravitational constant. The matrix $\mathbf{D}$ is then diagonal.

IMPLEMENTATION

The first choice that has to be made before this so-called *matrix method* can be implemented is that of the potential $\Phi_0(r)$ of the unperturbed state. This fixes the forms of the unperturbed orbits, their actions, and the percise shape of FIGURE 1. The calculations reported here have used the infinite Kuzmin[11]–Toomre[12] (KT) disk of mass M and length scale b with

$$\Phi_0(r) = \frac{-GM}{(b^2 + r^2)^{1/2}}, \qquad \sigma_0(r) = \frac{Mb}{2\pi(b^2 + r^2)^{3/2}}. \tag{24}$$

The action J_r and the frequencies Ω_r and Ω_θ can, for any given E and $L = J_\theta$, quickly be computed as elliptic integrals using the potential Φ_0 as integration variable and Carlson's[13] methods. One reason for this choice of potential is the availability of the following suitable biorthonormal set of potentials and densities, due to Clutton-Brock:[14]

$$\psi_j(r) = -G\left(\frac{2b}{r^2 + b^2}\right)^{1/2} p^m_{m+j}(\xi), \quad \mu_j(r) = \frac{(2m + 2j + 1)}{4\pi}\left(\frac{2b}{r^2 + b^2}\right)^{3/2} p^m_{m+j}(\xi). \tag{25}$$

Here

$$\xi = \frac{r^2 - b^2}{r^2 + b^2} \tag{26}$$

is a variable that maps the infinite range $[0, \infty)$ of r to the finite ξ-range of $[-1, 1]$, while the $p^m_{m+j}(\xi)$ are the usual associated Legendre functions $P^m_{m+j}(\xi)$ multiplied by a normalizing factor $[j!/(2m + j)!]^{1/2}$. These same potentials and densities were used by Aoki, Noguchi, and Iye[15] in their investigation of the modes of a gaseous disk.

One simple test of the suitability of functions (25) is to verify that they can well represent a (neutrally stable) sideways displacement of the KT disk. They do so with a single $j = 0$, $m = 1$ term. Weinberg[9] found Clutton-Brock's[16] analogous spherical set of potential/density functions to be useless for representing a sideways displacement of some infinite spherical models of interest to him. This situation was probably due to the fact that the large-r behavior of Clutton-Brock's functions, including their polynomial behavior in the variable ξ, did not mesh well with that of Weinberg's models. It was the lack of suitable available potential/density functions that led to the selection of the KT disk over the isochrone disk,[b] even though explicit formulas for J_r, Ω_r, and Ω_θ are available for the latter. The isochrone potential decays at large distances as $\Phi_0(r) \sim (GM/r)[1 + (b/r) + \cdots]$, while its surface density $\sigma_0(r)$ decays more awkwardly as $(M \ln r)/2\pi r^3$.[17] Saha[10] avoided these representation problems in his analysis of spherical isochrone models by "cooking up" functions involving polynomials in $r/(b + r)$. This is easier to do in spherical geometry, where differentiation only is needed and there is no awkward $\ln r$ term in the density, rather than disk geometry.

Another basic requirement is a representation of the infinite (J_r, J_θ) action-space over which the integrals (17) must be evaluated. We have made this region finite by working with the scaled potential variable

$$\tau = \frac{\Phi_0(r)}{\Phi_0(0)} = \frac{b}{(b^2 + r^2)^{1/2}} = \left(\frac{1 - \xi}{2}\right)^{1/2}, \tag{27}$$

which is also used for evaluating J_r, Ω_r, and Ω_θ. The two extreme values of τ reached by any orbit define its two *turning-point variables*

$$\tau_1 = \frac{\Phi_0(r_{max})}{\Phi_0(0)}, \qquad \tau_2 = \frac{\Phi_0(r_{min})}{\Phi_0(0)}. \tag{28}$$

These turning-point variables are easily related to E and L, and thence to the actions, and are yet another pair of independent integrals of motion for defining an orbit (apart from its direction of rotation). The action-space for the integrals (17), or equivalently the accessible region of (E, L^2)-space shown in FIGURE 1, is rectified as well as made finite by mapping into the right triangle $0 \leq \tau_1 \leq \tau_2 \leq 1$. Both to simplify the numerical integration and to deal with the variability that occurs near the vertex $\tau_1 = \tau_2 = 0$, that is, with nearly circular orbits at large distances, we map this triangle to a unit square by using the variables τ_1/τ_2 and τ_2.

A set of grid points in τ_1/τ_2 and τ_2 is then chosen for the evaluation of the integrals (17) by Guassian quadrature. This choice has to be adapted to the behavior of the integrands, including that of the Jacobian $\partial(J_r, J_\theta)/\partial(\tau_1, \tau_2)$, near the edges of the domain of integration. The Gaussian quadrature weights, as well as the values of Ω_r and Ω_θ for each grid point, are calculated and stored. Then the set of Fourier integrals (18) for a sufficient number of the infinite ranges of the indices k and l are calculated for each grid point. Each set of integrals may be evaluated simultaneously using a repeated trapezoidal rule. Because the integrands are all periodic in w_r, there is no better numerical method, and it gives a high degree of accuracy provided enough subdivisions are taken.[18] The Fourier coefficients $\hat{\Psi}_{k,l}$ ultimately decay to zero exponentially rapidly with l. For a nearly circular orbit, r and $(w_\theta - \theta)$ vary little, so that the coefficient $\hat{\Psi}_{k,0}$ is dominant and all the others are small. Highly eccentric orbits that reach to large distances have Fourier coefficients that vary little with l until l is large. Almost all of their $O[(r_{max})^{3/2}]$ period is spent at large distances, where

---

[b]Suitable potential/density functions for the isochrone disk have now been provided by E. Qian in 1992. Mon. Not. R. Astron. Soc. **257**: 581–592.

$\psi_k(r)$ is $O[(r_{max})^{-m-1}]$ and an amount of this magnitude is contributed to the integral. The short $O[(r_{max})^{-3/2}]$ fraction of the orbit spent at finite distances, where the integrand is $O(1)$, therefore gives the dominant $O[(r_{max})^{-3/2}]$ contribution to the integral for all m except $m = 0$. Because w_r is small and varies little in this region, the Fourier coefficients are relatively insensitive to l, and do not become so until l grows to be $O[(r_{max})^{3/2}]$, variations in the $\cos(lw_r)$ term begin to cause cancellations, and exponential decay finally occurs. The evaluation of the Fourier coefficients, and their rate of convergence can be tested using the formula (cf. [5, eq. (28)])

$$\sum_{l=-\infty}^{\infty} \hat{\Psi}_{j,l} \hat{\Psi}_{k,l} = \frac{1}{\pi} \int_0^{\pi} \psi_j(r) \psi_k(r) \, dw_r. \qquad (29)$$

Our estimates for eccentric orbits reaching to large distances and $m \geq 1$ are confirmed by this last relation; the integral is again $O[(r_{max})^{-3/2}]$ and is balanced only by summing a large $O[(r_{max})^{3/2}]$ number of $O[(r_{max})^{-3}]$ products of individual Fourier coefficients. The fact that many Fourier expansion coefficients may be required was noted by Zang,[19] though he had both a different and scale-free unperturbed potential and different perturbation potentials, and different estimates therefore apply in his case.

MODELS

The choice of a basic distribution function, f_0, from among the many that are possible for the choice (24) of potential and density, can be left until last. Provided that the grid chosen covers action-space sufficiently well for all the models of interest, it can be used to investigate modes of sequences of models, and to study how the modes vary along the sequence.

The models chosen for the first tests of our implementation of Kalnajs's method are ones that are basically due to Miyamoto,[20] but that we have modified by making all the orbits rotate the same direction. Their distribution functions, which can be found simply by Fricke's[21] method, are

$$f_0(E, L) = \frac{(2n + 3)}{2\pi^2 bG} \left(\frac{-bE}{GM}\right)^{2n+2} U(L) \, _2F_1\left(-n, -2n - 2; \frac{1}{2}; \frac{-L^2}{2b^2E}\right). \qquad (30)$$

Here $U(L)$ is a Heaviside step function, the $_2F_1$ function is a terminating hypergeometric series, and n is a parameter that Miyamoto restricted to be a nonnegative integer. The variation of f_0 with L, as well as with E, increases as n increases and the proportion of nearly circular orbits increases. In particular, the fraction of the total kinetic energy that is in the rotational rather than the radial motion is $(n + 1)/(n + 2)$. Toomre's[22] parameter Q, which gives a criterion for the local stability of the disk to axisymmetric disturbances, increases monotonically from the center outwards in all cases. Its central value of $2\pi/[3.36(1 + n/2)^{1/2}]$ exceeds the critical value of unity until $n = 5$. The mean streaming rotational velocity is

$$\langle v_\theta \rangle = \frac{\Gamma(2n + 4)}{\Gamma(2n + 9/2)} \left(\frac{-2\Phi_0(r)}{\pi}\right)^{1/2} \tau^{2n} \, _2F_1\left(1, -n; \frac{1}{2}; \frac{-r^2}{b^2}\right), \qquad (31)$$

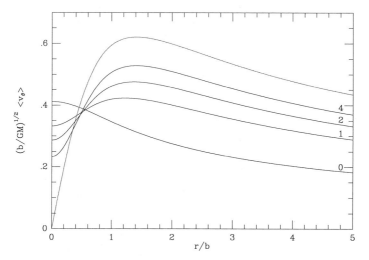

FIGURE 2. The circular velocity for the KT disk (*dotted curve*), and the mean streaming velocity $\langle v_\theta \rangle$ of (**31**) for four values of n as labeled. The mean streaming velocity tends to the circular velocity as $n \to \infty$.

which exceeds the circular velocity $[r d\Phi_0(r)/dr]^{1/2}$ in the inner regions, and is plotted in FIGURE 2 for several values of n.

BAR MODE INSTABILITIES

The complex frequencies for large-scale $m = 2$ instabilities of a range of our models are presented in TABLE 1. The justification for calling them bar modes is that the $k = 0$ term is the predominant one in the potential and density expansions. It has been known since the early N-body simulations of Hohl[23] that disks for which Toomre's parameter Q exceeds unity everywhere, and which are free of axisymmetric instabilities, can still have strong bar instabilities. The instabilities all propagate in the direction of the orbital motions. Their pattern speeds of $\omega_{\text{real}}/2$ exceed the maximum value 0.13 of $(\Omega_c - \kappa/2)$ in the units given, where Ω_c is the circular angular

TABLE 1. Bar Mode Instabilities

Model Number	ω	t_{OP}	$\sigma_r/\langle v_\theta \rangle$
5	$0.918 + 0.445i$	0.3884	0.3744
4	$0.823 + 0.371i$	0.3708	0.4153
3	$0.715 + 0.294i$	0.3468	0.4734
2	$0.594 + 0.204i$	0.3120	0.5647
1	$0.427 + 0.072i$	0.2581	0.7365

NOTE: Properties of the modified Miyamoto models given by the distribution function (**30**), and their bar mode instabilities. The frequencies ω are given in units of $(GM/b^3)^{1/2}$. The ratio in the fourth column is evaluated at $r = b\sqrt{2}$, $\sigma_r = [-\Phi_0/(2n + 4)]^{1/2}$ being the radial velocity dispersion.[20]

velocity and κ the epicyclic frequency for the KT potential, and hence they have no Lindblad resonances.[24] The bar instability is not present in our $n = 0$ model, and extrapolation from our table suggests that it has disappeared at $n = 0.6$. Although our sequence of models can be extended to noninteger values of n, the extended models resemble Dejonghe's[25] anisotropic spherical Plummer models in changing form with some degree of nonsmoothness when $-L^2/2b^2E = 1$. The integration to obtain their matrix elements (17) therefore requires a more elaborate treatment than that described earlier, and has not yet been undertaken.

TABLE 1 lists values of the Ostriker–Peebles[26] parameter t_{OP}, defined as half of the proportion of the total kinetic energy that is contained in the mean streaming rotational velocity (31). Its value is 0.1694 for the $n = 0$ model, and by interpolation, is 0.228 at $n = 0.6$. Hence it appears that models of the type considered here, with substantial rotational velocities persisting into the center, can overcome the bar instability at relatively high values of t_{OP}. The fourth column of TABLE 1 lists a ratio that Athanassoula and Sellwood[27] found effective in an empirical fit of computed growth rates of bisymmetric instabilities of a range of models for the KT disk. Their fit of $0.121 - 0.092(\sigma_r/\langle v_\theta \rangle)$, the ratio being evaluated at the turnover radius where the circular velocity is maximum (see the dotted curve of FIG. 2), predicts a rather mild variation of growth rates, which does not fit our growth rates well.

REFERENCES

1. VANDERVOORT, P. O. 1983. Astrophys. J. **273:** 511–529.
2. ———. 1989. Astrophys. J. **341:** 105–112.
3. ———. 1991. Astrophys. J. **377:** 49–71.
4. KALNAJS, A. J. 1971. Astrophys. J. **166:** 275–293.
5. ———. 1977. Astrophys. J. **212:** 637–644.
6. GOLDSTEIN, H. 1980. Classical Mechanics, 2d ed., Chap. 10. Addison-Wesley. Reading, Mass.
7. POLYACHENKO, V. L. & I. G. SHUKHMAN. 1981. Sov. Astron. **25:** 533–541.
8. WEINBERG, M. D. 1989. Mon. Not. R. Astron. Soc. **239:** 549–569.
9. ———. 1991. Astrophys. J. **368:** 66–78.
10. SAHA, P. 1991. Mon. Not. R. Astron. Soc. **248:** 494–502.
11. KUZMIN, G. G. 1956. Astron. Zh. **33:** 27–45.
12. TOOMRE, A. 1963. Astrophys. J. **138:** 385–392.
13. CARLSON, B. C. 1979. Numer. Math. **33:** 1–16.
14. CLUTTON-BROCK, M. 1972. Astrophys. Space Sci. **16:** 101–119.
15. AOKI, S., M. NOGUCHI & M. IYE. 1979. Publ. Astron. Soc. Japan **31:** 737–774.
16. CLUTTON-BROCK, M. 1973. Astrophys. Space Sci. **23:** 55–69.
17. KALNAJS, A. J. 1976. Astrophys. J. **205:** 751–761.
18. DAVIS, P. J. & P. RABINOWITZ. 1984. Methods of Numerical Integration, 2d ed. Academic Press. Orlando, Fla.
19. ZANG, T. A. 1976. The stability of a model galaxy. Ph.D. dissertation, M.I.T., Cambridge, Mass.
20. MIYAMOTO, M. 1971. Publ. Astron. Soc. Japan **23:** 21–32.
21. FRICKE, W. 1952. Astron. Nachr. **280:** 193–216.
22. TOOMRE, A. 1964. Astrophys. J. **139:** 1217–1238.
23. HOHL, F. 1971. Astrophys. J. **168:** 343–359.
24. BINNEY, J. & S. TREMAINE. 1987. Galactic Dynamics, Chap. 6. Princeton Univ. Press. Princeton, N.J.
25. DEJONGHE, H. 1986. Phys. Rep. **133:** 218–313.
26. OSTRIKER, J. P. & P. J. E. PEEBLES. 1973. Astrophys. J. **186:** 467–480.
27. ATHANASSOULA, E. & J. A. SELLWOOD. 1986. Mon. Not. R. Astron. Soc. **221:** 213–232.

Global Gravitational Instabilities in Accretion Disks[a]

JOEL E. TOHLINE AND JOHN W. WOODWARD

Department of Physics and Astronomy
Louisiana State University
Baton Rouge, Louisiana 70803

INTRODUCTION

As is apparent from the number and breadth of papers being presented at this conference, there are few structures in astronomical systems more ubiquitous than disks. In many systems—particularly accretion disk systems—the disk material can be treated as an essentially massless fluid (or particle) system that orbits in a potential well defined by a central point mass and, more often than not, the disk is geometrically thin. In such systems, the fluid moves in essentially Keplerian orbits with a radial angular velocity distribution given by $\Omega = \Omega_0 (r/r_0)^{-3/2}$. The general properties and dynamics of thin, Keplerian disk systems have been reviewed by Frank, King, and Raine.[1]

Here, we are not interested in studying massless accretion disks. We are interested, instead, in examining the dynamical stability of self-gravitating disks. Although this study may be relevant to a wide range of astrophysical systems, we are approaching it primarily with star formation in mind. Because of the basic angular momentum problem that is associated with star formation, massive disks may be extremely prevalent in protostellar environments. We want to determine under what conditions self-gravitating disks are unstable toward the development of nonaxisymmetric structure and, once nonaxisymmetric distortions develop, how angular momentum redistribution is effected and under what conditions (if any) disk fragmentation takes place.

In a self-gravitating disk system the fluid is not constrained to execute simple Keplerian motion, the disk need not be geometrically thin, and axisymmetric equilibria can be defined even in the absence of a central point mass. In our ongoing investigation into the stability of such systems, we have first confined our analysis to gaseous disks that have uniform specific entropy, obeying a barotropic equation of state (specifically, $n = \frac{3}{2}$ polytropes), and that (with few exceptions) initially possess uniform specific angular momentum. By varying only two parameters—the disk-to-central-object mass ratio (M_d/M_c) and the radial extent of the disk—we have constructed a wide variety of axisymmetric, equilibrium accretion disk systems and

[a]The extensive computational work required for this study has been conducted primarily at the Cornell National Supercomputer Facility, a resource of the Center for Theory and Simulation in Science and Engineering at Cornell University, which is funded in part by the National Science Foundation, New York State, and the IBM Corporation. This research has been supported in part by the U.S. National Science Foundation through Grant AST-9008166 and in part through NASA Grant NAGW-2447.

then, via nonlinear hydrodynamic simulations, have examined the relative stability of each system. One principal objective of this study has been to map out the locus of points in this two-dimensional parameter space that divides dynamically stable disk systems from unstable ones. It is the results relating to this particular objective that we report on here. Further details of this study can be found in Woodward[2] and Woodward and Tohline.[3]

NUMERICAL TECHNIQUES

In order for this study to be successful, it has been extremely important that we begin each hydrodynamic evolution with a good initial equilibrium state. A numerical code employing Hachisu's self-consistent-field (HSCF) technique has provided a versatile tool with which to acquire this necessary ingredient. The HSCF technique is a very powerful and efficient method for constructing equilibrium configurations of rapidly rotating, self-gravitating systems.[4,5] At each of four different system mass ratios—$M_d/M_c = 0.2, 1.0, 5.0$, and ∞—we have constructed as many as twelve disks of varying radial extent, for a total of some thirty-six unique models. Because we have imposed a rotation law of the form $\Omega = \Omega_0(r/r_0)^{-2}$, in general the resulting disk structures exhibit an off-axis pressure maximum (identified here at location $r = r_0$) and are geometrically thick, resembling tori. By varying r_-/r_+—the ratio of the inner to outer edges of the disk—we have effectively created disks of varying vertical thickness as well.[6] In practice, disks with small values of r_-/r_+ are very thick, obtaining much of their support from thermal pressure, while disks with r_-/r_+ near unity are quite slim, receiving their principal support from rotation. Because the ratio $T/|W|$ of rotational kinetic energy to gravitational potential energy can also be used to characterize the relative importance of rotational support in each disk, and because it has proved to be a physically meaningful parameter in many other studies of gravitationally driven instabilities,[7,8] we have used $T/|W|$ in place of r_-/r_+ as the second principal parameter to uniquely define the axisymmetric structure of our initial models.

The tool that we have used to analyze the stability of these systems has been derived from an extensively tested, three-dimensional hydrodynamic computer code that includes the effects of the disk material's self-gravity.[9-11] Employing the numerical techniques described by van Albada, van Leer, and Roberts,[12] we have extended this code to include an advection scheme that is second-order accurate both in space and time. Through this extension, numerical diffusion has been substantially reduced; there is, for example, no longer a need to supplement numerically measured growth rates with a correction factor to account for the effects of numerical diffusion. The code also has been modified to allow the central point mass to move in response to developing distortions in the disk. This additional generalization has been essential because it has enabled us to fully analyze the development of one-armed, spiral distortions such as the "eccentric instability" recently discussed by Adams, Ruden, and Shu[13] and Shu et al.[14] With this computational tool, we are able to study both the linear and nonlinear development of global, nonaxisymmetric instabilities in a wide variety of astrophysical systems.

MODELS EXAMINED

The thirty-six accretion disk structures whose relative stability have been studied to date are identified in TABLE 1. Specifically, columns 2 and 3 of TABLE 1 identify the values of the two dimensionless ratios—M_d/M_c and r_-/r_+—that have been required in order to uniquely specify the equilibrium structure of each axisymmetric, polytropic disk, and column 3 tabulates the corresponding value of $T/|W|$ for each initial model.

In the present study, we have transferred the axisymmetric equilibrium structure of each disk—as constructed numerically using the HSCF technique—into the three-dimensional grid of the hydrodynamic code; have perturbed the initial density distribution with a very low amplitude ($\delta\rho/\rho \approx 10^{-8}$), "white noise" perturbation; then, with no other outside intervention, have dynamically evolved the systems forward in time for as many as twenty rotation periods ($t_{rot} \equiv 2\pi/\Omega_0$), watching for the spontaneous development of nonaxisymmetric structure. By Fourier analyzing the azimuthal density distribution at many different discrete points during each evolution (typically, 300–500 integration time steps are taken each rotation period; see Williams and Tohline[11] for a detailed description of the analysis procedures), we have been able to thoroughly study the dynamical development of global, nonaxisymmetric eigenfunctions in these disks. Specifically, by expressing the fractional variation in the density from axisymmetry by

$$\frac{\delta\rho}{\rho} = A(r, z) \cdot e^{-i[\omega_m t - m\theta]},$$

where ω_m is a complex frequency and m is the associated azimuthal mode number, in most models we have been able to quantitatively measure growth rates, pattern speeds, and the radial structure of the most unstable eigenmodes, which usually have an azimuthal mode number of $m = 2$ or $m = 1$ (see additional discussion, below).

We should point out that, in more than half of the model evolutions that have been studied to date, a periodic boundary condition has been enforced in the azimuthal coordinate at $\theta = \pi$ instead of just at $\theta = 2\pi$ where, physically, it must occur. By imposing this "π-symmetry" constraint, we have been able to achieve twice the spatial resolution in the azimuthal direction at no additional computing cost, and we have been assured that the center of mass of the system remains fixed at the center of the computational coordinate mesh. At the same time, however, π-symmetry evolutions have artificially constrained the central point mass to remain at the center of the coordinate system (i.e., no motion of the point mass is permitted) and have completely suppressed the development of nonaxisymmetric eigenfunctions that have odd azimuthal mode numbers. For model evolutions in which π-symmetry has been imposed, the Greek letter "π" has been appended to the alphanumeric model name in column 1 of TABLE 1.

In evolutions where the π-symmetry constraint has not been employed, the central point mass has been permitted to wander freely in response to the gravitational field of the disk material. Indeed, at the outset of each such evolution, the point mass has been placed slightly off-axis, in a direction and with a radial offset calculated so as to position the center of mass of the combined disk-plus-central-

TABLE 1. Initial Model and Eigenfunction Data

				Pattern Speeds		Growth Rates		
Model (1)	M_d/M_c^* (2)	r_-/r_+ (3)	$T/\|W\|$ (4)	$y_1(m=1)$ (5)	$y_1(m=2)$ (6)	$y_2(m=1)$ (7)	$y_2(m=2)$ (8)	Type (9)
A08π†	∞	0.404	0.273		(−0.16)		0.36	I^a
A07π†	∞	0.325	0.253		−0.87		0.32	I
A06π†	∞	0.260	0.232		−0.94		0.39	I
A05π†	∞	0.215	0.215		−1.00		0.38	I
A04π†	∞	0.180	0.199		−1.00		0.34	I
A02π‡	∞	0.210	0.193		−1.01		0.30	I
A01π	∞	0.203	0.171		−0.85		0.08	I
B05π	5.0	0.425	0.317		−0.97		0.55	I
B04π	5.0	0.333	0.292		−0.96		0.49	I
E06	5.0	0.296	0.279	−0.91		0.31	0.36	III^b
E05	5.0	0.259	0.264	−0.90		0.30		III
B03π	5.0	0.240	0.256		−0.89		0.21	I
E04	5.0	0.222	0.248	−0.89		0.27		III
B02π	5.0	0.203	0.238		−0.93		0.03	I
E03	5.0	0.185	0.228	−0.88		0.25		III
B01π	5.0	0.166	0.217	—			(0.02)	?
E02	5.0	0.111	0.178	−0.83		0.13		III
E01	5.0	0.050	0.120	—		(0.09)		?
C06π	1.0	0.611	0.417		(+1.02)		0.60	I^c
C05π	1.0	0.462	0.400		−0.90		0.43	I
C04π	1.0	0.333	0.373		−0.82		0.20	I
C03π	1.0	0.314	0.368		−0.81		0.13	I
F06	1.0	0.296	0.362	−0.30		0.52		V
C02π	1.0	0.277	0.356		−0.77		0.06	I
F05	1.0	0.259	0.349	−0.34		0.48		V
C01π	1.0	0.240	0.342		−0.85		(0.00)	II?
F04	1.0	0.222	0.334	−0.34		0.49		V
F03	1.0	0.185	0.316	−0.37		0.46		V
F02	1.0	0.092	0.251	−0.50		0.18		IV
F01	1.0	0.055	0.212	−0.46		(0.03)		IV
D06π	0.2	0.611	0.468		(+0.67)		0.30	I^c
D05π	0.2	0.518	0.460		−0.74		0.13	I
D04π	0.2	0.462	0.453		+0.29		(0.21)	II
D03π	0.2	0.425	0.447		+0.10		(0.28)	II
D02π	0.2	0.351	0.432		(−0.23)		(0.04)	?
D01π	0.2	0.314	0.422		(+0.03)		(0.00)	?

*Models identified with $M_d/M_c = \infty$ actually employ values of M_d/M_c between 10^6 and 10^9.

†In order to allow direct comparison with Tohline and Hachisu,[15] a rotation law of $\Omega = \Omega_0(r/r_0)^{-3/2}$ has been employed instead of uniform specific angular momentum.

‡In order to allow direct comparison with Tohline and Hachisu,[15] a rotation law of $\Omega = \Omega_0(r/r_0)^{-7/4}$ has been employed instead of uniform specific angular momentum.

^{a}Fastest growing mode is actually $m = 4$.

^{b}Fastest growing mode is actually a Type I, $m = 2$ mode.

^{c}Mixing with the $m = 4$ mode is clearly evident.

object system precisely at the center of the computational coordinate mesh. In order to balance the very low amplitude "white-noise" density perturbation that has been initially imposed on each disk model, in practice the initial radial offset of the point mass has been extremely small—$\delta r/r_0 \approx 10^{-8}$.

RESULTS

The last five columns of TABLE 1 summarize the principal results, to date, of this stability study. The dimensionless parameter that quantifies the growth rate of an eigenmode,

$$y_2(m) \equiv \mathrm{Im}(\omega_m)/\Omega_0,$$

is tabulated in column 7 for the $m = 1$ azimuthal mode and in column 8 for the $m = 2$ mode; the dimensionless parameter

$$y_1(m) \equiv [\mathrm{Re}(\omega_m)/\Omega_0 - m],$$

which quantifies the pattern speed of each eigenmode, is tabulated in column 5 for the $m = 1$ mode and in column 6 for the $m = 2$ mode. Throughout TABLE 1, parentheses around a numerical value indicate a highly uncertain measurement (usually associated with marginally unstable models or models in which mode coupling has been observed; see further discussion below) and dashes indicate that a particular quantity could not be determined.

Typically, measured growth rates have fallen in the range $y_2 = 0.3$–0.5, which means that the amplitude of the nonaxisymmetric distortions are observed to e-fold every $\frac{1}{2}$–$\frac{1}{3}$ t_{rot}. However, among the set of models that has been studied at each selected system mass ratio, the "hottest" disks—that is, the disks with the lowest $T/|W|$ values—have exhibited growth rates that are roughly a factor of 10 slower than these typical values. Physically, these lowest growth rate models identify disks that have, or at least very nearly represent, marginally unstable structures. FIGURE 1 displays the measured y_2 growth rate information in a graphical form within the context of the two-dimensional, physical parameter space that we have explored. In the figure, circles have been drawn for 33 of the 36 models listed in TABLE 1 (only models C01π, D05π, and E06 are not represented). The centers of the circles identify the $T/|W|$ and M_d/M_c of each modeled system, and the diameter of each circle is directly proportional to the respective model's measured y_2 value. Open circles represent $m = 2$ growth rates derived from π-symmetry evolutions, while shaded circles represent $m = 1$ growth rates derived from evolutions in which the π-symmetry constraint has not been imposed.

With few exceptions, the measured values of y_1 are negative, which indicates that, for the vast majority of observed nonaxisymmetric modes, the corotation radius r_{cr} lies outside the pressure maximum r_0. In systems with relatively large disk masses, the y_1 values for both the $m = 1$ and the $m = 2$ modes have tended to group around -1.0 and -0.9, while values of y_1 ranging between -0.5 and $+0.3$ have been found in systems with $M_d/M_c \leq 1.0$. As we discuss presently, particular values of y_1 tend to be associated with particular "types" of nonaxisymmetric eigenmodes.

In addition to examining the time-evolutionary behavior of independent Fourier frequencies in these disk models, we have analyzed the radial structure of the developing, global eigenfunctions. Together with the measured y_2 and y_1 values, this information has allowed us to identify five characteristically different types of dynamically unstable eigenmodes. The Roman numerals I–V have been used in column 9 of TABLE 1 to denote which of these five modes has dominated the evolution of each of our evolved models. (A question mark appears in cases where

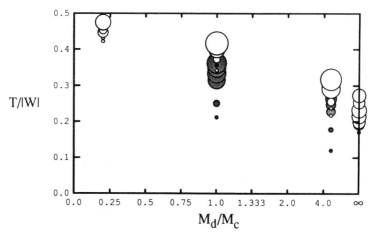

FIGURE 1. Measured values of the growth rate parameter y_2: The location of each circle identifies the $T/|W|$ and M_d/M_c of the model under consideration; the diameter of each circle is proportional to the respective model's measured value of y_2. *Open circles* represent $m = 2$ growth rates derived from π-symmetry evolutions, while *shaded circles* represent $m = 1$ growth rates derived from evolutions in which the π-symmetry constraint has not been imposed.

mode identification has been difficult or impossible to determine.) The basic characteristics associated with each eigenmode are as follows:

Type I:

- Azimuthal mode number $m = 2$.
- $y_1 \approx -1$ and $r_+ > r_{cr} > r_0$.
- In a plot of Fourier phase angle versus radius, the mode appears as a pair of oppositely positioned, coherent radial spokes (rather than as a pair of spiral-shaped arms) radiating from the axis of rotation, but near r_0 the orientation of both spokes abruptly shifts in phase by $\pi/2$ radians.
- Primarily observed as the dominant mode in relatively massive disks when the π-symmetry constraint has been imposed on an evolution (a notable exception was model E06 where this mode dominated even without this artificially imposed constraint).

Type II:

- Azimuthal mode number $m = 2$.
- $y_1 \approx +0.1$ to $+0.3$ and $r_{cr} \approx r_0$.

- In a plot of Fourier phase angle versus radius, the mode appears as a pair of oppositely positioned, coherent radial spokes (no abrupt phase shift is evident at any radius).
- Observed only in the hottest, relatively low disk-mass systems when the π-symmetry constraint has been imposed on an evolution.
- Instead of growing exponentially to nonlinear amplitudes, this mode grows only up to some limiting, *linear* ($\delta\rho/\rho \approx 5 \times 10^{-4}$) amplitude level. (For this reason, the growth rates reported in TABLE 1 for models D03π and D04π are quite uncertain.)

Type III:

- Azimuthal mode number $m = 1$.
- $y_1 \approx -1$, making $r_{cr} > r_+$!
- In a plot of Fourier phase angle versus radius, the mode appears as a single, coherent radial spoke radiating from the axis of rotation, but there is an abrupt phase shift of π radians near r_0.
- Observed in relatively high disk-mass systems.

Type IV:

- Azimuthal mode number $m = 1$.
- $y_1 \approx -\frac{1}{2}$ and $r_+ > r_{cr} > r_0$.
- In a plot of Fourier phase angle versus radius, the mode exhibits a fairly tightly wound, trailing spiral pattern that sweeps smoothly through more than 2π radians between r_- and r_+. (No abrupt phase shift is evident at any radius.)
- Observed only in the hottest, relatively low disk-mass systems.

Type V:

- Azimuthal mode number $m = 1$.
- $y_1 \approx -\frac{1}{3}$ and $r_+ > r_{cr} > r_0$.
- In a plot of Fourier phase angle versus radius, the mode exhibits a very open, trailing spiral character and there is an abrupt phase shift of approximately $-\pi/2$ radians near r_0 (i.e., the phase shift is in a direction opposite to the phase shifts observed in other types of modes).
- To date, has been observed only in the relatively cold systems with $M_d/M_c = 1.0$.

DISCUSSION

Relatively Massive Disks

We begin by discussing the dynamical stability of systems in which the disk has more mass than does the central, point-mass object that the disk surrounds. When the development of global eigenmodes with odd azimuthal mode numbers is suppressed (via our enforcement of the π-symmetry constraint) and, concurrently, the position of the point mass is held fixed at the center of mass of the system, we have found that disks are unstable toward the development of a Type I nonaxisymmetric instability. As the open circles in FIGURE 1 illustrate, moving from relatively hot disk structures to relatively cold ones, this instability first sets in at a value of $T/|W| \approx$ 0.24 for systems with $M_d/M_c = 5$, and (consistent with the results of Tohline and Hachisu[15]) at $T/|W| \approx 0.17$ for systems with $M_d/M_c = \infty$. The properties of this Type I eigenmode, including the abrupt $\pi/2$ phase shift previously reported, are consistent with a global, ellipsoidal (barlike) distortion of the initially axisymmetric torus/disk. Because $y_1 \approx -1$ for this unstable mode, we suspect that it is related to the I-mode identified in slim, self-gravitating annuli by Christodoulou and Narayan.[16]

When the π-symmetry constraint is removed from our simulations of systems with $M_d/M_c = 5$, a Type III nonaxisymmetric instability develops in disks that are too hot to support a Type I instability. As the shaded circles in FIGURE 1 illustrate, this instability sets in at a value of $T/|W| \approx 0.18$. However, a thorough examination of the properties of this Type III eigenfunction indicates that, in the linear amplitude regime, the instability actually does not give rise to a geometric distortion of the disk. Instead, while maintaining its axisymmetric structure, the disk/torus is found to be sliding off to one side of the cylindrical axis of the computational grid while the point mass is shifting off-center in the opposite direction. (Because y_1 is not precisely -1, there is some angular motion coupled with the radial motion, but the angular component is slight.) We therefore do not view this as an actual dynamical instability that is developing within the disk. By examining the problem from the viewpoint of the central point mass, we have deduced a more appropriate, physical description of this Type III instability. Finding itself in a dynamically unstable position at the top of the potential well that is created by the gravitationally dominate disk, the point mass "rolls off" to one side of the potential well and, in order to preserve the position of the center of mass of the entire system, the disk responds by sliding off to the other side. (See a similar discussion by G. Savonije.[17]) Restoring forces due to rotation are evidently not strong enough to corral the point mass in the vicinity of the initial symmetry axis of the system. Ultimately, in the nonlinear amplitude regime, the point mass should impact the inner edge of the disk.

Relatively Low-Mass Disks

In systems with $M_d/M_c = 1$, the Type I, $m = 2$ instability sets in at $T/|W| \approx 0.35$ (see the open circles in FIG. 1) and is the dominant mode of instability if the development of odd azimuthal modes is artificially suppressed. However, when the π-symmetry constraint is removed from our simulations, two distinctly different types of $m = 1$ modes arise in models that have lower values of $T/|W|$. First, at $T/|W| \approx$ 0.21 the Type IV instability sets in. This eigenmode displays a character that is very reminiscent of the "eccentric instability" first discussed by Adams, Ruden, and Shu.[13] As the smooth, one-armed spiral develops in the disk, the "central" point mass moves along a tightly wound spiral trajectory away from the system's center of mass. The separation between the center of mass and the point mass grows in direct proportion to the amplitude of the disk's spiral distortion, so development of this mode clearly depends on some type of constructive feedback between the gravitational fields of the point mass and the disk. We don't understand how the specific feedback mechanism proposed by Adams et al.[13] could have worked in our particular systems because our disks were homentropic and had uniform specific angular momentum (hence, formally the inner and outer Lindblad resonances laid directly on top of corotation). Because there is such a strong similarity between the two disk eigenmodes, however, we suspect that the Type IV instability observed in our simulations is, at the very least, closely related to the Adams et al.[13] eccentric instability.

As the disk in an $M_d/M_c = 1$ system is cooled somewhat, to a value of $T/|W| \approx 0.31$, the Type IV instability gives way to a Type V instability. As far as we have been able to determine, the Type V eigenmode does not resemble any previously discussed $m = 1$ mode that has been found to arise in self-gravitating accretion disks. At present, therefore, we cannot offer any physical explanation regarding the onset or development of this mode.

In the lowest disk-mass systems examined to date ($M_d/M_c = 0.2$), the Type I, $m = 2$ instability set in at $T/|W| \approx 0.46$. In disks that were slightly hotter than this—where we expected all $m = 2$ modes to be dynamically stable—the eigenmode that we have labeled as Type II developed. This mode exhibited properties that are quite different from any of the modes we observed in systems with larger disk masses. Of all its characteristics (previously itemized), the most peculiar and interesting was its limiting amplitude growth behavior. In many respects, the behavior of this eigenmode resembles the "supercritical stability" behavior first described by Landau[18] for certain modes near a point of marginal stability. According to the discussion presented by Drazin and Reid,[19] an isolated mode that would, via linear theory alone, be expected to grow exponentially without limit can encounter *supercritical stability* (due to nonlinear interactions) and equilibrate at a finite amplitude. We suggest that our Type II mode provides an "experimental" example of supercritical stability and that its development is closed associated with marginal stabilization of the Type I mode.

We have not yet completed our simulations of systems with $M_d/M_c = 0.2$ in which the π-symmetry constraint has been removed. Hence, we cannot comment on the relative susceptibility of these low-mass disks to the dynamical development of global $m = 1$ azimuthal modes.

REFERENCES

1. FRANK, J., A. R. KING & D. J. RAINE. 1985. Accretion Power in Astrophysics. Cambridge Univ. Press. New York.
2. WOODWARD, J. W. 1992. Ph. D. dissertation, Louisiana State University, Baton Rouge.
3. WOODWARD, J. W. & J. E. TOHLINE. 1992. In preparation.
4. HACHISU, I. 1986. Astrophys. J., Suppl. Ser. **61:** 479.
5. ———. 1986. Astrophys. J., Suppl. Ser. **62:** 461.
6. TOHLINE, J. E. 1991. In Structure and Emission Properties of Accretion Disks, C. Bertout, S. Collin-Souffrin, J. P. Lasota, and J. Tran Thanh Van, Eds.: 131. Editions Frontieres. Paris.
7. TASSOUL, J.-L. 1978. Theory of Rotating Stars. Princeton Univ. Press. Princeton, N.J.
8. DURISEN, R. H. & J. E. TOHLINE. 1985. In Protostars and Planets II, D. C. Black and M. S. Matthews, Eds.: 534. Univ. of Arizona Press. Tucson.
9. TOHLINE, J. E. 1980. Astrophys. J. **253:** 866.
10. TOHLINE, J. E., R. H. DURISEN & M. McCOLLOUGH. 1985. Astrophys. J. **298:** 220.

11. WILLIAMS, H. A. & J. E. TOHLINE. 1987. Astrophys. J. **315:** 594.
12. VAN ALBADA, G. D., B. VAN LEER & W. W. ROBERTS, JR. 1982. Astron. Astrophys. **108:** 76.
13. ADAMS, F. C., S. P. RUDEN & F. H. SHU. 1989. Astrophys. J. **347:** 959.
14. SHU, F. H., S. TREMAINE, F. C. ADAMS & S. P. RUDEN. 1990. Astrophys. J. **358:** 495.
15. TOHLINE, J. E. & I. HACHISU. 1989. Astrophys. J. **361:** 394.
16. CHRISTODOULOU, D. M. & R. NARAYAN. 1992. Astrophys. J. **388:** 451.
17. SAVONIJE, G. 1992. Unstable interaction between a self-gravitating gaseous disk and its central mass. This volume.
18. LANDAU, L. D. & E. M. LIFSHITZ. 1959. Fluid Mechanics. Pergamon. New York.
19. DRAZIN, P. G. & W. H. REID. 1981. Hydrodynamic Stability. Cambridge Univ. Press. Cambridge, England.

Stellar Mass Black Hole Accretion Disk Models with Physically Self-consistent Viscosities

WILLIAM K. ROSE

Department of Astronomy
University of Maryland
College Park, Maryland 20742

INTRODUCTION

Cygnus X-1 and SS 433 are compact galactic x-ray sources widely believed to be black holes. The OB supergiant HDE 226866 is the binary companion of Cygnus X-1. Similar supergiants are known to have masses $> 20M_\odot$. Estimates of the mass of Cygnus X-1 range from about 6 to $15M_\odot$. Efforts to establish the mass of Cygnus X-1 have been summarized by Shapiro and Teukolsky.[1] The upper limit to the mass of a neutron star is about $2M_\odot$ and therefore the $\simeq 6M_\odot$ lower mass limit of Cygnus X-1 implies that it is a black hole. The x-ray emission from Cygnus X-1 exhibits a wide range of time variability with the characteristic timescales of some x-ray bursts approximately equal to 1 ms. Moreover, x-ray variability is strictly aperiodic except at the binary star orbital period. These observations provide further evidence that Cygnus X-1 is a stellar mass black hole surrounded by an accretion disk.

The x-ray spectrum of Cygnus X-1 is much harder than observed from x-ray sources known to be neutron stars such as x-ray pulsars, bursters, and quasi-periodic objects (QPOs). A high-temperature ($T \simeq 10^8$–10^9 K) partially optically thin emitting region is required to explain the x-ray spectrum of Cygnus X-1, and therefore it has been suggested that the inner region of the accretion disk is thick in the vertical z-direction (Thorne and Price[2]). Standard constant α optically thick accretion disks (Shakura and Sunyaev[3]) have relatively soft x-ray spectra that are more consistent with those of low mass x-ray binaries than with the Cygnus X-1 spectrum. It has been suggested that the high-temperature inner disk around Cygnus X-1 is a consequence of viscous and/or thermal instabilities. In the calculations described in the next section we show that an accretion disk surrounding a black hole with the observationally inferred mass accretion rate of Cygnus X-1 is convective, and moreover convective velocities are sufficiently high to generate a hot corona. The presence of such a hot corona has been previously suggested (Ostriker,[4] Liang and Price,[5] Bisnovatyi-Kogan and Blinnikov[6]).

SS 433, which was initially identified as the emission line object V134 Aquilae, is surrounded by the supernova remnant W50. Strongly redshifted and blueshifted hydrogen and helium lines are observed from two counterstreaming, collimated jets whose inferred outflow velocities are $\pm 0.26c$. The symmetry axis of the jets emanating from SS 433 precesses with a period of 164 days. The orbital period of SS 433 and its massive, early-type binary companion is 13 days. Precession of the jets emitted from SS 433 has been interpreted as caused by precession of the accretion disk from which the jets are emitted. SS 433 is an intrinsically bright object since its inferred absolute optical magnitude is more luminous than −7. However, its x-ray luminosity is relatively low (i.e., ∼3 × 10³⁵ erg⁻¹). Variable radio emission is also observed. The large kinetic energies of the SS 433 jets indicate that they are powered by super-Eddington accretion. Estimates of the mass of SS 433 show that it is most probably about $10M_\odot$ and almost certainly greater than $4.3M_\odot$ (Zwitter and Calvani[7]). Other references to observations of SS 433 are given in a recent paper by Abramowicz.[8] In the second and third sections we describe accretion disk models with mass accretion rates intermediate between those inferred for Cygnus X-1 and SS 433, and qualitatively discuss the dynamics of jet formation and collimation. Some of our results are summarized in Rose.[9]

CALCULATIONS

Accretion disks form around black holes because infalling mass has appreciable specific angular momentum. If at some initial time an annulus of mass surrounds a star, then in order for mass accretion to take place a fraction of the mass of the annulus must be transported to greater radial distances. For steady-state accretion to occur viscous stresses must continuously transport angular momentum outwards. It is well known that viscosity caused by particle collisions is much too small to be important in disks surrounding stellar objects such as black holes. Magnetic fields and viscosity caused by thermal convection are the two most plausible sources of viscosity. Other forms of turbulence besides convection might also be significant (Pringle[10]). Magnetic fields are amplified by the inward spiral motions of mass elements in accretion disks, and therefore even if initial value magnetic fields are quite small, they may be amplified sufficiently for magnetic viscosity to maintain accretion. In the calculations described below magnetic pressure is small as compared to gas and radiation pressure, and consequently the structures of disks do not depend significantly on magnetic field strengths. Some of our accretion disk models are unstable to thermal convection. The dynamic viscosity η caused by convection is $\eta \sim \rho v_c h$ with ρ equal to the gas density, v_c equal to the convective velocity, and h equal to the disk half-thickness. Calculated convective viscosities are found to be either sufficient to maintain steady-state accretion or in some cases so large that viscous instability is indicated.

In a recent publication (Rose[11]) and Appendix A we show that the physical properties of a thin accretion disk undergoing constant mass accretion $\dot{M}$ can be described by the equations

$$v_s^{10}\left(1 + C_1\frac{T^3}{\rho}\right) = f_1^2 f_2 \tag{1}$$

and

$$\rho\left(1 + C_1\frac{T^3}{\rho}\right)^{6/5} = f_1^{2/5} f_2^{-3/10}, \tag{2}$$

where

$$f_1 = \frac{\dot{M}}{4\pi r^2 \alpha} \left(\frac{GM}{r^3}\right)^{1/2} [(GMr)^{1/2} - \beta(GMr_I)^{1/2}],$$

$$f_2 = \frac{9}{2} \frac{\kappa\alpha}{ac} \left(\frac{k}{\mu m_p}\right)^4 \left(\frac{r^2}{GM}\right)^{1/2}$$

and

$$C_1 = \frac{\mu m_p a}{3k}.$$

The dynamic viscosity η is given by the equation

$$\eta = \frac{2}{3} \alpha P \left(\frac{r^3}{GM}\right)^{1/2}. \tag{3}$$

In the preceding equations r_I is the inner edge of the accretion disk, $v_s = (kT/\mu m_p)^{1/2}$, κ the opacity, and a the radiation constant. The variable α, which must satisfy the inequality $\alpha \leq 1$, is known if the viscosity η is known. The constant β is close to unity for a black hole because angular momentum is transported into the black hole, but can be as small as zero if the accretion disk surrounds a neutron star, since the inner boundary layer of the disk interacts with the neutron star magnetosphere. The inner radius r_I is determined by general relativity. In computed accretion disk models we assume that $r_I = 6GM/c^2$, which is the innermost stable circular orbit of a spherical black hole, and $\beta = 0.9$.

The half-thickness h of an accretion disk described by (1)–(3) is

$$h = v_s \left(\frac{r^3}{GM}\right)^{1/2} \left(1 + C_1 \frac{T^3}{\rho}\right)^{1/2}. \tag{4}$$

Equation (4) shows that the disk half-thickness is increased as a consequence of radiation pressure.

Equations (1) and (2) do not give temperature T and density ρ explicitly; however, they can be solved iteratively for T and ρ if some value of α is assumed. If an accretion disk (or region of an accretion disk) is convective, then the dynamic viscosity is known at least approximately ($\eta \sim \rho v_c h$). After solving (1) and (2) with α assumed equal to a constant we can solve for η from (3) and then by varying α find physically self-consistent solutions of (1)–(3). In this manner the viscosity η (and also the parameter α) can be determined as a function of radial distance r. Our convective disk models are computed with $\eta = 0.5 \rho v_c h$.

Accretion disks are subject to thermal and viscous instabilities. The local heating rate equals the local cooling rate under equilibrium conditions. If Γ, Λ, and T are the heating rate, cooling rate, and equilibrium temperature, respectively, then the condition for thermal instability becomes

$$\frac{d \ln \Gamma}{d \ln T} > \frac{d \ln \Lambda}{d \ln T}. \tag{5}$$

It is well known that hot, optically thin gases often satisfy the instability condition given by (5). Thermal instability leads to the clumping of gas into hot and cool regions. A condition for viscous instability is (Pringle[10])

$$\frac{\partial \nu \Sigma}{\partial \Sigma} < 0, \tag{6}$$

where $\Sigma = \int \rho \, dz$ is the column density and $\nu = \eta / \rho$ is the kinematic viscosity. The presence of viscous instability implies that a slightly overdense region becomes even more overdense, and conversely a slightly underdense region becomes even more underdense.

Amplification of magnetic fields occurs as mass spirals in toward a black hole. The amount of initial magnetic field amplification depends on the ratio v_k / v_r, where v_k is the Kepler orbital velocity and v_r the radial inflow velocity. It can be shown that the dynamo mechanism for generating magnetic fields is probably effective in accretion disks. There are obvious uncertainties in estimates of magnetic field amplification. For this reason, after describing convective disk models we describe radiative disk models with α equal to a constant and changes in disk models that are a consequence of variable α before attempting to estimate disk magnetic field strengths.

Accretion disk models, which are solutions of (1) and (2), are described in FIGURES 1 and 2 for assumed mass accretion rates of 10^{-9} $M_\odot$/yr and 2×10^{-9} $M_\odot$/yr, respectively. The virial theorem implies that the luminosity of an accretion disk is

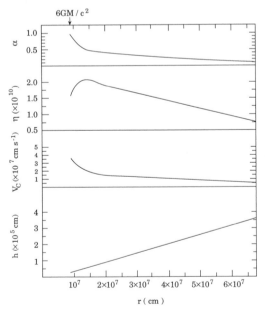

FIGURE 1. The parameter α, the viscosity $\eta = 0.5 \, \rho v_c h$, the convective velocity v_c, and the disk half-thickness h are shown as a function of radial distance r for $\dot{M} = 10^{-9}$ $M_\odot$/yr. All solutions are for $M = 10 M_\odot$.

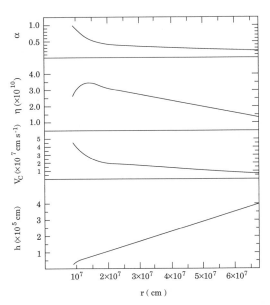

FIGURE 2. The parameter α, the viscosity $\eta = 0.5\,\rho v_c h$, the convective velocity v_c, and the disk half-thickness h are shown as a function of radial distance r for $\dot{M} = 2 \times 10^{-9}\,M_\odot/\text{yr}$.

$GM\dot{M}/2r_I$, where r_I is the inner edge of the disk. Since we assume $r_I = 6GM/c^2$ and $M = 10M_\odot$, the inner disk radius is 89 km. The observed x-ray luminosity of Cygnus X-1 is $\simeq 10^{37}$ erg^{-1}, which implies that the accretion rate is $\simeq 2 \times 10^{-9}\,M_\odot/\text{yr}$. Calculated disk models in FIGURES 1 and 2 are convective, and inferred convective velocities (Clayton[12]) are slightly supersonic or approximately sonic at radial distances relevant from the point of view of x-ray emission. It is physically clear that thermal convection with approximately sonic convective velocities can lead to the formation of a hot corona about the disk inner region, as previously inferred from x-ray measurements. For assumed values of $\dot{M}$ greater than $\simeq 2 \times 10^{-8}\,M_\odot/\text{yr}$ disk models are not convective, and therefore viscosities are not caused by turbulent convection. Using (3) it follows that α ranges from about 0.9 to 0.1 for the disk model given in FIGURE 1. The corresponding range in α is 1 to 0.2 for the disk model described in FIGURE 2. The actual turbulent dynamic viscosity may be somewhat less than we have assumed. If, for example, $\eta = 0.15\,\rho v_c h$, then predicted values of α are about a factor of 5–10 lower. The physical requirement that stress energy density not exceed pressure implies that α cannot exceed unity. If convective viscosities are such that α exceeds unity, then viscous instability exists. If the actual viscosity is $\eta = \rho v_c h$, then it follows that the Cygnus X-1 accretion disk is unstable.

In FIGURE 3 we show accretion disk half-thicknesses for models with $\dot{M}$ ranging from $10^{-8}\,M_\odot/\text{yr}$ to $5 \times 10^{-7}\,M_\odot/\text{yr}$. As expected, these models show that half-thicknesses increase as disk luminosities approach the Eddington limit. Because most of the disk models shown in FIGURE 3 are not convective, their viscosities are not as readily estimated, and therefore computed models are for $\alpha = 0.1$. Lower values of α imply smaller half-thicknesses, but radial variations in half-thickness are similar. Perhaps the most interesting implication of FIGURE 3 is that as radial distance decreases, disk thickness increases and then decreases close to the inner edge of the disk. This latter result is a consequence of angular momentum transport into the black hole. The sub-Eddington disk models shown in FIGURE 3 indicate that when disk luminosity exceeds the Eddington limit, radiation ejects mass from top and bottom sides of an annulus about the innermost disk region. Mass is driven from the accretion disk in the form of outflowing annular jets until the accretion disk luminosity becomes approximately equal to the Eddington limit. The condition for mass ejection is obtained by comparing the outward radiative force per unit mass,

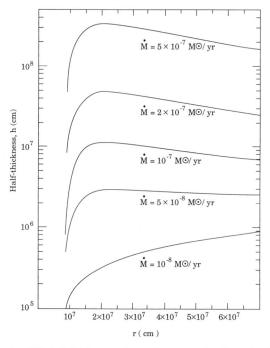

FIGURE 3. Accretion disk half-thicknesses h are shown as a function of radial distance r for assumed mass accretion rates $\dot{M}$ intermediate between those inferred for Cygnus X-1 and SS 433.

$\kappa L/c4\pi r^2$, to the inward gravitational force, GM/r^2. When the Eddington luminosity is exceeded, $G - \kappa L/M4\pi c$ is negative, and therefore mass is accelerated outwards. We can as a first approximation assume radial symmetry because, as shown in FIGURE 3, disk thickness becomes large before the Eddington luminosity is reached. If $G - \kappa L/M4\pi c$ is negative, then conservation of energy between initial radial distance $r = R$ and final radial distance $r = \infty$ implies

$$v^2 = \frac{2}{R}\left(\frac{\kappa L}{4\pi c} - GM\right), \tag{7}$$

where v is the outflow velocity at $r = \infty$ and R is the radial distance from the black hole. Assuming $L = 2L_{crit}$ and $R = 400$ km in (7), we obtain

$$v = 0.25c, \tag{8}$$

which is approximately equal to the outflow velocity from SS 433. The observed jet cone angles are about 20° (Zwitter and Calvani[7]), and therefore the velocity perpendicular to the symmetry axis is $\simeq 1 - 2 \times 10^9$ cms^{-1}. This latter velocity is appreciably less than the orbital velocity at $r \simeq 400$ km. It follows that gas in an outflowing jet continues to rotate differentially after ejection from the accretion disk.

Since jets are emitted by radiation and optically thick, the momentum of outflowing gas cannot exceed photon momentum by a factor of order unity, and we expect the relation

$$\frac{L}{c} = \dot{M}v \tag{9}$$

to hold approximately. Similar arguments have been used to explain mass outflow rates from red giants (e.g., Zuckerman[13]). Setting $L = 2L_{crit}$ and $v = 0.26c$, we have

$$\dot{M} \simeq 5 \times 10^{-7} M_\odot/\text{yr}. \tag{10}$$

Equations (9) and (10) imply that about half of the mass in the outer disk is ejected as jets, and the remainder is accreted into the black hole.

Initial disk magnetic fields are amplified by differential rotation. They also undergo dissipation, and therefore disk magnetic field strengths can be estimated by equating amplification and dissipation timescales. The amount of magnetic field amplification by rotation is limited because winding reduces length scales (Eardley and Lightman[14]). Assuming that magnetic fields are frozen into the gas, the initial growth of the ϕ component is given by the equation

$$\frac{1}{B_\phi}\frac{dB_\phi}{dr} = \frac{\omega(r)}{v_r}, \tag{11}$$

where $\omega(r)$ and v_r are the circular orbital angular velocity and the radial infall velocity, respectively. Since $v_r = dr/dt$, we have

$$B_\phi = B_{\phi_0}e^{\int(\omega/v_r)\,dr} = B_{\phi_0}e^{\int \omega\,dt}. \tag{12}$$

Equation (12) implies that the amplification timescale is $1/\omega$. The corresponding magnetic dissipation timescale is L/v_A, with L equal to the scale length of B_ϕ and $v_A = B(4\pi\rho)^{-1/2}$, the Alfvén velocity. The length scale L decreases as a consequence of rotation because winding causes adjacent magnetic lines of force to have opposite polarities, and therefore L decreases in the same manner as B_ϕ in (12) increases. Setting amplification and dissipation timescales equal we obtain

$$\frac{1}{\omega} = \left(\frac{R^3}{GM}\right)^{1/2} = \frac{L(4\pi\rho)^{1/2}}{B_\phi} = \frac{R(4\pi\rho)^{1/2}}{B_{\phi_0}e^{2\omega\tau}}, \tag{13}$$

where we have assumed that the initial magnetic length scale is R and that the radial infall timescale R/v_r is much greater than τ, the time interval required for magnetic dissipation to equal the amplification timescale $1/\omega$. Solving for τ in **(13)**, we find

$$\tau = \frac{1}{2\omega} \ln \left[\frac{\omega R (4\pi\rho)^{1/2}}{B_{\phi_0}} \right]. \tag{14}$$

For $R = 10^9$ cm and $B_{\phi_0} = 1$ G, **(14)** implies that τ is ~ 10 s, which is much less than

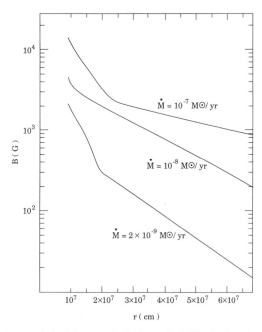

FIGURE 4. The characteristic disk magnetic field $B = (B_r B_\phi)^{1/2}$ obtained by equating magnetic and Coriolis forces is shown as a function of radial distance r for several disk models. The model with $\dot{M} = 10^{-7} M_\odot/\mathrm{yr}$ was computed with $\alpha = 10^{-5}$, whereas the $\dot{M} = 10^{-8} M_\odot/\mathrm{yr}$ model is for $\alpha = 0.1$. Most of the latter disk is convective and therefore physical viscosities are caused by convection. Sufficient magnetic viscosity to maintain steady-state accretion implies $\alpha < 10^{-6}$ in the radiative region of the disk. The dynamo magnetic field strength labeled $2 \times 10^{-9} M_\odot/\mathrm{yr}$ is for the convective Cygnus X-1 model shown in FIGURE 2.

R/v_r. Therefore, from **(12)** we have

$$B_\phi = B_{\phi_0} e^{\omega\tau} \sim 10^2 \text{ G}. \tag{15}$$

Equation **(15)** shows that magnetic field strengths adequate to cause disk viscosities are not generated entirely by rotation. Even if initial conditions are such that strong fields are produced in a region of a disk, the rate of inward decrease in magnetic length scales implies that interior field strengths are too weak to cause disk viscosity. However, the helicity due to rotation and vertical density gradients can lead to dynamo magnetic field generation in accretion disks surrounding black holes (Zeldovich *et al.*[15]). The characteristic limiting amplitude field strengths found by equating Coriolis and magnetic forces (Levy and Rose[16]) are given by the equation

$$\frac{B_r B_\phi}{4\pi} = 2\rho v_r \omega, \tag{16}$$

where v_r is the radial infall velocity. The predicted dynamo magnetic fields shown in FIGURE 4 for the convective disks with $\dot{M} = 2 \times 10^{-9} M_\odot/\mathrm{yr}$ and $M = 10^{-8} M_\odot/\mathrm{yr}$ are too weak to explain disk viscosity. However, the predicted field strength in the disk with $\dot{M} = 10^{-7} M_\odot/\mathrm{yr}$, which was computed with $\alpha = 10^{-5}$, is sufficient to explain viscosity close to the inner disk boundary. Dynamo field strengths adequate to explain disk viscosity are generated for α between 10^{-7} and 10^{-5}. For SS433, where the mass accretion rate is $5–10 \times 10^{-7} M_\odot/\mathrm{yr}$, magnetic viscosities are consistent with much higher values of α (i.e., $\sim 0.1–10^{-3}$). We conclude that the SS433 disk viscosity is probably caused by dynamo magnetic fields.

DISCUSSION OF RESULTS

X-ray emission from Cygnus X-1 is characterized by short-term variability with some x-ray bursts of $\simeq 1$-ms duration. It can be shown (Lightman *et al.*[17]) that in a Schwarzschild geometry the orbital angular frequency observed at large distances is equal to the Kepler orbital angular velocity $\omega = \sqrt{GM/r^3}$. Assuming $M = 10 M_\odot$ and $r = 89$ km the orbital period is equal to 4.6×10^{-3} s, which is somewhat too large to explain the 1-ms x-ray bursts from Cygnus X-1. The time interval for radial infall from $3r_g$, the innermost stable orbit, and $1.5r_g$ the innermost orbit about a Schwarzschild black hole, is given by the equation (Lawden[18])

$$t = \frac{1}{c} \left(\frac{R}{r_g} - 1 \right)^{1/2} \int_{3/2 r_g}^{R = 3r_g} \frac{r^{3/2} \, dr}{(r - r_g)(R - r)^{1/2}}. \tag{17}$$

Evaluating (17), we find $t \simeq 1$ ms, and therefore it is reasonable to associate the presence of $\simeq 1$-ms bursts with the radial infall timescale implied by (17).

Observations of Cygnus X-1 with the Einstein x-ray observatory recently reported by Balucinska and Chlebowski[19] show a soft x-ray (< 2.5 keV) component that is attributable to the relatively low-temperature disk given by model calculations. The Cygnus X-1 hard x-ray spectrum can be interpreted as radiation from a hot corona ($T \simeq 10^8–10^9$ K) of optical depth approximately equal to unity surrounding a relatively low-temperature ($T \simeq 2 \times 10^7$ K) optically thick disk. Our model calculations indicate that the high-temperature corona is formed by sonic or slightly supersonic convective velocities in the disk. The presence of magnetic fields may also contribute to heating the disk corona. There appears to be no evidence for a two-temperature disk of very hot ions ($T_i \simeq 10^{11}$ K) and relatively cool ($T_e \simeq 10^9$ K) electrons as proposed by Eardley, Lightman, and Shapiro.[20] The two-component optically thick disk and hot corona model supported by our calculations may even provide an explanation for the so-called high and low Cygnus X-1 states distinguished by differing hard x-ray emission. Our calculations suggest that small changes in disk physical characteristics (e.g., mass accretion rate) might cause the disk to become unstable to viscous instability. The presence or absence of strong disk magnetic fields, which could also appreciably affect hard x-ray intensity, might also depend sensitively on disk physical characteristics.

In the last section we argued that the SS 433 jets are generated by super-Eddington accretion. FIGURE 3 gives a qualitative explanation for jet formation and collimation. The inner disk region expands to larger thickness than the outer disk where the radiative flux is much lower. It follows that the Eddington flux limit can be exceeded in the inner disk, but radiative fluxes remain sub-Eddington in the outer disk. The innermost disk is likely to be below the Eddington limit, because ejected mass lowers disk luminosity and also because angular momentum is transported into the black hole. It is possible that high-energy photons (x-rays, γ-rays) radiated close to the black hole are observable, since SS 433 jets are probably annular (i.e., hollow). Detection of γ-rays from SS 433 has been reported (Lamb et al.[21]). More recent observations (Geldzahler et al.[22]) place upper limits on γ-ray fluxes that are lower than those previously reported. Changes in inner jet geometry could possibly explain the apparent disagreement between published γ-ray observations. Abramowicz[8] has recently estimated that the optical spectrum of SS 433 is similar to that of a star of radius $R = 30R_\odot$ and effective temperature $T = 32,000$ K. The corresponding luminosity is approximately 4×10^{39} erg s^{-1} if the radiation is assumed to be isotropic. The inferred large projected area and high luminosity provide additional evidence that SS 433 is a black hole well above the neutron star mass limit. However, because the radiation from SS 433 is not emitted isotropically and the Eddington limit depends on helium abundance, the luminosity probably does not exceed the Eddington limit of a 10–15 $M_\odot$ spherical star.

APPENDIX A

Following the discussion given in [1, sect. 14.5] it can readily be shown that the structure of a thin, optically thick accretion disk is described by the equations

$$P = \rho \frac{GM}{r^3} h^2 \tag{A-1}$$

$$\frac{ac}{3\kappa\rho} \frac{T}{h} = \frac{3}{8\pi r^2} \dot{M} \frac{GM}{r} \left[1 - \beta \left(\frac{r_I}{r} \right)^{1/2} \right] \tag{A-2}$$

$$\frac{ac}{3\kappa\rho} \frac{T^4}{h} = \frac{9}{4} \eta h \frac{GM}{r^3} \tag{A-3}$$

$$P = \rho \frac{kT}{\mu m_p} + \frac{1}{3} aT^4 = \rho v_s^2 (1 + C_1 T^3/\rho) \tag{A-4}$$

where

$$v_s = \left(\frac{kT}{\mu m_p} \right)^{1/2} \simeq 10^4 T^{1/2} \quad \text{and} \quad C_1 = \frac{\mu m_p a}{3k}.$$

Substituting $t_{\theta r} = -\alpha P$ with $\alpha = \alpha(r)$ into eqs. 14.5.11, 14.5.15, and 14.5.16 of [1], we obtain

$$\alpha P = \frac{M}{4\pi r^2 h}[(GMr)^{1/2} - \beta(GMr)^{1/2}] \qquad \text{(A-5)}$$

and

$$\eta = \frac{2}{3}\alpha P\left(\frac{r^3}{GM}\right)^{1/2}. \qquad \text{(A-6)}$$

Equations **(A-3)** and **(A-6)** imply

$$\frac{ac}{\kappa\rho}\frac{T^4}{h} = \frac{9}{2}\alpha Ph\left(\frac{GM}{r^3}\right)^{1/2}. \qquad \text{(A-7)}$$

From **(A-1)** and **(A-4)** we have

$$h = v_s\left(\frac{r^3}{GM}\right)^{1/2}\left(1 + C_1\frac{T^3}{\rho}\right)^{1/2}. \qquad \text{(A-8)}$$

Equations **(A-4)**, **(A-5)**, and **(A-8)** imply

$$\rho v_s^3\left(1 + C_1\frac{T^3}{\rho}\right)^{3/2} = \frac{\dot{M}}{4\pi r^2\alpha}\left(\frac{GM}{r^3}\right)^{1/2}[(GMr)^{1/2} - \beta(GMr_I)^{1/2}]. \qquad \text{(A-9)}$$

From **(A-4)**, **(A-7)**, and **(A-8)** we obtain

$$\frac{v_s^4}{\rho^2} = \left(1 + C_1\frac{T^3}{\rho}\right)^2 f_2(r) \qquad \text{(A-10)}$$

with

$$f_2(r) = \frac{9}{2}\frac{\kappa\alpha}{ac}\left(\frac{k}{\mu m_p}\right)^4\left(\frac{r^3}{GM}\right)^{1/2}.$$

Equations **(1)** and **(2)** follow directly from **(A-9)** and **(A-10)**.

REFERENCES

1. SHAPIRO, S. L. & S. A. TEUKOLSKY. 1983. Black Holes, White Dwarfs and Neutron Stars. Wiley. New York.
2. THORNE, K. S. & R. H. PRICE. 1975. Astrophys. J., Lett. **195**: L101.
3. SHAKURA, N. I. & R. A. SUNYAEV. 1976. Mon. Not. R. Astron. Soc. **175**: 613.
4. OSTRIKER, J. P. 1976. Cited in Liang and Price.
5. LIANG, E. P. T. & R. H. PRICE. 1977. Astrophys. J. **218**: 247.
6. BISNOVATYI-KOGAN, G. S. & S. I. BLINNIKOV. 1977. Astron. Astrophys. **59**: 111.
7. ZWITTER, T. & M. CALVANI. 1989. Mon. Not. R. Astron. Soc. **236**: 581.
8. ABRAMOWICZ, M. A. 1989. *In* The Physics of Compact Objects. N. E. White and L. G. Filipov, Eds. Pergamon. Oxford.

9. ROSE, W. K. 1991. *In* Structure and Emission Properties of Accretion Disks, C. Bertout *et al.*, Eds. Editions Frontiers: Paris.
10. PRINGLE, J. E. 1981. Annu. Rev. Astron. Astrophys. **19:** 137.
11. ROSE, W. K. 1991. *In* Extreme Ultraviolet Astronomy, R. F. Malina and S. Bowyer, Eds. Pergamon. Oxford.
12. CLAYTON, D. D. 1968. Principles of Stellar Evolution and Nucleosynthesis. McGraw-Hill. New York.
13. ZUCKERMAN, B. 1987. *In* Spectroscopy of Astrophysical Plasmas, A. Dalgarno and D. Layzer, Eds. Cambridge Univ. Press. Cambridge, England.
14. EARDLEY, D. M. & A. P. LIGHTMAN. 1975. Astrophys. J. **200:** 187.
15. ZELDOVICH, YA. B., A. A. RUZMAIKIN & D. D. SOKOLOFF. 1989. Magnetic Fields in Astrophysics. Gordon & Breach. New York.
16. LEVY, E. & W. K. ROSE. 1974. Astrophys. J. **193:** 419.
17. LIGHTMAN, A. P., W. H. PRESS, R. H. PRICE & S. A. TEUKOLSKY. 1975. Problem Book in Relativity and Gravitation. Princeton Univ. Press. Princeton, N.J.
18. LAWDEN, D. F. 1982. An Introduction to Tensor Calculus, Relativity and Cosmology, 3d ed. Wiley. New York.
19. BALUCINSKA, M. & T. CHLEBOWSKI. 1989. *In* The Physics of Compact Objects, N. E. White and L. G. Filipov, Eds. Pergamon. Oxford.
20. EARDLEY, D. M., A. P. LIGHTMAN & S. L. SHAPIRO. 1975. Astrophys. J., Lett. **199:** L153.
21. LAMB, R. C., J. L. LING, W. A. MAHONEY, G. R. RIEGLER, W. A. WHEATON & A. S. JACOBSON. 1983. Nature **305:** 37.
22. GELDZAHLER, B. J., G. H. SHARE, R. L. KINZER, J. MAGURA, E. L. CHUPP & E. RIEGER. 1989. Astrophys. J. **342:** 1123.

Global Equilibria of Turbulent Accretion Disks

N. J. BALMFORTH,[a] S. P. MEACHAM,[b] E. A. SPIEGEL,[a]
AND W. R. YOUNG[c]

[a]*Astronomy Department*
Columbia University
New York, New York 10027

[b]*Department of Oceanography*
Florida State University
Tallahassee, Florida 32306

[c]*Scripps Institute of Oceanography*
University of California at San Diego
San Diego, California 92037

In Shallow Water Dragons become the Laughing-Stock of Shrimps
—Ernest Bramah, "Kai Lung's Golden Hours"

INTRODUCTION

In the study of accretion disks around central objects with specified gravitational potentials, it is commonly assumed that the distribution of the mean azimuthal velocity is Keplerian. A similar assumption of centrifugal balance underlies the usual determinations of galactic mass distributions from rotation curves. In this paper, we offer a justification for this assumption for the case of fully turbulent disks, starting from ideas about the general influence of turbulence on the mean state of a fluid. In this introductory section, we begin by describing our basic premises for thin axisymmetric disks.

Let the fluid velocity be denoted $\mathbf{u}(\mathbf{x}, \mathbf{t})$. Then if $S(\mathbf{x}, t)$ is a scalar field such that

$$\frac{DS}{Dt} = 0, \qquad \frac{D}{Dt} = \partial_t + \mathbf{u} \cdot \nabla, \qquad (1)$$

one says that S is a *material invariant*. In turbulence theory, as in other parts of physics, invariants have played an important part in the development of general arguments in problems that are too complicated for detailed solution. For turbulent disks, we assume that S becomes completely homogenized as a result of mixing within the disk, whatever initial conditions are given on $S(\mathbf{x}, t)$. Arguments supporting this can be given in the two distinct cases of mild and strong turbulence, and have been laid out in the former case by Rhines and Young[1] in an oceanographic context.

For strong homogeneous turbulence, horizontal eddy scales larger than the thickness of the disk, are present. These scales will readily mix an S that is conserved by fluid parcels into a distribution with a homogeneous average, but with possibly

53

large instantaneous fluctuations. In the mild case, mixing is relatively weak and homogenization proceeds as azimuthal gradients of S are rapidly effaced by Taylor's[2] shear dispersal mechanism as a result of differential rotation in the disk. The radial gradients are subsequently removed more slowly. Eventually S becomes uniform. These arguments can be expected to break down near the edges of the disk, but, for simplicity, we shall assume here that S is uniform everywhere.

In what follows, we shall implicitly allow for the effects of turbulence by assuming that material invariant scalar fields are homogenized. We realize that there is much more to be said about this issue, but in this introductory account we are more interested in showing the advantage that a simplifying principle such as this form of *turbulent equilibrium* may provide in devising models for the mean structure of disks. From either point of view, the question of what causes turbulence in disks remains open.

SPECIFIC ENTROPY AND POTENTIAL VORTICITY

The specific entropy is a material invariant. We therefore assume that it is uniform and, since $S = c_v \log(p / \rho^\gamma)$, we have

$$p = K\rho^\gamma, \tag{2}$$

with constant K.

This assumption was used to construct equilibrium models of stars with turbulent convection zones in the nineteenth century. There is more to the justification of this condition of "convective equilibrium," as it was usually called,[3] than we have mentioned. In stars, in which turbulence is caused by convection, the instability is generally driven by negative radial entropy gradients. So, in homogenizing the specific entropy, one is also renormalizing the convective growth rates by the effect of turbulence. In such cases, we have this second, compelling reason for assumption (2).

However, when the turbulence is caused by some mechanical process, such as shear instability, we may expect entropy homogenization whenever the Péclet number of the turbulence is large. (For optically thick media, $Pe = vl/\kappa$, where l and v are the typical length and speed of the turbulence, and κ is the radiative diffusivity.) In many current models of accretion disks, heat flow in the axial direction, z (a direction we loosely call the vertical), is usually assumed to occur through radiative transfer. In such cases S will depend on z, possibly on r, but not on the azimuthal coordinate, θ. Here we have assumed homentropy. This is sufficient to permit the calculation of the mean state of spherical stars from the equilibrium equations without further details of the turbulent process itself.

When large-scale motions occur, the situation is ambiguous once more, both for rotating stars and disks, because the distribution of angular momentum is not known. To resolve this ambiguity, we propose to introduce another material invariant, *potential vorticity,* whose homogenization will remove the indeterminacy of the mean motion. This quantity is one that has featured in many treatments of geophysical fluid dynamics, and the version we use here is the one that is normally used in the shallow water theory basic to that subject. In this application, we take advantage of the parallelism between the basic shallow water theory of dynamical meteorology and the equations of disk dynamics that has been long appreciated.[4] This was reflected in the title of Spiegel's lecture on this work in the conference: "Shallow water, shallow gas; much of a muchness." A telling observation on these lines was made by Lovelace and Hohlfeld,[5] who derived results indicating that our galaxy has almost constant potential vorticity.

Let us introduce the vorticity $\boldsymbol{\omega} = \nabla \times \mathbf{u}$. A prognostic equation for $\boldsymbol{\omega}$ may be obtained by taking the curl of the equation of motion for $\mathbf{u}$, which is here the Euler equation for an inviscid fluid. With the condition (2), we readily find that

$$\frac{D\boldsymbol{\omega}}{Dt} + \boldsymbol{\omega}\nabla \cdot \mathbf{u} = \boldsymbol{\omega} \cdot \nabla\mathbf{u}. \tag{3}$$

In a thin disk, $\boldsymbol{\omega}$ is dominated by its z-component, ζ. Since the large-scale motion is nearly horizontal and independent of z, the content of (3) is contained in

$$\frac{D\zeta}{Dt} + \zeta\nabla \cdot \mathbf{u}_H = 0, \tag{4}$$

where $\mathbf{u}_H$ is the horizontal velocity.

The conservation of mass is expressed as

$$\frac{D\rho}{Dt} + \rho\nabla \cdot \mathbf{u} = 0, \tag{5}$$

where ρ is the density. We assume that the surface of the disk is defined by $z = \pm h(r)$, where the cylindrical coordinates are r, θ, z. Then the surface density is

$$\sigma(r) = \int_{-h}^{h} \rho \, dz. \tag{6}$$

If we integrate (5) over the depth of the disk for fixed r, θ, we obtain, as is usual for shallow fluid layers.

$$\frac{D\sigma}{Dt} + \sigma\nabla \cdot \mathbf{u}_H = 0. \tag{7}$$

The main ingredient in passing from (5) to (7) is the neglect of the variation of the velocity with z. This is a standard feature of shallow water theory, and the arguments supporting it carry over to shallow gas theory.

Now we may combine (4) and (7) to obtain the material invariant,

$$\frac{Dq}{Dt} = 0, \qquad q = \frac{\zeta}{\sigma}, \tag{8}$$

which is called a *potential vorticity*.

EQUILIBRIUM CONDITIONS

Our allowances for the effects of turbulence are made in the statements that S and q are constants. Now we can look at the mean structures of turbulent disks by simply writing the equilibrium conditions for axisymmetric, steady disks. These are the radial and vertical force balances,

$$0 = -\partial_r p - \rho\partial_r\varphi + \rho\frac{u^2}{r} \tag{9}$$

$$0 = -\partial_z p - \rho\partial_z\varphi \tag{10}$$

where p is pressure,

$$\varphi = -\frac{GM}{\sqrt{r^2 + z^2}}, \tag{11}$$

and $u(r)$ is the azimuthal component of the motion.

An isolated, self-maintaining vortex cannot remain in a time-independent state because of viscous diffusion. However, in the presence of a slow inflow of material the viscous spreading of the vortex can be balanced[6] and a steady state can then be achieved. This idea originates in aeronautics in the context of flow around airfoils and must also apply to the gyre of accretion disks. We discuss the balance of advective inflow and tangential stress, which is the azimuthal component of the equations of motion, in the seventh section.

Because of (2), we can integrate (10) as

$$\eta + \varphi = f(r), \tag{12}$$

where η is the specific enthalpy,

$$\eta = n\gamma K\rho^{1/n}, \qquad n = \frac{1}{\gamma - 1}, \tag{13}$$

f is, as yet, an arbitrary function, and n is the polytropic index. In fact, f is the centrifugal potential, since (9) can now be written as

$$u^2(r) = rf'(r). \tag{14}$$

In galactic studies, one observes $f(r)$ and uses it to infer the mass distribution. Here we cannot do this, and instead use the condition of uniform potential vorticity.

FORMULATION

The upper and lower edges of the disk, as already stated, define the surface

$$z = \pm h(r), \tag{15}$$

the disk being presumed symmetric about the plane $z = 0$. Since η must vanish on the disk surface, we have the condition

$$\varphi(r, h(r)) = f(r), \tag{16}$$

whence

$$\eta(r, z) = \varphi(r, h) - \varphi(r, z), \tag{17}$$

and

$$\rho(r, z) = \left[\frac{\varphi(r, h) - \varphi(r, z)}{n\gamma K} \right]^n. \tag{18}$$

The radial balance equation becomes

$$r\partial_r[\varphi(r, h)] = u^2. \tag{19}$$

And the constant parameter q is expressed through

$$\frac{1}{r} \partial_r(ru) = q\sigma. \tag{20}$$

We have two equations [(19) and (20)] for the three unknowns u, σ, and h. A third relation is obtained by inserting (18) into (6); this gives σ as an explicit function of h, but it is hard to work with. Instead, we adopt a formula derived by assuming that $h/r \ll 1$, and have further verified that this expression is in good accord with numerical results for all $h/r < 1$. Explicitly it is

$$\sigma = \left(\frac{GM}{n\gamma Kr} \right)^n \left[1 - \frac{r}{\sqrt{r^2 + h^2}} \right]^n \beta_n h, \tag{21}$$

where $\beta_n = B(n + 1, \frac{1}{2})$ is a beta function. The system (19)–(21) describes the mean fields of thin, turbulent disks.

At the outer edge of the disk ($r = r_*$) we have the boundary condition,

$$h = 0 \quad \text{at} \quad r = r_*. \tag{22}$$

At the inner edge of the disk $r = r_i$, several different boundary conditions are plausible. In the numerical calculations presented in the eighth section, we have adopted the condition

$$h = 0 \quad \text{at} \quad r = r_i. \tag{23}$$

When the dimensions of the central object are much smaller than the typical disk thickness, $r_i = 0$ and the central mass may be regarded as a point singularity. We can also look for toroidal solutions that have an inner edge separated from the surface of the central object, for which $r_i > 0$.

If the central object is a massive star with a radius larger than the disk thickness, then a more complicated matching is required that includes a boundary layer in which the potential vorticity *must* vary in order to match the disk solution to that of the stellar interior.[7-9] We do not enter into such complications here.

NONDIMENSIONALIZATION

The calculations and their meanings are simplified by the use of natural units. We use the radius of the disk, r_*, as the length scale for the radial direction and introduce the maximum semithickness, h_*, for the unit of length in the z-direction.

For a thin disk, the ratio

$$\epsilon = \frac{h_*}{r_*} \tag{24}$$

is small.

Let the unit of surface density be

$$\sigma_* = \left(\frac{GM\epsilon^2}{n\gamma Kr_*}\right)^n \beta_n h_*. \tag{25}$$

We write

$$r = r_* R; \qquad h = d_* H; \qquad \sigma = \sigma_* \Sigma$$

and

$$u(r) = \sqrt{\frac{GM}{r_*}} U(R); \qquad \varphi(r, h) = \frac{GM}{r_*} \Phi(R, H). \tag{26}$$

The nondimensional equations for the equilibria of disks become

$$R \frac{d}{dR} \Phi(R, H) = U^2, \tag{27}$$

$$\frac{d}{dR} (RU) = RQ\Sigma, \tag{28}$$

and

$$\Sigma = \left[\frac{1 + R\Phi(R, H)}{\epsilon^2 R}\right]^n H, \tag{29}$$

where

$$\Phi(R, H) = \frac{-1}{\sqrt{R^2 + \epsilon^2 H^2}} \tag{30}$$

and

$$Q = q\sigma_* (r_*^3 / GM)^{1/2}. \tag{31}$$

ASYMPTOTICS

We now seek asymptotic solutions for small ϵ. Let

$$Y = \left(\frac{\Sigma}{H}\right)^{1/n}. \tag{32}$$

Then the equations can be rewritten in this way:

$$\epsilon^2 R \frac{dY}{dR} = U^2 - \frac{1}{R},$$ (33)

$$\frac{d(RU)}{dR} = QRHY^n$$ (34)

and

$$H = \frac{R[2RY(1 - \frac{1}{2}\epsilon^2 RY)]^{1/2}}{1 - \epsilon^2 RY}.$$ (35)

The nondimensional potential vorticity, Q, that appears in (34) can be scaled out completely by rescaling

$$\hat{H} = \lambda H \qquad \hat{Y} = \lambda^2 Y \qquad \hat{\epsilon} = \lambda^{-1}\epsilon,$$

where

$$\lambda = Q^{(\gamma-1)/(\gamma+1)} = Q^{1/(2n+1)}.$$

After dropping the circumflex, the resulting equations are the same as (33)–(35), but with Q set equal to 1 in (34). This demonstrates that there is a single family of solutions parametrized by

$$\epsilon = \frac{h_*}{r_*} Q^{-1/(2n+1)},$$ (36)

which groups together many of the key parameters of the problem. This would have emerged more naturally if we had defined the unit of surface density with a suitable dependence on Q in the first place.

Equation (29) becomes

$$\epsilon^2 Y = \frac{1}{R}\left[1 - \left(1 + \epsilon^2 \frac{H^2}{R^2}\right)^{-1/2}\right],$$ (37)

which we can approximate further by assuming that $\epsilon^2 H/R \ll 1$. In general, this approximation does not hold in an inner boundary layer near $R = 0$, but for the bulk of the disk we find

$$Y \sim \frac{1}{2}\frac{H^2}{R^3} - \frac{3}{8}\epsilon^2 \frac{H^4}{R^5} + \frac{5}{16}\epsilon^4 \frac{H^6}{R^7} + \cdots$$

$$= Y_0 + \epsilon^2 Y_1 + \epsilon^4 Y_2 + \cdots.$$ (38)

Then (33) and (34) become

$$RU^2 - 1 = \epsilon^2 R^2 \partial_R Y_0 + \cdots$$

$$\partial_R(RU) = RH[Y_0^n + \epsilon^2 Y_0^{n-1} Y_1 + \cdots]. \tag{39}$$

We seek asymptotic expansions of H and U

$$H \sim H_0 + \epsilon^2 H_2 + \cdots, \qquad U \sim U_0 + \epsilon^2 U_2 + \cdots. \tag{40}$$

At leading order, we obtain

$$RU_0^2 - 1 = 0,$$

$$\partial_R(RU_0) = \left(\frac{1}{2} H_0^2 R^{-3}\right)^n RH_0. \tag{41}$$

Thus

$$U_0 = R^{1/2}, \qquad H_0 = 2^{(n-1)/(2n+1)} R^{(6n-3)/(4n+2)}. \tag{42}$$

We therefore recover the usually assumed result that the azimuthal velocity in the main part of the disk is Keplerian to leading order of thinness. The assumption of uniform potential vorticity also tells us how H varies with R. From (42), we see that for $n > 1/2(\gamma < 3)$, the thickness increases monotonically with R in the main part of the disk. The corresponding solution for the surface density is

$$\Sigma_0 = 2^{-(2n^2+1)/(2n+1)} R^{-(4n+3)/(4n+2)}, \tag{43}$$

which indicates that the surface density declines with R, regardless of the value of n.

It is straightforward to go to higher order and to discover that the asymptotic expansion fails when R is small, so corrections are needed in a boundary layer about $R = 0$. Moreover, the solution does not satisfy the boundary condition $H = 0$ at $R = 1$, and a boundary layer is required there as well. Both the higher order terms and the boundary layer solutions can be obtained analytically, and we shall provide the details elsewhere. For now, it suffices to present numerical solutions of the theory to illustrate its content.

NUMERICAL SOLUTIONS

In this section we show some solutions to (33)–(35) graphically.

FIGURE 1 presents solutions for the condition (23) with $r_i = 0$, the case where the central mass is a point singularity and the disk goes all the way to the origin. Panel (a) displays the half thickness, H, as a function of radius for various values of the polytropic index and $\epsilon = 1/3$. For low values of n the polytropic disks form sharp polar funnels about the central object, and are reminiscent of some features of Lynden-Bell's[10] speculations concerning the nucleii of active galaxies. This is illustrated

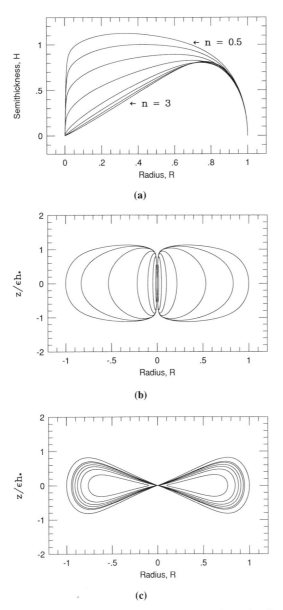

(a)

(b)

(c)

FIGURE 1. Numerical solutions for disk equilibria. Panel **(a)** shows the dimensionless half-thickness H against radius R for various values for the polytropic index n. The particular polytropes with $n = 0.5, 0.6, 0.75, 1.0, 1.25, 1.5, 2.0, 2.5$, and 3.0 are shown. The aspect ratio $\epsilon = 0.2$. Panels **(b)** and **(c)** show contours of constant density for two of these models—specifically the two with indices $n = 0.5$ and $n = 3$. The particular density levels shown (in dimensionless units for which the central density takes the value 1.0) are 0, 0.01, 0.02, 0.05, 0.1, 0.2, and 0.5. The vertical coordinate is the dimensionless, stretched variable $z/\epsilon h_*$.

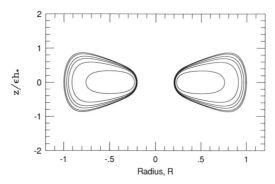

FIGURE 2. Contours of constant density for a toroidal polytropic model surrounding a central point mass. The polytropic index $n = 1.5$, the aspect ratio $\epsilon = 0.2$, and the inner edge of the object has the radius $r_i = 0.2$. The particular density levels shown (in dimensionless units for which the density maximum has the value 1.0) are those for which $\rho = 0, 0.01, 0.05, 0.1, 0.2$, and 0.5. The vertical coordinate is the dimensionless, stretched variable $z/\epsilon h_*$.

further in panel (b) in which contours of constant density are plotted for the polytrope with the lowest value of n. For possibly more physical values of n, the funnel is wider and the shape is more toroidal [as indicated in panel (c) for the polytrope with $n = 3$].

FIGURE 2 shows a toroidal solution that satisfies (23) and $r_i = 0.2$. It is characterized by the parameter values $n = 3/2$ and $\epsilon = 0.2$. This solution is not connected to the central object. It is therefore distinct from the models displayed in FIGURE 1 because there will be no net flow of material through the torus. In the accretion disk solutions the continual transfer of mass and angular momentum can be modeled by the method we now outline.

TURBULENT MOMENTUM TRANSPORT

In the leading order balance discussed previously, there are no explicit terms describing accretion and the radial transfer of angular momentum. In the inviscid, axisymmetric limit, all of the terms in the azimuthal momentum balance vanish. When there are weak azimuthal viscous stresses, a small, net inward flow, v, arises. In the manner of standard disk theory[11,12] the azimuthal momentum equation can be written in the form

$$\Sigma v \partial_R (RU) = \partial_R(\mu R U_R) - U\partial_R(\mu R)/R. \qquad (44)$$

As we have mentioned, this is a standard balance of aeronautical theory,[6] with μ the traditional shear viscosity parameter, suitably nondimensionalized.

The continuity equation has the integral

$$2\pi R \Sigma v = -\dot{M}, \qquad (45)$$

where $\dot{M}$ is the net, inward, radial flux of mass. Combining these, we obtain

$$\partial_R[\mu R^3 \partial_R(U/R)] = -\frac{1}{2\pi}\dot{M}\partial_R(RU). \tag{46}$$

After substituting the equilibrium azimuthal velocity field previously derived and choosing a value for the accretion rate $\dot{M}$, we obtain a first-order ordinary differential equation for the form of the viscosity required for a steady-state model with constant potential vorticity. For the solution given by expressions (42), that differential equation can be integrated to

$$\mu = \mu_1 R^{-1/2} + \frac{|\dot{M}|}{3\pi}, \tag{47}$$

where μ_1 is a constant of integration. The spatially dependent part of this expression, $\mu_1 R^{-1/2}$, is not determined by the requirements that the potential vorticity is uniform and that the velocity field is prescribed by (42) and (45). The azimuthal shear stress always vanishes with this spatial dependence of the viscosity coefficient and so shear is irrelevant. The physically important term in (47) is the constant quantity $|\dot{M}|/3\pi$, which provides a nonvanishing tangential stress and drives accretion. Therefore, without loss of generality, we may take $\mu_1 = 0$. (Were we to retain stress terms in the radial momentum equation, this would not be possible.)

DISCUSSION

We have proceeded in analogy with the modeling of convective stars in the previous century to model turbulent accretion disks. We note that entropy and potential vorticity are material invariants for this problem, and we presume that a turbulent velocity field exists within the disk. Then we assume that, as a result, the mean state has uniform specific entropy and uniform potential vorticity. The former implies a polytropic equation of state, the latter allows us to close the problem for the azimuthal velocity and thickness. We find that, for thin disks, the solution for the interior of the disk has an approximately Keplerian balance without assuming this *ab initio*. Boundary layers are needed at the edges of the disk.

Our central assumption is that the disk is essentially turbulent. We have not specified the source of this eddy activity, but are motivated by the general fluid dynamical prejudice that flows at very high Reynolds numbers are turbulent. There is a great deal of kinetic energy locked in our equilibrium solutions, and there are many potential instabilities that could release this energy. Some arise purely from the behavior of weakly viscous fluids. For example, incompressible plane Couette flow is linearly stable, but such flows rarely remain laminar at Reynolds numbers above $O(10^3)$. Other instabilities may arise from the action of additional physics not included here. As examples we cite the instability of plane shear flows in the presence of stratification[13] and planar magnetic fields.[14,15] These are what we may call *catalytic instabilities,* in which some extra degree of freedom allows the fluid to convert shear energy into turbulent energy.

Our speculations about stability are limited by the fact that our theory is developed as an average over a turbulent flow. We cannot therefore be precise about the nature of energetic fluctuations of this flow without deeper consideration of the way that the basic state is forced by the accretion of material and angular momentum from outside the disk (though observed velocity curves for disk galaxies point to the existence of such fluctuations). As for many rotating turbulent fluids, we may expect to see transient vortices within the disk, associated with those fluctuations. Coherent structures of this kind may modify the observable features of the disk such as the emergent radiation from the disks associated with active galactic nuclei.[16] Such features of turbulence cannot be discussed without looking into the fluctuations that occur in the disk, and for that we need to go beyond the elementary equilibria described here. It will therefore be of interest to numerically simulate forced, turbulent shallow disks. The equilibria described here will remain interesting as they should describe the mean state of the bulk of the disk.

ACKNOWLEDGMENT

We are happy to acknowledge that a part of this work was done at the Geophysical Fluid Dynamics Summer School at the Woods Hole Oceanographic Institution.

REFERENCES

1. RHINES, P. B. & W. R. YOUNG. 1982. J. Fluid Mech. **122:** 347.
2. TAYLOR, G. I. 1953. Proc. R. Soc. London **A219:** 186.
3. LAMB, H. 1932. Hydrodynamics, 6th ed. Cambridge Univ. Press. Cambridge, England.
4. DICKERSON, R. E. 1964. Pure Appl. Geophys., No. 59, p. 155.
5. LOVELACE, R. V. E. & R. G. HOHLFELD. 1978. Astrophys. J. **221:** 51.
6. BATCHELOR, G. 1967. An Introduction to Fluid Dynamics. Cambridge Univ. Press. Cambridge, England.
7. PAPALOIZOU, J. C. B. & G. Q. G. STANLEY. 1985. Mon. Not. R. Astron. Soc. **370:** 597.
8. PACZINSKI, B. 1990. Astrophys. J. **370:** 597.
9. POPHAM, R. & R. NARAYAN. 1990. Astrophys. J. **370:** 604.
10. LYNDEN-BELL, D. 1978. Phys. Scr. **17:** 185.
11. PRINGLE, J. 1981. Annu. Rev. Astron. Astrophys. **19:** 137.
12. SHAKURA, N. I. & R. A. SUNYAEV. 1973. Astron. Astrophys. **24:** 337.
13. DRAZIN, P. G. & W. R. REID. 1981. Hydrodynamic Stability. Cambridge Univ. Press. Cambridge, England.
14. STERN, M. 1963. Phys. Fluids **6:** 636.
15. CHEN, X. L. & P. J. MORRISON. 1991. Phys. Fluids B **3:** 863.
16. ABRAMOWICZ, M. A., A. LANZA, E. A. SPIEGEL & E. SZUSZKIEWICZ. 1992. Nature **356:** 41.

Learning about Algol Disks—Learning from Algol Disks[a]

R. E. WILSON AND DIRK TERRELL

Astronomy Department
University of Florida
Gainesville, Florida 32601

ALGOLS AND W SERPENTIS STARS

Discussion of disks in Algol-type binaries at this time may stimulate new theoretical work on disks around normal stars and disk accretion onto normal stars. Most of the theory about disks around stars concerns cataclysmic variables (CVs), which is to say white dwarfs accreting from low mass main sequence stars, yet there are interesting problems of normal star disks that have not been solved, even in the first order. Why all the interest in CVs? First, active problem areas tend to be those in which the theory is difficult but not hopeless, and a properly developed thin disk theory (difficult, but not hopeless) should be adequate for CVs. Second, there should be a good observational base. Cataclysmic variables do not score so well here because they are very faint objects for spectroscopy, which is the most critically needed kind of observation, although the disks often do account for a significantly high percentage of the light of these dim objects. Third, the CV problem is one that we all know about, while disks around normal stars are not so well known for a variety of reasons—for one, they do not lead so directly to explosions. The disks of this paper result from Roche lobe overflow of subgiant stars onto unevolved or little-evolved companions. They progress through several stages, each with its own very difficult theoretical problems. It is clear that thin disk theory will not do, because at some stages the disks are not even close to a steady state, while at other stages they are effectively thick. To our advantage, however, is that some of the objects are quite bright (even constellation stars!), and they are orders of magnitude brighter than CVs as a class. There already exist large collections of observed spectral energy distributions (SEDs), and many other kinds of observations. An advantage for theory is that the behavior of these normal star disks is not so much dominated by shock waves (not so easy to treat) as are the CV disks, although of course there are shock waves. So the theory of accretion disks around normal stars is in some ways easier and in some ways harder than that of CV disks. Observing them is in some ways easier and in some ways harder. Selecting one or the other problem from a cold start would be a close call. However, CVs have had their attention, so let us see where we now are with disks in the Algol and related binaries and let us give Algols a chance.

For the purposes of this paper, the term *Algol* will include the W Serpentis-type binaries. So what are the W Sers? To be strictly correct, the W Sers are at present

[a]The work of one of the authors (D. T.) was fully supported by a NASA Graduate Student Researcher Fellowship, and the work of the other author (R. E. W.) was supported in 1991 by a NASA ISRP grant through the Space Grant Consortium of Florida Universities.

primarily, or perhaps for some persons entirely, an observationally defined class. There are not very many members of the class—of the order of ten. Examples are W Ser, β Lyrae, SX Cas, KX And, RX Cas, W Cru, V367 Cyg, and AR Pav. Recognition of the W Serpentis stars came about when Plavec and Koch[1] (viz., Plavec,[2] for a review) noticed unusually bright far ultraviolet emission lines in IUE (International Ultraviolet Explorer satellite) spectra, and realized that they were seeing the signature of mass transfer and mass loss on a grand scale. The best known W Ser is the infamous β Lyrae, whose thick disk and general circumstellar and circumbinary activity have teased stellar astronomers for a century. The notariety of β Lyrae relative to other W Ser's is partly due to its being much brighter than its classmates. W Sers are particularly interesting because of the likelihood that at least some are the missing evolutionary link between detached pretransfer binaries and the Algols. Some of the W Sers may not lead to Algols, but consider that some of them do. In that case, lobe overflow of an expanding star begins a rapid stage of mass transfer (viz., Plavec[3]) that is very brief compared to the overall evolutionary time scale, and that would be the W Ser stage. If we want optically and geometrically thick disks, this is where they should be. The system will have an evolved star in contact with its Roche lobe, an accreting star that is detached from its Roche lobe (usually well-detached), and major circumstellar flow activity. A severe observational problem is that, for high inclinations, such an accumulation of circumstellar gas, may largely or even entirely block our view of the central star and, of course, of the inner parts of the disk. This idea is in accord with observations of W Sers. When the major flow stops and a slow phase of mass transfer begins, we have, for some starting configurations, an ordinary Algol binary. There may be an interesting transition stage in which the rapid stage is just dying out, during which the accreting star is spinning very fast because of assimilated angular momentum, yet is in direct view because the disk is largely gone. Such Algols are known (e.g., Van Hamme and Wilson,[4] and references contained therein), and rotation that is faster than synchronous is not at all rare among Algols.

The morphology of the W Sers might be called semidetached if we were to think only of the Roche lobes of synchronous rotators, but it is more interesting to extend the idea of a limiting lobe to asynchronous rotators. A star that spins faster than synchronously will be limited to a size smaller than its Roche lobe, with a null point of effective gravity on the binary line of centers. For very fast rotation, the limiting lobe will be much smaller than the Roche lobe. The analogy with the Roche lobe is complete, since the limit is a combined gravity-rotation limit, just as is the Roche lobe, and in fact the Roche lobe is just the special case that one obtains for synchronous rotation. With the matter-donating star of a W Ser filling its Roche lobe and the accreting star filling its smaller lobe, we have a double contact binary (Wilson[5]). Of course, it is not necessary for the entire star to spin rapidly, since only the behavior of the outer envelope is relevant to the size limitation. Notice that the double contact condition is essentially inevitable when there is large-scale mass transfer, because only modest accretion of orbital angular momentum is needed to spin the surface layers up to quite fast rotation. Some observational confirmation of this idea exists in the rotation statistics of Algols (Van Hamme and Wilson[4]), which indicates rotation comparable to the limit in a few Algols. Recognition of double contact as the fourth morphological type (after detached, semidetached, and overcontact) offers a way to comprehend why W Sers are so qualitatively different from other close binaries and provides a structural-evolutionary basis for understanding W Sers as a class.

THICK DISKS AND BETA LYRAE

The thick disks of W Serpentis binaries will require a thick disk theory— something we do not need for the CVs. The distinction made here is that in thin disks the pressure gradient affects only vertical structure (normal to the disk plane) and has negligible influence on radial structure. The simplifying consequence is that thin disks can be treated as consisting of independent rings, whereas thick disks cannot. In his review of thin disk theory, Pringle[6] (under "Breakdown of Thin Disk Approximation") wrote:

> . . . Thus, the disk is no longer Keplerian, and the splitting of disk structure into a radial part and a part perpendicular to the disk plane is no longer valid. The disk behaves as if it is a rapidly rotating centrally condensed star and should, strictly, be treated accordingly.

It was good to see this remark, because at the time one of us (R. E. W.) was computing a thick disk structural model for β Lyrae exactly along those lines—as a differentially rotating, centrally condensed star (Wilson[7]). The model is of a steady-state, self-gravitating, toroidal object that derives its energy from viscous dissipation (so the fundamental energy source is gravitation), and that utilizes mixing length theory for convective transport. Other approaches could involve dynamical computations of time-variable thick disks, with or without self-gravity, although steady thick disks around normal stars require self-gravity for hydrostatic self-consistency, at least under the reasonable assumptions of Wilson.[7,8] In any case, a major breakthrough is needed if realistic models are to be generated for W Ser-type thick disks.

It is not clear whether or not the Wilson[7] disk model is a step in the right direction, but its foundations will be described here because so far it is the only attempt at a thick disk around a normal star. The 1982 structural thick disk models were computed with geometry from the equipotential formulation of Wilson[8] and the differential equations of stellar structure, with the geometrical correction factors defined by Kippenhahn and Thomas.[9] In computing both the gravitational and the centrifugal potentials there are significant problems, and the steps taken to circumvent those problems can be given here only in condensed form. The full equipotential method is contained in Wilson.[8] The gravitational potential is that of two mass points for the stars plus a circular wire for the disk mass. Thus it is a natural extension of the idea of the Roche model, which represents the stars as mass points. The centrifugal potential is more difficult, and is reached by a sequence of thought experiments and numerical experiments that rule out broad classes of rotation laws as being impossible to realize self-consistently. We are left with disk rotation that is not exactly uniquely defined, but is boxed within very narrow limits. This is done by establishing two radial distances within the disk plane at which local rotation must be Keplerian, where "Keplerian" means that there is no pressure gradient force, so that motion is influenced only by net gravitational (two stars plus disk) and centrifugal force. The inner Keplerian distance is where the disk joins onto its central star, which is presumed to rotate at its centrifugal limit, at least at one point on the equator. Centrifugally limited rotation for the star seems inevitable because it is well known that only modest accretion in binary star mass transfer will spin the outer envelope of a star up to the centrifugal limit. The outer Keplerian distance is at the disk's idealized wirelike mass concentration. This is a consequence of having a pressure maximum that coincides with the density maximum of the mass concentration. Of course, the radial pressure derivative is zero at a pressure maximum. With these two constraints on the differential rotation of the disk, little freedom is left, and it turns out that rotation cannot be much different from Keplerian anywhere (see Wilson[8] for a quantitative treatment). However, it may be surprising to have this problem cast in terms of a self-gravitating disk in the first place—why not dispense with self-gravity? This is a consequence of the requirements of a closed equipotential structure and a common rotation rate for the star and disk where they join. It then turns out to be impossible to have self-consistent equipotentials without arbitrary and unphysical discontinuities if there is no disk gravity to close the equipotentials. Interestingly enough, Hubeny and Plavec[10] recently published a non-self-gravitating thick disk model for β Lyrae, but they had to attach a region with constant angular momentum at the outside in order to close equipotentials. Their model probably is useful for predicting approximately correct spectral energy distributions, but a simple argument shows that the region of constant angular momentum has major negative consequences for its viability as a valid structural model. The argument is as follows. Constant angular momentum in radius means that local rotation drops considerably faster outwardly than for pressure-free (p-f) Keplerian motion (the exponent in the angular velocity–radial distance law is -2 rather than the -1.5 of p-f Keplerian). Only a little distance beyond the beginning of the region of constant angular momentum, the local rotation will be substantially slower than p-f Keplerian, and will require a large pressure gradient for support against radial collapse. What is to generate this large pressure gradient, which would have to be of a greater order of magnitude than in the Keplerian region just inward? The only candidate is turbulence, which Hubeny and Plavec in fact discuss, but turbulent pressure requires turbulent motions, and these are not permitted by celestial mechanical considerations. That is, if we compute the orbital motion of mass elements that depart significantly from the "smoothest possible" behavior near the boundary of the Roche lobe (which is where the disk edge is in β Lyrae), we find that they leave the lobe entirely. Even well within the lobe they will have large radial excursions. However, light curves of β Lyrae over many decades show that the disk has a fairly clean outer edge that produces reasonably consistent and well-defined eclipses of the subgiant companion star. It therefore is not possible to have turbulence on a scale sufficient to produce a pressure far larger than the gas pressure.

The reason for investigating self-gravitating disk models should now be clear. If the aim is to have a disk that is bounded by closed equipotentials and that also interfaces with its central star in a logically consistent way, disk gravity is needed in order to close the equipotentials. It turns out that the disk mass can be as small as a few percent of the central star's mass, but it cannot be negligibly small. Topological properties of self-gravitating disks are discussed by Abramowicz et al.[11] Before seeing how well the model predicts observed disks quantitatively, let us make sure that at least one disk of this sort really exists.

IS THIS PROBLEM REAL?

The existence of opaque, steady, thick disks might not stand up to challenge, except for the existence of β Lyrae. The other ten or so binaries of the W Serpentis class have signs of such disks, but the orbital inclinations are not always favorable or some needed observations are lacking, or there is some other problem. With β Lyrae there is no escape. β Lyrae has a long history of excellent observations of every imaginable kind, but basic recognition of "what is going on" did not come until S. Huang[12] published his disk model. Prior to that, β Lyrae was simply upsetting to everyone's mental equilibrium. Huang's disk model provided the key to understanding the geometry of β Lyrae, although his disk was much too small in both radius and thickness to satisfy the light curves quantitatively. The essential quantitative geometry came with light curve fitting of a decade later (Wilson[13]). The disk geometry of that work was very simple, but did establish the approximately correct disk thickness and disk radius, which are roughly in the ratio 1 to 3 (so the disk is really very thick). Now for the basic questions.

1. *Is the disk optically thick?* Eclipses of the subgiant companion by the disk are cleanly defined. The ingress and egress light curve behavior is in full agreement with models that have no semitransparent fringe. Also, absence of photospheric spectral lines of the central object shows that either it is blocked completely from view or is of an entirely different nature from the massive main sequence star indicated by several lines of indirect evidence.

2. *Is the disk radius large (similar to that of the Roche lobe)?* According to simple geometrical considerations, the duration of eclipse determines the sum of the radii of the involved objects. The eclipse of the subgiant star by the disk has a well-determined duration and the subgiant can account for only a minor part of that duration, so the disk radius can be boxed within fairly narrow limits that make it roughly the size of its Roche lobe. Sizes of both the primary Roche lobe and the subgiant secondary star's Roche lobe are fixed by a chosen mass ratio, and the preceding statements remain true for all reasonable mass ratios.

3. *Is the disk geometrically thick?* Assuming the disk to be essentially symmetrical about the orbit plane, there is a maximum fractional obscuration of the subgiant with varying inclination. For $i = 90$ degrees (edge-on), the fractional obscuration by an arbitrarily thin disk would be zero. For some lower inclination it would again be zero because the projected boundaries do not overlap. Somewhere in between there is maximum obscuration for a thin disk, and numerical experiments (Wilson[13]) show that it is far less than that which is observed. Therefore the disk must be thick.

4. *Is the disk stable (in approximate steady state)?* Most models of β Lyrae postulate a rather massive main sequence star that is completely, but just barely, covered by the disk. Beta Lyrae would have been among the brightest constellation stars if the disk should ever have receded enough to reveal that star. If the central object is much smaller and fainter than a main sequence star, long-term disk fluctuations might not be in conflict with the observational record, but major fluctuations on a time scale much shorter than a century definitely would be, from the

evidence of modern accurate light curves. The disk appears to be remarkably stable on a time scale of decades and perhaps centuries.

From the preceding four points, there seems to be no escape from recognizing the existence in β Lyrae of a large, steady disk that is optically and geometrically thick, and that therefore is quite unlike the thin disks of conventional theory. It seems rather like Pringle's "rapidly rotating centrally condensed star." Let us "treat it accordingly." To begin, it is obvious to ask what can be learned from equipotentials. It can already be seen from the experiences of Hubeny and Plavec[10] that equipotentials without disk self-gravity require an outer patched-on region of slow rotation if they are to close, and from the previous discussion that there is no substitute for rotation to provide support against radial collapse. Also, the main message of Wilson[8] is that disk self-gravity is essential if anything resembling a coherent, reasonably consistent, equipotential structure is to apply to the problem. In fact, the Wilson models also require the outer disk to rotate more slowly than Keplerian, but with the disk having a little self-gravity it is possible to find configurations with global coherence. Perhaps more important is that it actually is possible to integrate the differential equations of stellar structure for such equipotentials (Wilson[7]) and arrive at structural disk models that are rather like the disk in β Lyrae and that have quite reasonable interior temperatures, pressures, and densities. They also have considerable self-consistency, in that the integrated density agrees with the gravitational mass used to compute the equipotentials, and the viscously generated luminosity is about right for the β Lyrae disk, although perhaps a little high in the published models.

What is *in* the structural disk models? Essentially they are built from the following.

(a) The four differential equations of stellar structure, modified for geometrical distortion via the correction factors of Kippenhahn and Thomas,[9] and the usual boundary conditions.
(b) The equipotential formulation of Wilson[8] for a differentially rotating, self-gravitating disk.
(c) The condition of rotational continuity with the central star.
(d) Mixing length convection theory.
(e) Luminosity generation by viscous dissipation. (There is an error in this part that probably is inconsequential to overall success of the models, and that will be corrected later.)

What comes out of the models? Given a disk of 0.5 solar masses (0.04 of the assumed star mass) and normal chemical abundances, and with the only free parameter being the viscosity, typical solutions have the following.

(a) An "equivalent sphere" equal volume radius of about 17 solar radii for a 0.5 solar mass object. This is just about right for the β Lyrae disk. No parameter was tuned to reach this number, which is of the order of 25 times that of a star of the same mass.
(b) About 5×10^3 solar luminosities. This is high, but the right order of magnitude.
(c) An interior that is convective and significantly superadiabatic throughout, and

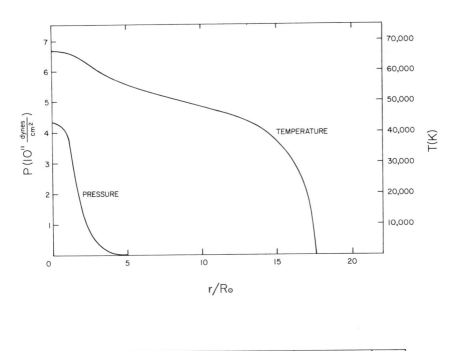

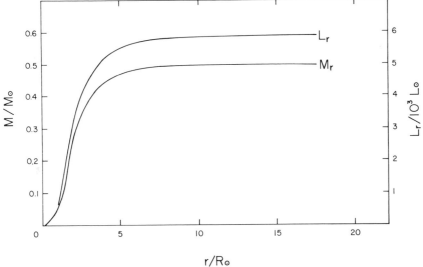

FIGURE 1. The run of pressure and temperature (**upper panel**) and Mr and Lr (**lower panel**) within the Wilson[7] self-gravitating thick disk model for β Lyrae. Note the rather high "central" mass concentration, which shows that the wire approximation for computing the equipotentials is satisfactory. (From Wilson.[7] Reproduced by permission.)

that has its mass strongly concentrated around the idealized ring that was used to generate the equipotentials.

FIGURE 1, which is reproduced from Wilson,[7] illustrates the run of physical variables in the disk. So if we ask "do equipotentials have much to do with any real disks?", the answer comes in two parts. From the observational side, we note that β Lyrae has a large, thick, opaque, sharply bounded, essentially steady disk. The observational record is quite clear on these points. This sounds like a quasi-static object with an equipotential structure. From the theoretical side we can construct models that closely resemble the β Lyrae disk, provided that we include disk self-gravity and that we compute equipotentials according to a few rather reasonable rules (Wilson[8]). On the other hand, if we compute disk models without self-gravity, consisting of rings whose vertical structure is decoupled from their radial structure, we immediately run into an inconsistency in formulating the equipotentials. Suppose, however, that we persist and compute such models anyway, by patching up the inconsistency and closing the equipotentials by fiat. We can then derive no satisfaction by structural matching of the observed β Lyrae disk because the freedom gained by decoupling the vertical and radial structures will permit a wide range of disk dimensions. The theory begins to lose our interest due to a surplus of free parameters. So the β Lyrae disk cannot be treated satisfactorily as a puffed up thin disk, and equipotentials with self-gravity are necessary. The β Lyrae disk problem is real, and we have a candidate for its solution on hand.

THE ALGOL STAGE

Now let the rapid phase of mass transfer come to its natural end and a slow phase begin, as in the standard picture. Of course, for some binaries the mass loser will detach from its Roche lobe and transfer will cease entirely, but for many systems a long stage of intermittent slow transfer is expected (viz., e.g., Plavec[3]). With only a trickle of matter flow available for spin-up, tidal braking will quickly synchronize rotation. The thick disk will be assimilated by the accreting star, and we shall have a normal slowly rotating Algol. Now the mass receiving star is uncovered and we can see it very well, but the main activity is over and what we have to see is rather boring (except, of course, for real astronomers). Fortunately, our frustration is not complete, because some observed Algols appear to be in a transition state between the "interesting but hidden" and "visable but uninteresting" stages. Examples are S Cnc, U Cep, SW Cyg, RY Gem, TT Hya, AQ Peg, AW Peg, RW Per, RY Per, and RZ Sct (Van Hamme and Wilson[4]). Furthermore, accumulating observations show that many Algols have a kind of disk, in the sense of a flattened distribution of gas, although the weaker examples may be detected only occasionally and only a few can be detected outside total eclipse. The state of such a disk cannot be expected to be remotely close to steady, nor should the disk have even rough axial symmetry. However, the disk is optically thin, so we can observe all of it, at least in principle. These transition cases provide opportunities to learn about the overall mass transfer process if we can model the ephemeral disks. A noteworthy point is that although mass transfer activity and rapid rotation are highly correlated, there are individual exceptions. Such an exception is S Cnc, which rotates at about 13 times the synchronous rate, yet shows little evidence of circumstellar gas (viz., Van Hamme and Wilson,[14] and references contained therein). There the fast rotation probably measures intermittent transfer activity averaged over recent millenia, while the (comparative lack of) circumstellar matter tells us what is happening now.

Over the past two decades there have been several important contributions to computing the behavior of thin disks of the kind found in Algols and other binaries in slow or intermediate transfer (e.g., Prendergast and Taam,[15] Lubow and Shu,[16] Lin and Pringle[17]). Briefly, such a disk can be approximated as non-self-gravitating and is governed by celestial mechanics in the first approximation, but with nonnegligible viscous and pressure interactions. We have taken an interest in a neglected but important aspect of this problem, which is to synthesize observable quantities from disk matter distributions and motions (Terrell and Wilson[18]). The hydrodynamic scheme is essentially that of Lin and Pringle,[17] with various refinements. The program follows a large number of gas elements and includes viscosity via progressively weighted momentum averaging within an interaction length, such that viscous coupling increases as element separation decreases. Pressure gradient forces are computed by smoothed particle hydrodynamics (SPH), as in Lucy,[19] and Gingold and Monaghan.[20-23] Several kinds of programming efficiency permit including larger numbers of gas elements and running larger numbers of experiments than have been usual in earlier contributions. The new step is to synthesize spectral line profiles for quantitative comparison with observed spectral energy distributions. Our main early emphasis is on emission profiles, but absorption profiles will receive due attention. Quantitative confrontations between observed and theoretical line profiles should lead to several kinds of progress. First and very important is validation of the hydrodynamical treatment in binaries that have optically thin but bright and readily observable disks. The idea is to test the hydrodynamics on selected Algols, where disk radiation is strong and the systems are generally bright, so that we then can apply the theory with confidence to CVs and other accreting binaries. For the Algols themselves, an initial goal is to make the first reasonably reliable estimates of average mass transfer rates, for comparison with evolutionary computations. Intimately involved with all of this is the understanding of mass and angular momentum exchange between a disk and its accreting star. When that is well in place, it should be possible to predict rates of mass loss from the entire binary system. We are already learning about ejection angles from the inner Lagrangian point, and will be able to relate our experiments to predictions (Lubow and Shu[16]). A future development will be to compute the polarization properties of photospheric radiation that is scattered by the disk, along the lines of the work by Wilson and Liou,[24] but with dynamical disk evolution. This should make it possible to follow timewise behavior of circumstellar polarization, for comparison with observations (from space) over several or many binary cycles.

After models of thin and thick disks have passed various tests of credibility and reliability, a long range overall goal is to use the models to predict evolution beyond the W Serpentis and Algol stages. For example, a full evolutionary model should be able to produce Wolf-Rayet binaries and immediate precursors (precollapse) for the several varieties of neutron star and black hole binaries. It should be able to do this quantitatively, with essentially correct masses and structural properties of the stars. This now appears to be an extremely difficult problem because the end results are likely to be sensitive to initial conditions and to minor shortcomings of the physical treatment that have little effect on instantaneous structure. The problem is reminiscent of weather prediction, but then what is the joy in solving an easy problem? A good early aim would be to validate (or invalidate) the role of centrifugally limited accretion and to understand more fully the interaction between fast-rotating stars and accretion disks. The laboratory for this experiment is stocked with rapidly rotating Algols.

REFERENCES

1. PLAVEC, M. J. & R. H. KOCH. 1978. Inf. Bull. Var. Stars No. 1482.
2. PLAVEC, M. J. 1980. In Close Binary Stars, Observations and Interpretation, M. J. Plavec, D. M. Popper, and R. K. Ulrich, Eds.: 251. Reidel. Dordrecht, the Netherlands.
3. ———. 1968. Adv. Astron. Astrophys. 6: 201.
4. VAN HAMME, W. & R. E. WILSON. 1990. Astrophys. J. 100: 1981.
5. WILSON, R. E. 1979. Astrophys. J. 234: 1054.
6. PRINGLE, J. 1981. Annu. Rev. Astron. Astrophys. 19: 137.
7. WILSON, R. E. 1982. In Binary and Multiple Stars as Tracers of Stellar Evolution, Z. Kopal and J. Rahe Eds.: 261. Reidel. Dordrecht, the Netherlands.
8. ———. 1981. Astrophys. J. 251: 246.
9. KIPPENHAHN, R. & H. C. THOMAS. 1970. In Stellar Rotation, A. Slettebak, Ed.: 20. Reidel. Dordrecht, the Netherlands.
10. HUBENY, I. & M. J. PLAVEC. 1991. Astrophys. J. 102: 1156.
11. ABRAMOWICZ, M. A., A. CURIR, A. SCHWARZENBERG-CZERNY & R. E. WILSON. 1984. Mon. Not. R. Astron. Soc. 208: 279.
12. HUANG, S. 1963. Astrophys. J. 138: 342.
13. WILSON, R. E. 1974. Astrophys. J. 189: 319.
14. VAN HAMME, W. & R. E. WILSON. 1992. Astron. J. To be published.
15. PRENDERGAST, K. H. & R. E. TAAM. 1974. Astrophys. J. 189: 125.
16. LUBOW, S. H. & F. H. SHU. 1975. Astrophys. J. 198: 383.
17. LIN, D. N. C. & J. E. PRINGLE. 1976. In Structure and Evolution of Close Binary Systems, P. Eggleton, S. Mitton, and J. Whelan, Eds.: 237. Reidel. Dordrecht, the Netherlands.
18. TERRELL, D. & R. E. WILSON. 1992. In Light Curve Modeling of Binary Stars, E. F. Milone, Ed.: 7. Springer-Verlag. New York.
19. LUCY, 1977. Astrophys. J. 82: 1013.
20. GINGOLD, R. A. & J. J. MONAGHAN. 1977. Mon. Not. R. Astron. Soc. 181: 375.
21. ———. 1978. Mon. Not. R. Astron. Soc. 184: 481.
22. ———. 1979. Mon. Not. R. Astron. Soc. 188: 39.
23. ———. 1979. Mon. Not. R. Astron. Soc. 188: 45.
24. WILSON, R. E. & J. C. LIOU. 1992. To be published.

Observations of Disks in Algol and Cataclysmic Binaries

RONALD H. KAITCHUCK

Department of Physics and Astronomy
Ball State University
Muncie, Indiana 47306

INTRODUCTION

The first detection of an accretion disk was made by Wyse[1] in 1934. Arthur Wyse was conducting a program to obtain spectra of the secondary stars in Algol-type binaries by observing during primary eclipse. A spectrum obtained near the end of totality of the system RW Tau showed emission on either side of the stellar absorption lines. These emission lines were very difficult to see outside of totality because of the brilliance of the uneclipsed primary star.

Years later A. Joy[2] began a study of RW Tau. Because of the limitations of the technology of the time, he could obtain no more than two to three spectra during totality. However, he sampled enough eclipses so that a typical pattern became apparent. Near the beginning of totality the emission lines were redshifted by 350 km s^{-1}, while at the end of totality they were blueshifted 350 km s^{-1}. Joy offered a simple but ingenious model to explain the observations. He proposed that the primary star was surrounded by a rotating gaseous ring. The observed emission line behavior could be explained as an eclipse of this ring by the secondary star. No doubt, for most people this model brought to mind an image of the thin, Keplerian ring of Saturn.

In the next few years, Struve and collaborators[3-5] discovered many more binary systems with gaseous rings. Rings were found to be fairly common in Algol-type binaries. In systems with orbital periods less than about 5 days (like RW Tau) the emission was weak and was only visible near the bottom of eclipse. For systems with periods greater than about 5 days the emission was strong enough to be detectable outside of eclipse. Also, as Joy had noted earlier in RW Tau, the emission lines in the short-period Algols were highly variable with asymmetries in the emission strength of the red- and blueshifted sides of the ring.

In the years that followed, the concept of mass transfer between the component stars of a binary system was introduced (Crawford[6]), and gaseous rings became recognized as a result of mass transfer and the accretion process. The rings became known as accretion disks. The theory of accretion disk structure is now quite extensive. The "standard" picture is that of a thin, axisymmetric disk rotating in a very nearly Keplerian fashion. Viscosity in the gas causes it to radiate and lose kinetic energy. The process also transfers the angular momentum of the infalling gas outward where it is given to the orbital momentum via tidal interactions of the outer disk with the secondary star (Frank, King, and Raine[7]). The disk provides a way to slowly lower gas down the potential well of the mass-gaining star and liberate its potential energy.

TYPES OF ACCRETION DISKS

Binary stars span a vast range in their parameters such as orbital period, masses, and mass transfer rates. Consequently, we shouldn't expect the accretion disks in these systems to look the same. The disks found in short-period Algol systems like RW Tau are rather small (see below) and with rather low accretion rates. As a consequence, the disks appear to be optically thin in the continuum, but often they are optically thick in the emission lines (as judged from the Balmer decrement). In cataclysmic binaries, the disks are even smaller with higher accretion rates. In this case, a large portion is optically thick in the continuum and the disk is a dominant source of continuum light.

For some binaries, especially those with noncompact stars, the size of the mass-gaining star is relatively large compared to the stellar separation. In these cases when the stream attempts to sweep around the trailing side of the star (due to the Coriolis effect) the stream will strike the star (Lubow and Shu,[8] Kaitchuck, Honeycutt, and Schlegel[9]). We know that a type of disk still manages to form, because such binaries are the short-period Algol systems like RW Tau. For these systems we perhaps are seeing the impact debris of a star/stream collision. Evidence for the penetration of the stream into the primary star of U Cep has been reported by Olson.[10] For the long-period Algols and cataclysmic variables the mass-gaining star is relatively small and the stream will sweep around the star without collision, forming a more normal, stable disk. Given that the formation of some disks involve a collision of the stream with the star and others do not, we expect these disks to look rather different.

DISKS IN SHORT-PERIOD ALGOL BINARIES

The eclipses in short-period Algol systems involve occultations of both the primary star and its accretion disk. Time-resolved spectroscopy of the disk emission lines during eclipse can be used to map the disk structure. This was first done for RW Tau (Kaitchuck and Honeycutt[11]). It was possible to obtain 30 spectra during the 80-minute totality. The results largely confirm the expectations for the unusual nature of this disk. The disk is extremely variable on a time scale of one orbital period. It sometimes disappeared for months at a time. For this reason, it was labeled a *transient* disk. Analysis of the changing Doppler components showed the disk to be smaller than previously estimated (on the assumption of Keplerian motion), with radii that varied from 1.1 to 1.7 times that of the central star. The leading and trailing sides of the disk are very asymmetric, both in terms of the line strengths and the radial velocities. The observed radial velocities were significantly smaller than expected for gas moving in circular orbits at the measured radii. In at least two cases the velocity field on the leading side of the disk appeared reversed, that is, the highest velocities occurred at the *outer* edge. Furthermore, the line widths were usually at least a factor of 2 greater than that expected for a line broadened by rotation of a Keplerian disk. Similar results have been obtained for U Cep (Kaitchuck, Honeycutt, and Faulkner[12]), TZ Eri (Kaitchuck and Park[13]), and SW Cyg (Kaitchuck[14]). This has lead to the conclusion that the disks in these binaries have supersonic turbulence.

The same conclusion was independently reached for U Cep by Crawford.[15] Strong support for this picture came from International Ultraviolet Explorer (IUE) observations of emission lines in RW Tau (Plavec and Dobias[16]) and absorption lines in other Algol-like binaries (Peters and Polidan[17]). These observations showed high excitation lines characteristic of plasma with an electron temperature of 10^5 K. The latter authors coined the term the hot turbulent accretion region (HTAR) to describe this accretion flow.

PERMANENT DISKS IN LONG-PERIOD ALGOLS

We expect that the long-period Algols will have disks closer to our expectations given the fact that the stream does not strike the mass-gaining star. In many ways the study of these systems is more difficult than it is for the short-period Algols. Due to their long orbital periods it is difficult or impossible to follow a complete eclipse in the course of a single night. Partial coverage of an eclipse doesn't map the disk very well. Using data from several different eclipses is subject to misinterpretation if the disk has changed between the various epochs of observation. Consequently, there have been few attempts to study the emission line behavior through eclipse. In one case, RY Gem ($P = 9.3$ days), the total phase of eclipse lasts 4.5 hours and, with luck, it is possible to observe this in a single night. The results of such observations (Kaitchuck[18]) seem to show many of the same effects that are seen in the short-period Algols. The size of the primary star in RY Gem is such that a portion of the stream may still graze the limb of the mass-gaining star, producing many of the characteristics of a transient disk.

The most extensive survey of the disk structure in long-period Algols is that of Peters.[19] She finds that for systems with periods greater than 6 days the disks appear to be stable with little variability in their emission lines. These disks are large, filling most of the Roche lobe of the mass-gaining star. The trailing side of the disk is usually brighter than the leading side, while the leading side is often more extended. Presumably, both these effects are due to the impact of the stream on this disk. That is, the stream makes the trailing side of the disk denser and brighter, and disturbs the flow in the outer periphery, producing a noncircular disk. While these systems show some differences from the standard disk model, they may come much closer to this picture than any other type of disk.

DISKS IN CATACLYSMIC VARIABLES

Today, accretion disks in binary systems are most widely discussed in the context of cataclysmic variables (CVs). Our knowledge of the disk structures in these binaries has been recently reviewed by Horne,[20] therefore only certain points are discussed here.

In CVs the dominant light source is the accretion disk (due to the deep potential well of the mass-gaining white dwarf). The spectrum shows both continuum disk emission and emission lines. In high inclination systems these lines are double peaked because roughly half of the disk is rotating toward us and half is rotating

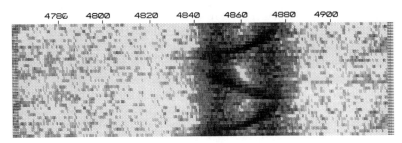

FIGURE 1. A trailed spectrogram of the $H\beta$ emission line of the binary WZ Sge. This image is displayed as a photographic negative with time running downward. Half the data are repeated to make one and a half orbital cycles. The two parallel disk components are clearly seen as is the s-wave that moves between them. The s-wave shows a nonsinusoidal shape.

away. In addition, there is often significant line emission from one or more of the following: the stream/disk impact shock; the stream overflow of the disk; the stream itself. These processes, either collectively or individually, produce what is known as the "s-wave" emission (Kaitchuck, Schlegel, and Hantzios[21]). The name comes from its appearance in trailed spectrograms. FIGURE 1 shows a trailed spectrogram of WZ Sge (Honeycutt, Kaitchuck, and Schlegel[22]), the first system in which an s-wave was identified (Kraft[23]). This image was produced from 160 spectra that were averaged into phase bins and displayed as a gray-scale image. Orbital phase increases down the image and half of the data are repeated to make 1.5 orbital cycles. The two Doppler components from the disk are visible as is the s-wave that moves back and forth across the disk components. (See Honeycutt, Kaitchuck, and Schlegel[22] for more details and other examples.) While the s-wave usually has a velocity amplitude equal to the separation of the disk components, it almost always shows a radial velocity phasing that differs from the orbital motion of the white dwarf. This is not apparent in FIGURE 1 because the orbital motion is very difficult to see. FIGURE 2 shows a trailed spectrogram of U Gem. Here the orbital motion is evident, as is the complex nature of the s-wave. It is clearly nonsinusoidal and appears to split at some phases.

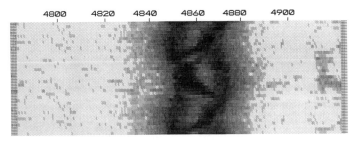

FIGURE 2. A trailed spectrogram of the $H\beta$ emission line of the binary U Gem. In this image the orbital motion is clearly seen in the disk components. The s-wave is complex and appears to double for a portion of the orbit.

Of course, these extra emission sources complicate our study of the disks themselves. It must also be kept in mind that the majority of the gas in these disks is optically thick in the continuum. In many cases, the emission line studies represent a minor component of the disk. In fact, it is still not entirely clear where the line emission originates. It may come from the outer edge or, more likely, from a coronalike region above and below the plane of the disk. In systems with high mass transfer rates, such as novalike binaries and dwarf novae in outburst, the emission lines are weak or absent, and instead we see broad absorption lines from the disk. In systems with low mass transfer rates, such as dwarf novae in quiescence, the emission lines are quite strong relative to the continuum. These considerations indicate that line emission may not always be the best way to learn about the bulk of the disk structure.

While continuum light does not tell us anything about a disk's kinematics, it can reveal details of its temperature structure. Horne[24] has developed a technique that uses multicolor photometry of the eclipses of high inclination CVs to map the disk temperature as a function of radius. Of course, the observational data are a one-dimensional mapping of a two-dimensional emitting surface, so there is no unique solution. Since the disk is expected to be at least approximately axisymmetric, Horne picks the most axisymmetric solution that fits the data. The results for RW Tri (Horne and Stiening[25]) show the disk to be an optically thick radiator with colors intermediate between blackbodies and stellar atmospheres. The derived temperature–radius profile was compared to a steady-state disk model to derive a mass transfer rate of $10^{-8} M_\odot / \mathrm{yr}$.

While the line emission in CVs may not tell us about the bulk of the matter in the disk, it is our only source of information about the kinematics. But one of the great difficulties of studying the emission lines in CVs is the complexities of the line profiles created by the presence of the s-wave and perhaps other sources of line emission. Recently, Marsh and Horne[26] have introduced the technique of Doppler tomography, which can be used to disentangle the emission components. Doppler tomography is very similar to x-ray tomography used in the medical field (Gordon, Herman, and Johnson[27]). While Marsh and Horne have used a maximum entropy algorithm to process the data, almost as much can be learned by a simpler technique of "back projection" (Horne,[28] Kaitchuck[29]).

The back-projection technique involves a transformation of the data from the trailed spectrogram format into velocity space. The line profile observed at any phase is pictured as a projection of a velocity space image along the line of sight at that phase angle. To begin this transformation, a coordinate system is defined that is fixed in the rotating frame of the stars. The X axis runs between the stars with the intersection of the Y axis at the center of mass of the system. The positive Y axis points in the direction of the secondary star's motion. The Z axis is then perpendicular to the orbital plane. This coordinate system rotates with the stars. Any velocity vector (V_x, V_y) in this coordinate system will have a corresponding sine curve in the trailed spectrum. At the same time, it will be represented by a point in the $V_x - V_y$ plane (velocity space). A trailed spectrogram can be thought of as a collection of sinusoids produced by each emitting point in the binary rest frame. The $V_x - V_y$ plane is pictured as being composed of a series of "pixels" like a CCD image. For each pixel (each V_x, V_y pair) the observed radial velocity is calculated by

$$V(\phi) = V_x \cos(\phi) + V_y \sin(\phi)$$

where ϕ is the orbital phase. At each phase, the line flux at the calculated radial velocity is found and a running total is kept. The process is repeated for each pixel in velocity space. The result is a velocity space map that can be displayed as a gray-scale or false-color image.

The velocity maps are a little difficult to understand at first. The double-peaked emission line profiles from a symmetric disk become a doughnut-shaped region in this map. The disk is turned inside out because the high-velocity gas of the inner disk (extreme line wings) falls at the outer portions of the doughnut, and the low-velocity gas of the outer disk maps to near the origin. The advantage of viewing the data in velocity space is that the physical location of the emission line components in the stellar rest frame can often be identified. For instance, if the emission were coming from along the length of the stream, this would produce a pattern in the trailed spectrogram that would not be easily recognized. But in the velocity map, the stream trajectory has a very predictable location and is easily interpreted. The locations of

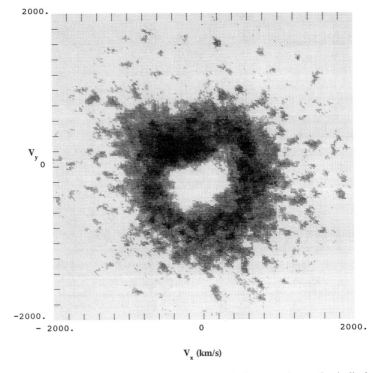

V_x (km/s)

FIGURE 3. A Doppler tomogram of U Gem. This is a velocity–space image that is displayed as a photographic negative. Note the ring structure that is due to the disk and the brighter, elongated s-wave emitting region.

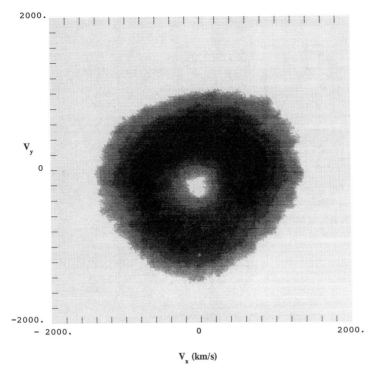

V_x (km/s)

FIGURE 4. A Doppler tomogram of the system IP Peg. Note the nonuniformity of the disk emission. The brightest portion of the disk falls on the opposite side of the V_y axis from the expected s-wave emission site.

the stars and the Roche lobes can also be positioned in the velocity map when the system parameters are known. So, any emission from the heated face of the secondary star is readily identified.

Application of this technique to the very complex line profile structure of U Gem seen in FIGURE 2 results in the velocity-space map of FIGURE 3. The doughnut-shaped feature of the disk is clearly seen, as is a bright, elongated emission region. These data have been analyzed by Marsh et al.[30] They found that part of this emission is located on the secondary star. The remainder (extending to the left of the Y axis) did not fall on the expected stream trajectory, nor did it show the expected disk motion. They suggest that this emission arises from the portion of the stream that is slowed after it passes the stream/disk shock region, but has not yet slowed enough to match the local disk velocity.

Application of this technique to several CVs (Kaitchuck et al.[31]) has shown some fascinating features and differences between systems. For instance, some binaries, like IP Peg (FIG. 4), show very clumpy emission in the doughnut region, indicating very clumpy azimuthal emission structure in the disks. Most novalike systems show little or no indication of disk line emission, but instead are dominated by emission from the s-wave region.

SUMMARY

Observations have shown that there are at least two types of accretion disks in binary star systems. The short-period Algol systems have transient disks that are a product of the collision of the mass stream with the accreting star. These disks are far from the simple, Keplerian disks pictured in most stationary models. The long-period Algol systems and the cataclysmic variables do not suffer a star/stream collision. The long orbital periods in the former makes them difficult to observe in an optimum manner. The later group suffers from the complicated emission line profiles. Eclipse mapping and Doppler tomography are new and important tools in our understanding of disk emission. The application of Doppler emission line mapping of CVs has just begun, and it will undoubtedly reveal new aspects of the disk structure. This technique has equally exciting applications to Algol-type binaries, where it has yet to be applied. Full orbit studies of long-period Algols may give us our best look at disks that do not have the complications of CVs or the short-period Algols. They may be the disks that we can most directly compare with theory.

REFERENCES

1. WYSE, A. B. 1934. Lick Obs. Bull. No. 464 **17**: 37.
2. JOY, A. H. 1942. Publ. Astron. Soc. Pac. **54:** 35.
3. STRUVE, O. 1948. Publ. Astron. Soc. Pac. **60:** 160.
4. ———. 1949. Mon. Not. R. Astron. Soc. **109:** 487.
5. STRUVE, O. & S.-S. HUANG. 1957. O.N.R.A.S. 3(19): 161.
6. CRAWFORD, J. A. 1955. Astrophys. J. **121:** 71.
7. FRANK, J., A. R. KING & D. J. RAINE. 1985. Accretion Power in Astrophysics. Cambridge Univ. Press. Cambridge, England.
8. LUBOW, S. H. & F. H. SHU. 1975. Astrophys. J. **198:** 383.
9. KAITCHUCK, R. H., R. K. HONEYCUTT & E. M. SCHLEGEL. 1985. Publ. Astron. Soc. Pac. **97:** 1178.
10. OLSON, E. C. 1980. Astrophys. J. **241:** 257.
11. KAITCHUCK, R. H. & R. K. HONEYCUTT. 1982. Astrophys. J. **258:** 224.
12. KAITCHUCK, R. H., R. K. HONEYCUTT & D. R. FAULKNER. 1989. Astrophys. J. **339:** 420.
13. KAITCHUCK, R. H. & E. A. PARK. 1988. Astrophys. J. **325:** 225.
14. KAITCHUCK, R. H. 1989. Space Sci. Rev. **50:** 51.
15. CRAWFORD, R. C. 1981. Ph.D. dissertation, Univ. of California, Los Angeles.
16. PLAVEC, M. J. & J. J. DOBIAS. 1983. Astrophys. J. **272:** 206.
17. PETERS, G. J. & R. S. POLIDAN. 1984. Astrophys. J. **282:** 745.
18. KAITCHUCK, R. H. 1988. Publ. Astron. Soc. Pac. **100:** 594.
19. PETERS, G. J. 1989. Space Sci. Rev. **50:** 9.
20. HORNE, K. 1991. *In* Structure and Emission Properties of Accretion Disks, Int. Astronomical Union Colloquium No. 129. In press.
21. KAITCHUCK, R. H., E. M. SCHLEGEL & P. A. HANTZIOS. 1990. *In* Accretion-Powered Compact Binaries, C. W. Mauche, Ed.: 83. Cambridge Univ. Press. Cambridge, England.
22. HONEYCUTT, R. K., R. H. KAITCHUCK & E. M. SCHLEGEL. 1987. Astrophys. J., Suppl. Ser. **65:** 451.
23. KRAFT, R. P. 1961. Science **134:** 1433.
24. HORNE, K. 1985. Mon. Not. R. Astron. Soc. **213:** 129.
25. HORNE, K. & R. F. STIENING. 1985. Mon. Not. R. Astron. Soc. **216:** 933.
26. MARSH, T. R. & K. HORNE. 1988. Mon. Not. R. Astron. Soc. **235:** 269.

27. GORDON, R., G. T. HERMAN & S. A. JOHNSON. 1975. Sci. Am. **233:** 56, Oct.
28. HORNE, K. 1991. Paper presented at the 12th North American Conference on Cataclysmic Variables and Related Objects.
29. KAITCHUCK, R. H. 1991. Paper presented at the 12th North American Conference on Cataclysmic Variables and Related Objects.
30. MARSH, T. R., K. HORNE, E. M. SCHLEGEL, R. K. HONEYCUTT & R. H. KAITCHUCK. 1990. Astrophys. J. **364:** 637.
31. KAITCHUCK, R. H., *et al.* In preparation.

The Oscillations and Stability of Rotating Fluids: The Two-Potential Formalism[a]

JAMES R. IPSER[b] AND LEE LINDBLOM[c]

[b]Department of Physics
University of Florida
Gainesville, Florida 32611

[c]Department of Physics
Montana State University
Bozeman, Montana 59717

INTRODUCTION

Rotation plays an essential role in determining the observable properties of a number of interesting astrophysical phenomena, for example, the accretion disks that we observe as compact x-ray sources and active galactic nuclei, and the rapidly rotating neutron stars that we observe as pulsars. This paper is concerned with the mathematical problem of describing the oscillations and determining the stability of these objects. Such oscillations may eventually be observed as temporal variations in the radiation emitted by these sources. And, the effects of such instabilities may eventually be observed either directly—by watching the dynamical evolution of unstable objects, such as too-rapidly rotating supernova cores—or indirectly—by measuring the physically allowed range of equilibrium states, such as the maximum angular velocities of neutron stars. The quantitative understanding of the oscillations and stability of rotating self-gravitating fluids must form the foundation for any deep understanding of those observations that measure the dynamics of these astrophysical phenomena.

A mathematical technique—the two-potential formalism—has been developed in recent years[1-3] that provides a relatively simple and elegant description of the oscillations of rotating self-gravitating fluids. In this approach the equations that describe these pulsations are reduced to an eigenvalue problem whose eigenfunctions are a pair of scalar potentials: one potential that describes the hydrodynamic perturbations and a second that describes the gravitational perturbations of the fluid. All other perturbation quantities, such as the fluid's velocity perturbation or the Lagrangian displacement, are determined as linear combinations of these potentials and their derivatives. This formalism was designed to describe the adiabatic oscillations of equilibrium fluid states that may have arbitrary differential rotation, and an arbitrary—possibly nonbarotropic—equation of state.[3] The first application of this formalism was to evaluate numerically the modes of rapidly rotating neutron stars.[4,5] The effects of gravitational radiation and viscosity on the stability of those modes have also been determined using these techniques.[6] The mathematical simplification

[a]This research was supported by National Science Foundation Grants PHY-8906915 and PHY-9019753, and by National Aeronautics and Space Administration Grant NAGW-2951.

that leads to the two-potential formalism has proved to be remarkably adaptable. It has been extended to include post-Newtonian effects on the oscillations of rotating stars.[7,8] It has also been adapted to describe the perturbations of a rotating fully general-relativistic fluid in terms of one scalar potential—to describe the hydrodynamic perturbations—and one tensor—to describe the perturbations in the space–time metric.[9] For nonrotating relativistic fluids this description reduces to an eigenvalue problem that again involves only a pair of scalar potentials.[10,11]

We believe that the two-potential formalism is a powerful tool that will have numerous additional astrophysical applications. In particular, we believe that these techniques will be useful in the study of astrophysical disks. One motivation for preparing this paper for this volume, then, is to provide a succinct review of this formalism in a representation that is appropriate for the study of disks. In particular, we present the formalism here for the case of the general adiabatic perturbations of differentially rotating fluid states that may have nonbarotropic equations of state. We also give explicit representations of the differential equations and the integral variational-principle expression for the frequencies of these modes in cylindrical coordinates. These new coordinate representations of the equations are probably the most suitable for the analysis of disks. The explicit coordinate representations of the equations presented here reveal an interesting fact that was not transparent in previous covariant discussions:[3] the variational-principle expression for the pulsation frequencies is valid even when those frequencies are complex. Thus, we think that the variational principle may be a useful tool for investigating the dynamical stability of rotating fluids.

THE TWO-POTENTIAL FORMALISM

The oscillations of a rotating self-gravitating fluid are described by the solutions of the linearized fluid equations:

$$\partial_t \delta\rho + v^a \nabla_a \delta\rho + \nabla_a(\rho \delta v^a) = 0, \tag{1}$$

$$\partial_t \delta v^a + v^b \nabla_b \delta v^a + \delta v^b \nabla_b v^a = -\frac{\nabla^a \delta p}{\rho} + \frac{\delta\rho \nabla^a p}{\rho^2} + \nabla^a \delta\Phi, \tag{2}$$

$$\nabla^a \nabla_a \delta\Phi = -4\pi G \delta\rho. \tag{3}$$

In these equations $\delta\rho$ represents the perturbation in the fluid density, δp the perturbed pressure, δv^a the perturbed fluid velocity, and $\delta\Phi$ the perturbed gravitational potential. Those quantities without the prefix δ represent the equilibrium values of those fields. The equilibrium state whose perturbations are being studied is assumed to be stationary and rotationally symmetric, and the equilibrium fluid velocity is assumed to be purely rotational. Time derivatives in these equations are denoted ∂_t, while ∇_a represents the three-dimensional spatial covariant derivative (i.e., just the partial derivatives $\partial/\partial x^a$ in Cartesian coordinates).

We are interested in the normal mode solutions to (1)–(3), that is, those solutions having time dependence $e^{i\omega t}$, where the frequency ω is a constant. Since the equilibrium configurations are axisymmetric, the angular dependence of the separated solutions has the form $e^{im\varphi}$, where φ is the angle that measures rotations about the symmetry axis of the star and m is an integer. The solutions to (1)–(3) having these properties are completely determined by two scalar potentials, δU and $\delta\Phi$, which have the form

$$\delta U = \delta U_0 e^{i\omega t + im\varphi}, \tag{4}$$

$$\delta\Phi = \delta\Phi_0 e^{i\omega t + im\varphi}, \tag{5}$$

where δU_0 and $\delta\Phi_0$ are independent of t and φ. All of the fluid perturbations are determined by these two potentials and their derivatives:

$$\delta p = \rho(\delta U + \delta\Phi), \tag{6}$$

$$\delta\rho = \left(\frac{\partial\rho}{\partial p}\right)_s \delta p + i\frac{\rho^2}{\sigma}\delta v^a A_a, \tag{7}$$

$$\delta v^a = iQ^{ab}[\nabla_b \delta U + \rho(\delta U + \delta\Phi)A_b]. \tag{8}$$

Equation (6) is essentially the definition of δU, (7) is the condition that the perturbation be adiabatic, and (8) is equivalent to (2) for these perturbations. In these expressions $\sigma = \omega + m\Omega$ is the frequency of the mode as measured in a frame rotating with the (position = dependent) angular velocity of the fluid Ω. The thermodynamic derivative $(\partial\rho/\partial p)_s$ is to be computed at constant entropy per unit mass s. The vector A_a and the tensor Q^{ab} depend only on the equilibrium configuration and the frequency of the mode σ:

$$A_a = \frac{1}{\rho^2}\left[\nabla_a\rho - \left(\frac{\partial\rho}{\partial p}\right)_s \nabla_a p\right], \tag{9}$$

$$Q^{ab} = \frac{\lambda}{\sigma^3}\left[(\sigma^2 - A^c\nabla_c p)g^{ab} + 2i\hat{\varphi}^b\epsilon^{ac}\left(\sigma\Omega_c - \frac{\Omega^d\nabla_d p}{\sigma}A_c\right)\right.$$

$$\left. - 2\omega^a\Omega^b + \nabla^a p A^b - i\hat{\varphi}^a\epsilon^{bc}\left(\sigma\omega_c - \frac{\omega^d A_d}{\sigma}\nabla_c p\right)\right]. \tag{10}$$

The scalar λ, which is proportional to the determinant of Q^{ab}, is given by

$$\lambda = \sigma^4[\sigma^4 - \sigma^2 A^a\nabla_a p - 2\sigma^2\Omega^a\omega_a + 2A^a\omega_a\Omega^b\nabla_b p]^{-1}. \tag{11}$$

The vector $\omega^a = (\nabla \times v)^a = \epsilon^{abc}\nabla_b v_c$ is the vorticity of the fluid; $\Omega^a = \Omega z^a$ is the angular velocity vector; z^a is the unit vector that is parallel to the rotation axis, and $\hat{\varphi}^a$ is the unit vector in the φ direction; spatial indices are lowered and raised by the metric g_{ab} (i.e., the identity matrix in Cartesian coordinates) and its inverse g^{ab}, and finally $\epsilon^{ab} = \epsilon^{abc}\hat{\varphi}_c$ where ϵ^{abc} is the totally antisymmetric tensor whose components have the values ± 1 or 0 in Cartesian coordinates. The Lagrangian displacement ξ_a is also determined by the two potentials δU and $\delta\Phi$ via (8) and the formula:

$$\xi_a = -i\left(\frac{g_{ab}}{\sigma} - i\frac{v_a\nabla_b\Omega}{\sigma^2\Omega}\right)\delta v^b. \tag{12}$$

The two potentials δU and $\delta\Phi$ are determined in turn by the two second-order partial differential equations:

$$\nabla_a(\rho Q^{ab}\nabla_b\delta U) + \Psi_3\delta U = -\rho^2 Q^{ab}A_b\nabla_a\delta\Phi - \Psi_2\delta\Phi, \tag{13}$$

$$\nabla^a\nabla_a\delta\Phi + 4\pi G\Psi_1\delta\Phi = \frac{4\pi G\rho^2}{\sigma}A_a Q^{ab}\nabla_b\delta U - 4\pi G\Psi_1\delta U, \tag{14}$$

which are equivalent to (1) and (3) for these perturbations. The scalars Ψ_1, Ψ_2, and Ψ_3 depend only on the equilibrium fluid state and the frequency of the mode σ:

$$\Psi_1 = \rho\left(\frac{\partial\rho}{\partial p}\right)_s - \frac{\rho^3}{\sigma}A_a Q^{ab}A_b, \tag{15}$$

$$\Psi_2 = \sigma\Psi_1 + \nabla_a(\rho^2 Q^{ab}A_b), \tag{16}$$

$$\Psi_3 = \Psi_2 + im\frac{\rho^2}{\varpi}(Q^{ab} - Q^{ba})\hat{\varphi}_a A_b, \tag{17}$$

where ϖ is the radial distance from the rotation axis. The solution of (13) and (14) for the functions δU and $\delta\Phi$ that satisfy the appropriate boundary conditions is an eigenvalue problem. One boundary condition is that the perturbed gravitational potential $\delta\Phi$ must vanish at infinity. The second boundary condition, that the Lagrangian perturbation in the pressure $\Delta p = \delta p + \xi^a\nabla_a p$ must vanish on the surface of the fluid, is automatically satisfied by the bounded solutions of these equations if the density ρ vanishes on the surface of the equilibrium configuration.

It is often helpful to have a variational principle for the pulsation equations that can be used as a tool for estimating the frequencies of the modes. Such a variational principle for (13) and (14) is given by

$$S = \frac{1}{2\pi}\int\left\{\rho(\sigma Q^{ab} - i\varpi Q^{ac}\nabla_c\Omega\hat{\varphi}^b)\nabla_a\left(\frac{\delta U^\dagger}{\sigma}\right)\nabla_b\left(\frac{\delta U}{\sigma}\right) - \frac{\Psi_3}{\sigma}\delta U^\dagger\delta U\right.$$

$$+ \frac{\rho^2}{\sigma}(\sigma Q^{ab} - i\varpi Q^{ac}\nabla_c\Omega\hat{\varphi}^b)\left[\delta\Phi^\dagger A_a\nabla_b\left(\frac{\delta U}{\sigma}\right) + \delta\Phi A_b\nabla_a\left(\frac{\delta U^\dagger}{\sigma}\right)\right]$$

$$+ \frac{\nabla^a\delta\Phi^\dagger\nabla_a\delta\Phi}{4\pi G} - \Psi_1\left(\delta\Phi^\dagger\delta\Phi + \delta\Phi^\dagger\delta U + \delta\Phi\delta U^\dagger\right)\right\}d^3x, \tag{18}$$

where d^3x is the proper spatial volume element, and the adjoints $\delta U^\dagger$ and $\delta\Phi^\dagger$ are defined by

$$\delta U^\dagger = \delta U_0 e^{-i\omega t - im\varphi}, \tag{19}$$

$$\delta\Phi^\dagger = \delta\Phi_0 e^{-i\omega t - im\varphi}. \tag{20}$$

This expression (18) is a variational principle in the sense that arbitrary independent variations of S with respect to δU_0 and $\delta\Phi_0$ vanish if and only if (13) and (14) are satisfied. The proof of this is given by Ipser and Lindblom[3] for the case of real ω. A proof is given in the last section of this paper for the case of complex ω. The frequencies of the modes are estimated by using the equation $S = 0$ to "define" ω as a function of δU_0, $\delta\Phi_0$, and m. For given δU_0, $\delta\Phi_0$, and m, S depends only on ω, and consequently the zeros of S determine ω. The stationary values of ω—with respect to infinitesimal variations in δU_0 and $\delta\Phi_0$—are eigenvalues therefore of (13) and (14). In practice the eigenvalues ω of (13) and (14) may be estimated using (18) by first selecting a set of trial eigenfunctions $\delta U_0(\lambda_i)$ and $\delta\Phi_0(\lambda_i)$ that depend on N parameters λ_i. The optimal values of these parameters and the best estimate of ω are then obtained by solving $S = 0$ together with $\partial S/\partial\lambda_i = 0$ for each λ_i, keeping $\partial\omega/\partial\lambda_i = 0$ (the Ritz method). We note that this version of the variational principle involves parameterizing both trial potentials δU_0 and $\delta\Phi_0$. When (14) does not depend on ω, a more efficient variational principle exists[3] that involves parameterizing only the single potential δU_0. In this case, $\delta\Phi_0$ is considered to be the function of δU_0 that is obtained by solving (14). However, in the case of fluids where $A_a \neq 0$ (like the hot material in an accretion disk), (14) does depend on ω, and so the more complicated variational principle given in (18) must be used.

Self-gravitational effects are often negligible in accretion disks. In this case (the Cowling approximation), the two-potential formalism simplifies considerably: The fluid perturbations are determined from the single potential δU by setting $\delta\Phi = 0$ in (6)–(8). The potential δU is determined in turn by the single partial differential equation obtained by setting $\delta\Phi = 0$ in (13). The frequencies of the modes in this approximation may be estimated with the aid of the variational principle obtained by setting $\delta\Phi = 0$ in (18).

CYLINDRICAL COORDINATES

The covariant form of the two-potential equations, (14) and (13), is simple and compact. The equations are most conveniently derived in this form,[3] and abstract manipulations of the equations are often easiest using this form as well. The covariant form of the equations also has the advantage that it can be transformed into any convenient choice of coordinates in a perfectly straightforward manner. However, before any explicit solution of the equations can be found it is inevitable that the equations must be expressed in some particular choice of coordinates. For the study of accretion disks, we feel that cylindrical coordinates are the most natural choice. Therefore, we present in this section the explicit representation of the two-potential equations in cylindrical coordinates.

Let z, ϖ, and φ denote the standard cylindrical coordinates: z measuring translations parallel to the rotation axis, ϖ the radial distance from the axis, and φ measuring rotations about the axis. In cylindrical coordinates, then, the equations that express $\delta\rho$ and the components of δv^a in terms of the two potentials δU_0 and $\delta\Phi_0$ are given, via (4), (5), (7), and (8), by

$$\delta\rho = \left\{ \Psi_1(\delta U_0 + \delta\Phi_0) - \frac{2m\Omega\lambda\rho^2}{\varpi\sigma^3} A_\varpi\delta U_0 - \frac{\lambda\rho^2}{\sigma^2} A_\varpi \frac{\partial\delta U_0}{\partial\varpi} \right.$$

$$\left. - \frac{\lambda\rho^2}{\sigma^4}\left[\sigma^2 A_z - 2\Omega(A_z\omega_z + A_\varpi\omega_\varpi)\right]\frac{\partial\delta U_0}{\partial z} \right\} e^{i\omega t + im\varphi}, \tag{21}$$

$$\delta v^z = i\,\frac{\lambda}{\sigma^3}\left\{\rho\left[\sigma^2 A_z - 2\Omega(A_z\omega_z + A_\varpi\omega_\varpi)\right](\delta U_0 + \delta\Phi_0) + \frac{2m\Omega}{\varpi\sigma}A_\varpi\partial_z p\,\delta U_0\right.$$

$$\left. + (\sigma^2 - A_\varpi\partial_\varpi p - 2\Omega\omega_z)\frac{\partial\delta U_0}{\partial z} + A_\varpi\partial_z p\,\frac{\partial\delta U_0}{\partial\varpi}\right\}e^{i\omega t + im\varphi}, \tag{22}$$

$$\delta v^\varpi = i\,\frac{\lambda}{\sigma^3}\left\{\rho\sigma^2 A_\varpi(\delta U_0 + \delta\Phi_0) + \frac{2m\Omega}{\varpi\sigma}(\sigma^2 - A_z\partial_z p)\delta U_0\right.$$

$$\left. + (\sigma^2 - A_z\partial_z p)\frac{\partial\delta U_0}{\partial\varpi} + A_\varpi\partial_z p\,\frac{\partial\delta U_0}{\partial z}\right\}e^{i\omega t + im\varphi}, \tag{23}$$

$$\delta v^\varphi = \frac{\lambda}{\varpi\sigma^4}\left\{\rho\left[\sigma^2(A_z\omega_\varpi - A_\varpi\omega_z) - 2\Omega\omega_\varpi(A_z\omega_z + A_\varpi\omega_\varpi)\right](\delta U_0 + \delta\Phi_0)\right.$$

$$-\frac{m\sigma}{\varpi}(\sigma^2 - A_z\partial_z p - A_\varpi\partial_\varpi p)\delta U_0 + \sigma^2\left(\omega_\varpi\frac{\partial\delta U_0}{\partial z} - \omega_z\frac{\partial\delta U_0}{\partial\varpi}\right)$$

$$\left. + (A_z\omega_z + A_\varpi\omega_\varpi)\left(\partial_z p\,\frac{\partial\delta U_0}{\partial\varpi} - \partial_\varpi p\,\frac{\partial\delta U_0}{\partial z}\right)\right\}e^{i\omega t + im\varphi}. \tag{24}$$

The components of A_a and ω_a used in these expressions are given by

$$\begin{pmatrix}A_z\\A_\varpi\\A_\varphi\end{pmatrix} = \frac{1}{\rho^2}\begin{pmatrix}\partial_z\rho\\\partial_\varpi\rho\\0\end{pmatrix} - \frac{1}{\rho^2}\left(\frac{\partial\rho}{\partial p}\right)_s\begin{pmatrix}\partial_z p\\\partial_\varpi p\\0\end{pmatrix}, \tag{25}$$

$$\begin{pmatrix}\omega_z\\\omega_\varpi\\\omega_\varphi\end{pmatrix} = \begin{pmatrix}2\Omega + \varpi\partial_\varpi\Omega\\-\varpi\partial_z\Omega\\0\end{pmatrix}, \tag{26}$$

and the scalars λ and Ψ_1 are given by

$$\lambda = \sigma^4\left[\sigma^4 - \sigma^2(A_z\partial_z p + A_\varpi\partial_\varpi p + 2\Omega\omega_z) + 2\Omega(A_z\omega_z + A_\varpi\omega_\varpi)\partial_z p\right]^{-1}, \tag{27}'$$

$$\Psi_1 = \rho\left(\frac{\partial\rho}{\partial p}\right)_s - \frac{\rho^3\lambda}{\sigma^2}(A_z^2 + A_\varpi^2) + \frac{2\rho^3\lambda\Omega}{\sigma^4}A_z(A_z\omega_z + A_\varpi\omega_\varpi). \tag{28}$$

In transcribing the covariant expressions for these quantities into cylindrical coordinates we have made repeated use of the identity $2\Omega\omega_\varpi = A_z\,\partial_\varpi\,p - A_\varpi\,\partial_z p$, which is satisfied by these equilibrium fluid configurations. The shorthand $\partial_z p = \partial p/\partial z$, $\partial_\varpi p = \partial p/\partial\varpi$, etc., is sometimes used to denote partial differentiation in these expressions. We note that the covariant and contravariant z- and ϖ-components of vectors are equal, $\delta v^z = \delta v_z$ and $\delta v^\varpi = \delta v_\varpi$, while the φ-components are related by $\delta v_\varphi = \varpi^2\delta v^\varphi$. The components of the Lagrangian displacement ξ^a are related to the components of the perturbed velocity, via **(12)**, by

$$
\begin{pmatrix} \xi^z \\ \xi^\varpi \\ \xi^\varphi \end{pmatrix} = -\frac{i}{\sigma^2} \begin{pmatrix} \sigma\delta v^z \\ \sigma\delta v^\varpi \\ \sigma\delta v^\varphi - i\delta v^z \partial_z \Omega - i\delta v^\varpi \partial_\varpi \Omega \end{pmatrix}.
\tag{29}
$$

The potentials δU_0 and $\delta\Phi_0$, which depend only on z and ϖ, are determined by the cylindrical coordinate representations of **(13)** and **(14)**:

$$
\frac{\partial}{\partial z}\left[\frac{\rho\lambda}{\sigma^2}(\sigma^2 - A_\varpi \partial_\varpi p - 2\Omega\omega_z)\frac{\partial}{\partial z}\left(\frac{\delta U_0}{\sigma}\right) + \frac{\rho\lambda}{\sigma^2}A_\varpi\partial_z p\frac{\partial}{\partial\varpi}\left(\frac{\delta U_0}{\sigma}\right)\right]
$$

$$
+ \frac{1}{\varpi}\frac{\partial}{\partial\varpi}\left[\frac{\rho\lambda\varpi}{\sigma^2}(\sigma^2 - A_z\partial_z p)\frac{\partial}{\partial\varpi}\left(\frac{\delta U_0}{\sigma}\right) + \frac{\rho\lambda\varpi}{\sigma^2}A_\varpi\partial_z p\frac{\partial}{\partial z}\left(\frac{\delta U_0}{\sigma}\right)\right]
$$

$$
+ \left[\sigma\Psi_3 - m\sigma\frac{\partial}{\partial z}\left(\frac{\rho\Lambda_z}{\sigma}\right) - \frac{m\sigma}{\varpi}\frac{\partial}{\partial\varpi}\left(\frac{\rho\varpi\Lambda_\varpi}{\sigma}\right) - m^2\rho\Lambda_\varphi\right]\frac{\delta U_0}{\sigma}
$$

$$
= -\frac{\rho^2\lambda}{\sigma}\left\{\left[A_z - \frac{2\Omega}{\sigma^2}(A_z\omega_z + A_\varpi\omega_\varpi)\right]\frac{\partial\delta\Phi_0}{\partial z} + A_\varpi\frac{\partial\delta\Phi_0}{\partial\varpi}\right\}
$$

$$
- \left[\Psi_2 + \frac{m\rho^2}{\sigma}(\Lambda_z A_z + \Lambda_\varpi A_\varpi)\right]\delta\Phi_0,
\tag{30}
$$

$$
\frac{1}{4\pi G}\left[\frac{\partial^2\delta\Phi_0}{\partial z^2} + \frac{1}{\varpi}\frac{\partial}{\partial\varpi}\left(\varpi\frac{\partial\delta\Phi_0}{\partial\varpi}\right) + \left(4\pi G\Psi_1 - \frac{m^2}{\varpi^2}\right)\delta\Phi_0\right]
$$

$$
= \frac{\rho^2\lambda}{\sigma}\left\{\left[A_z - \frac{2\Omega}{\sigma^2}(A_z\omega_z + A_\varpi\omega_\varpi)\right]\frac{\partial}{\partial z}\left(\frac{\delta U_0}{\sigma}\right) + A_\varpi\frac{\partial}{\partial\varpi}\left(\frac{\delta U_0}{\sigma}\right)\right\}
$$

$$
- \left[\Psi_1 + \frac{m\rho^2}{\sigma^2}(\Lambda_z A_z + \Lambda_\varpi A_\varpi)\right]\delta U_0.
\tag{31}
$$

The scalars Ψ_1, Ψ_2, and Ψ_3 that appear in these equations are given by **(28)** and

$$
\Psi_2 = \sigma\Psi_1 + \frac{\partial}{\partial z}\left\{\frac{\rho^2\lambda}{\sigma}\left[A_z - \frac{2\Omega}{\sigma^2}(A_z\omega_z + A_\varpi\omega_\varpi)\right]\right\} + \frac{1}{\varpi}\frac{\partial}{\partial\varpi}\left(\frac{\rho^2\lambda\varpi}{\sigma}A_\varpi\right),
\tag{32}
$$

$$
\Psi_3 = \Psi_2 + \frac{m\rho^2\lambda}{\sigma^4\varpi}(A_\varpi\partial_z p - A_z\partial_\varpi p)(A_z\omega_z + A_\varpi\omega_\varpi)
$$

$$
+ \frac{m\rho^2\lambda}{\sigma^2\varpi}(A_z\omega_\varpi - A_\varpi\omega_z - 2\Omega A_\varpi),
\tag{33}
$$

and the quantities Λ_z, Λ_ϖ, and Λ_φ are defined by

$$
\begin{pmatrix} \Lambda_z \\ \Lambda_\varpi \\ \Lambda_\varphi \end{pmatrix} = \frac{\lambda}{\varpi\sigma^3} \begin{pmatrix} \sigma^2\omega_\varpi - (A_z\omega_z + A_\varpi\omega_\varpi)\partial_\varpi p \\ -\sigma^2\omega_z + (A_z\omega_z + A_\varpi\omega_\varpi)\partial_z p \\ \sigma(\sigma^2 - A_z\partial_z p - A_\varpi\partial_\varpi p)/\varpi \end{pmatrix}.
\tag{34}
$$

For real values of the frequency ω, (30) and (31) are real; thus the potentials δU_0 and $\delta \Phi_0$ may be taken (without loss of generality) to be real. For cases where the frequency is complex, however, these potentials will necessarily be complex as well. We point out that these coordinate representations of the equations are significantly more complicated than their covariant counterparts. This illustrates why the covariant expressions are in many cases a more convenient choice for abstract manipulations.

THE VARIATIONAL PRINCIPLE

As we remarked earlier, a variational principle is often a useful tool for estimating the eigenvalues of partial differential equations. In order to facilitate the use of (18) for the study of the pulsations and stability of accretion disks, we present here its transcription into cylindrical coordinates:

$$
S = \int\int \left\{ \frac{\rho\lambda}{\sigma^2} \left(\sigma^2 - A_\varpi \partial_\varpi p - 2\Omega\omega_z \right) \left[\frac{\partial}{\partial z} \left(\frac{\delta U_0}{\sigma} \right) \right]^2 \right.
$$

$$
+ \frac{\rho\lambda}{\sigma^2} \left(\sigma^2 - A_z \partial_z p \right) \left[\frac{\partial}{\partial \varpi} \left(\frac{\delta U_0}{\sigma} \right) \right]^2 + \frac{2\rho\lambda}{\sigma^2} A_\varpi \partial_z p \frac{\partial}{\partial z} \left(\frac{\delta U_0}{\sigma} \right) \frac{\partial}{\partial \varpi} \left(\frac{\delta U_0}{\sigma} \right)
$$

$$
- \left[\sigma \Psi_3 - m\sigma \frac{\partial}{\partial z} \left(\frac{\rho \Lambda_z}{\sigma} \right) - \frac{m\sigma}{\varpi} \frac{\partial}{\partial \varpi} \left(\frac{\rho \varpi \Lambda_\varpi}{\sigma} \right) - m^2 \rho \Lambda_\varphi \right] \left(\frac{\delta U_0}{\sigma} \right)^2
$$

$$
+ \frac{2\rho^2 \lambda}{\sigma} \left[A_z - \frac{2\Omega}{\sigma^2} \left(A_z \omega_z + A_\varpi \omega_\varpi \right) \right] \delta \Phi_0 \frac{\partial}{\partial z} \left(\frac{\partial U_0}{\sigma} \right)
$$

$$
+ \frac{2\rho^2 \lambda}{\sigma} A_\varpi \delta \Phi_0 \frac{\partial}{\partial \varpi} \left(\frac{\delta U_0}{\sigma} \right) - 2 \left[\Psi_1 + \frac{m\rho^2}{\sigma^2} \left(\Lambda_z A_z + \Lambda_\varpi A_\varpi \right) \right] \delta U_0 \delta \Phi_0
$$

$$
+ \frac{1}{4\pi G} \left[\left(\frac{\partial \delta \Phi_0}{\partial z} \right)^2 + \left(\frac{\partial \delta \Phi_0}{\partial \varpi} \right)^2 \right] + \left[\frac{m^2}{4\pi G \varpi^2} - \Psi_1 \right] \left(\delta \Phi_0 \right)^2 \right\} \varpi d\varpi dz, \qquad (35)
$$

where the integral is to be carried out over the $\varpi \geq 0$ half-plane. The various functions that appear in (35), for example, λ, Ψ_1, Λ_z, etc., are expressed in terms of cylindrical coordinates in the previous section. It is straightforward (but somewhat tedious) to verify that the variation of this S with respect to δU_0 vanishes if and only if (30) is satisfied, and its variation with respect to $\delta \Phi_0$ vanishes if and only if (31) is satisfied. It is also straightforward to verify that $S = 0$ when (30) and (31) are satisfied. The calculations needed to verify these relationships do not depend on the frequency ω being real. It follows, then, that this variational principle is valid even for modes having complex frequencies. It should be suitable therefore for the study of the dynamical instabilities of rotating stars and accretion disks. The derivation of the variational principle presented here generalizes the work of Ipser and Lindblom[3] by showing that it applies to modes having complex frequencies. The original argument was based on a covariant analysis of the equations and used the fact that the tensor $\sigma Q^{ab} - i\varpi Q^{ac} \nabla_c \Omega \hat\varphi^b$ was Hermitian. This tensor is *not* Hermitian unless the frequency ω is real, however. Thus, the proof given by Ipser and Lindblom[3] fails for complex ω. However, as we have shown here, the vanishing of the variations of the functional S is equivalent to the pulsation equations even for complex ω. Thus the variational principle *is valid* even in this more general case. This is one example, then, when the analysis of the coordinate representations of the equations lead to an important insight that was not apparent in the covariant analysis.

ACKNOWLEDGMENT

We thank Curt Cutler for stimulating our interest in the question of the validity of the variational principle for modes having complex frequencies, and we thank him for several enlightening conversations pertaining to this point.

REFERENCES

1. IPSER, J. R. & R. A. MANAGAN. 1985. Astrophys. J. **292:** 517.
2. MANAGAN, R. A. 1985. Astrophys. J. **294:** 463.
3. IPSER, J. R. & L. LINDBLOM. 1991. Astrophys. J. **379:** 285.
4. ———. 1989. Phys. Rev. Lett. **62:** 2777; also ——— 1989. Phys. Rev. Lett. **63:** 1327.
5. ———. 1990. Astrophys. J. **355:** 226.
6. ———. 1991. Astrophys. J. **373:** 213.
7. CUTLER, C. & L. LINDBLOM. 1991. Ann. N. Y. Acad. Sci. **631:** 97.
8. ———. 1992. Astrophys. J. **385:** In press.
9. IPSER, J. R. & L. LINDBLOM. 1992. Astrophys. J. **389:** 392.
10. IPSER, J. R. 1991. Ann. N. Y. Acad. Sci. **631:** 110.
11. IPSER, J. R. & R. PRICE. 1991. Phys. Rev. D **43:** 1768.

Gas Dynamics of Cloudy Galactic Disks[a]

WILLIAM W. ROBERTS, JR.

Department of Applied Mathematics
University of Virginia and Virginia Institute
for Theoretical Astronomy
Charlottesville, Virginia 22903
and
Mathematical-Computational Modeling Laboratory
University of Virginia
Charlottesville, Virginia 22903

INTRODUCTION

One of the central problems in galactic dynamics concerns the important relationship between the cloudy interstellar medium and galactic spiral structure. In many galaxies a grand design of spiral structure is prominent on the global scale. This prominence can be strong even though the major arms of the grand design on local and intermediate scales may be quite broken, patchy, and knotty (e.g., M81, NGC 4321, and NGC 5364). In other galaxies numerous spurs, arm branchings, and interarm bridges are evident eminating from the major spiral arms. For many such systems these features on local and intermediate scales appear to coexist as manifestations with a global grand design of spiral structure (e.g., M51 and NGC 1232). Other galaxies exhibit even more dominant local and intermediate scale features as well as multiple arm structures (e.g., M101) in place of a clearcut grand design. In other systems only flocculent patterns are apparent (e.g., NGC 2841).

What underlies the dynamical behavior of galaxies that can make possible such dramatically complex morphologies? What provides for the diverse variety of morphological structures? What role does the cloudy interstellar medium play? Are the dominant physical mechanisms and fundamental dynamical processes that underlie the cloudy interstellar medium instrumental in helping to account for such spiral structures and morphologies?

Roberts *et al.*[1] address these and other questions focused on the important relationship between the cloudy interstellar medium and galactic spiral structure. In the present paper, we provide an overview of the underlying gas dynamics of cloudy galactic disks and report further results. By the use of computer simulation of the *self-gravitating gaseous and young stellar association component* of cloudy galactic disks–*Pop I matter* in general, we find that the interstellar medium can contribute numerous, substantial irregular features to the observed appearances of galaxies. While this effect is not surprising in principle, the details of the structures produced by the self-gravitating Pop I component are intriguing.

[a]This work was supported in part by the National Science Foundation under Grant AST-87-12084 and NASA under Grant NAGW-929. The computations were carried out on the CDC 855, the IBM RS/6000s, and the AMSUN workstation cluster at the University of Virginia and the Cray Y-MP at the Pittsburgh Supercomputing Center under Grant AST880019P.

Of particular interest is the behavior of this medium[1-3] in the *presence* of a *smooth bisymmetric spiral potential*, such as that which would result from a *modal density wave* in the Pop II stellar component (Bertin *et al.*[4,5]). Even a small amount of gas can lead to a rather ragged appearance for the global spiral structure. In cases with low gas content, the resultant composite structure is found to be well organized on the large scale, but broken and knotty on local scales—highly reminiscent of that in observed galaxies. In cases with moderate gas content, the local and intermediate scale features that appear in the simulations closely resemble observed spurs, feathers, arm branchings, and interarm bridges. The shorter features resemble spurs, whereas the longer features often evolve into interarm bridges. They are seen to assemble and disassemble in the computational simulations through natural evolutionary processes underlying their formation and destruction over time. In their initial stages, most of these local irregular features are found to originate from density clumps and knots that form within the major spiral arms. Subsequently, they appear to open outwards at higher pitch angles than the main arms. Finally, they are seen to experience considerable shear and stretching under galactic differential rotation.

In contrast in the *absence* of a global spiral field, the self-gravity of the Pop I "gas and young stellar association" matter is found to produce flocculent structure.[1] This is a striking result, since it indicates that spiral features constituting flocculent structure without a global grand design can be produced by the *Pop I component alone,* even if the Pop II stellar component is completely unresponsive (i.e., stable). These flocculent features originate in the Pop I component at locations spanning the full angular extent of the disk. This is in contrast to the stubbier spurs that appear to eminate from the major arms in the grand design cases.

MODEL OF THE CLOUDY INTERSTELLAR MEDIUM

Before viewing selected types of the spiral structures and morphologies found in the computations, we shall focus on the *physical model* adopted and the dominant physical mechanisms and fundamental dynamical processes captured in the model. Constituents of the physical model include (1) a system of gas clouds with finite cross sections, initially distributed randomly over a two-dimensional disk out to a maximum radius R_{max} and given the appropriate local circular velocity plus small peculiar velocities, and (2) a system of young stellar associations that form through star formation processes within the cloudy gas. The physical model differs from earlier work[6-8] primarily through the inclusion of the self-gravity of the Pop I "gas and young stellar association" component and the inclusion in selected cases of an underlying global density wave mode that is computed.[1] The motion of the gas clouds and young stellar associations are governed gravitationally by their own self-gravity as well as by the underlying gravitational force field of the background galaxy. Cases are considered both without and with a modal spiral-perturbed component to this underlying force field with spiral forcing amplitude ranging as high as 10 percent of the background central gravitational force.

Young stellar associations assume the mass of those clouds from which they form for short periods of time corresponding to the *star formation–active stages* of the associations, after which time the associations redeposit their mass back into clouds through supernovae events. Consequently, the total mass attributed to and interchanged between these two *mobile* systems—(1) gas clouds and (2) young stellar associations—is taken together in the definition of *total gas mass* and is intended to include all *Pop I matter* in general. The ratio of the *total gas mass,* constituting these two *mobile* systems of Pop I matter, to the total mass underlying the basic-state rotation of the galaxy (prescribed as the fixed background component) is defined as the *gas mass fraction.*

In a *rotating* frame centered at the galactic center and rotating with angular speed Ω_p appropriate for the density wave mode computed,[1] we denote the position of the ith cloud in polar coordinates as $(r_i(t), \psi_i(t))$. The acceleration on the ith cloud can be decomposed as

$$\mathbf{a}_i(t) = \mathbf{a}_{0i}(t) + \mathbf{a}_{vi}(t) + \mathbf{a}_{1i}(t) + \mathbf{a}_{gi}(t) + \mathbf{a}_{ci}(t) + \mathbf{a}_{si}(t). \tag{1}$$

The six contributions of the acceleration are, respectively, that due to the axisymmetric central field (including the centrifugal acceleration), the velocity-dependent rotating frame (Coriolis) acceleration, the fixed spiral forcing, the self-gravity of the gas clouds and young stellar associations, cloud–cloud collisions, and supernova boosts. The first four contributions of (1) equally well represent the acceleration on the ith stellar association. In what follows, we focus briefly on several of these contributions to the acceleration.

Spiral Perturbed Force

The spiral-perturbed potential field $\mathcal{U}_1(r_i(t), \psi_i(t), t)$ is that of the density wave mode[4,5] utilized to drive the mobile self-gravitating Pop I "gas and young stellar association" component in several cases considered. The mode adopted is a representative one computed by Roberts *et al.*[1] by means of a procedure developed by Pannatoni[9] and used for extensive surveys of galaxy models by Thurstans[10] and Lowe.[11] Given a choice of basic state, Pannatoni's procedure determines a pattern speed Ω_p, growth rate γ, potential amplitude $\overline{U}_1(r)$, and phase $\phi(r)$ for the potential perturbation

$$\mathcal{U}_1(r, \psi, t) = C\overline{U}_1(r)e^{\gamma t}\cos(m\psi + \phi(r)). \tag{2}$$

Local spiral features of interest are found to develop on a much faster time scale than the time scale determined for the growth of the mode. In part for this reason and in part because the growth of the mode is expected to equilibrate in the presence of dissipative processes, we neglect the growth rate γ. Once the constant amplitude factor C is prescribed, the radial variation of the modal spiral forcing amplitude relative to the central gravitational force underlying the basic-state rotation of the system is fully determined (e.g., values for this ratio are typically within the range from zero to 10 percent). Such a spiral-perturbed potential field contributes to the acceleration on the ith cloud or the ith young stellar association as

$$\mathbf{a}_{1i}(t) = -\nabla\mathcal{U}_1(r_i(t), \psi_i(t)). \tag{3}$$

Self-gravity of Gas Clouds and Young Stellar Associations

The acceleration on the ith gas cloud or the ith stellar association due to the self-gravitational field of the Pop I gaseous and young stellar association component

$$\mathbf{a}_{gi}(t) = -\nabla \mathscr{U}_g(r_i(t), \psi_i(t), t) \tag{4}$$

is calculated by a Fourier decomposition technique developed by Miller[12] and Miller and Smith.[13,14] It is an *approximation* to the field produced by N point masses of mass m at positions $(r_i(t), \psi_i(t))$ and for which each mass produces a softened Coulomb field:

$$\mathscr{U}_g(\mathbf{r}, t) = \sum_{j=1}^{N} \frac{Gm}{\sqrt{|\mathbf{r}(t) - \mathbf{r}_j(t)|^2 + a_s^2}}, \tag{5}$$

where G is the universal gravitational constant. Following Roberts et al.,[1] we choose the softening length scale a_s for the Pop I matter to be comparable to the thickness of the gaseous disk. The *gas mass fraction* determines the mass m of an individual cloud and governs the magnitude of the self-gravitational field of the gas cloud and young stellar association systems relative to the underlying background gravitational field.

Cloud–Cloud Collisions

Of paramount importance is the *dissipative* character of the cold cloudy component of the gaseous interstellar medium that largely distinguishes it from the stellar component.[15–17] First of all, it is the presence of this cold, cloudy component that makes possible an overall velocity dispersion sufficiently low to promote regimes of unstable, growing global spiral density wave modes.[4,5,18,19] Secondly, in real galaxies it is likely to be the balance achieved between such moderately to rapidly growing global modes on the one hand and the dissipative nonlinear gaseous response on the other that allows the emergence of finely tuned, coherent grand designs of global spiral structures. Without the presence of a cold and dissipative gaseous component, real galactic disks may be hard pressed to produce and exhibit any such sharp, clear-cut structures on global scales. Likewise, such cold cloud systems maintained by dissipative cloud–cloud collisions are better able to provide the appropriate environment for the effective assembling of massive cloud complexes within the spiral arms and thereby to produce fertile beds for star formation activity.

In the physical model, dissipation of the energy contained in cloud random motions takes place through carefully monitored, inelastic cloud–cloud collisions. One cloud may collide inelastically with another cloud, and a fraction of the energy contained in their relative motion is dissipated. Let

$$C_i(t) = \left\{ j \,\middle|\, \begin{array}{l} \text{clouds } i \text{ and } j \text{ are in the same bin, are ap-} \\ \text{proaching each other, and } |\mathbf{r}_i - \mathbf{r}_j| < a_c \end{array} \right\}, \tag{6}$$

where a_c is the collision length scale. The collision algorithm in the computational code checks for collisions at discrete time steps. At time step k, cloud i receives an impulsive velocity change from each cloud j for which $j \in C_i(k\Delta t)$, where Δt is the time step. The effect of this change is to reverse the component of the relative approach velocity that is along the line connecting the two clouds, and to reduce the magnitude of this velocity to f_r of its previous value. If we define $\mathbf{r}_{ij} = \mathbf{r}_i - \mathbf{r}_j$ and $\hat{r}_{ij} = \mathbf{r}_{ij}/|\mathbf{r}_{ij}|$, this prescription may be written as

$$\mathbf{a}_{ci}(t) = \sum_{k=0}^{K} \sum_{j \in C_i(k\Delta t)} \left(-\frac{1}{2}(1 + f_{r_{ij}})\right)\left[\left(\frac{d\mathbf{r}_i}{dt} - \frac{d\mathbf{r}_j}{dt}\right) \cdot \hat{r}_{ij}\right] \delta(t - k\Delta t)\hat{r}_{ij},\tag{7}$$

where K denotes the total number of time steps in the computations.

The restitution coefficient f_r is defined by

$$f_{r_{ij}} = \frac{b^{-1} + f_{r_{min}}\{[(d\mathbf{r}_i/dt) - (d\mathbf{r}_j/dt)] \cdot r_{ij}\}}{b^{-1} + \{[(d\mathbf{r}_i/dt) - (d\mathbf{r}_j/dt)] \cdot \hat{r}_{ij}\}}\tag{8}$$

$$b^{-1} = \left(\frac{f_{r_0} - f_{r_{min}}}{1 - f_{r_0}}\right)\sqrt{\pi}\, v_d,\tag{9}$$

where representative values are adopted for v_d, $f_{r_{min}}$, and f_{r_0} in various cases considered.

The computational evolution proceeds in fixed time steps of duration Δt; however, the collision algorithm is more sophisticated in that it captures every collision at the appropriate time and location of occurrence within each time step. It should be noted that colliding clouds are not assumed to have to coalesce into larger individual entities; instead, the assembling of clouds into *loosely associated* aggregations of large cloud complexes takes place as a natural dynamical process in which dissipative cloud–cloud collisions and local self-gravitational forces play their respective important roles.

Supernova Boosts

Replenishment of a portion of the gas cloud system's energy in random motions is allowed to take place through velocity impulses to clouds by carefully monitored supernova explosions in regions of active star formation activity.[20] When a supernova explodes within a specified distance, R_{snr}, of a cloud, the cloud is given a small velocity impulse in the opposite direction. These randomizing impulses are able to replace a portion of the random kinetic energy that is lost from the cloud system due to dissipative cloud–cloud collisions.

Formation of Stellar Associations

In the physical model adopted, clouds may give birth to stellar associations in either one of two ways. When "susceptible" clouds collide, a stellar association may be formed at the center of mass position and velocity. Since cloud collisions are strongly localized in regions of high cloud number density (collision rate goes as number density squared), this star formation process is roughly analogous to the high gas-density instabilities postulated by continuum models of the interstellar medium in spiral galaxies.

A stellar association is also allowed to form when a susceptible cloud receives a velocity impulse from an expanding supernova remnant; the resulting stellar association is given the (postboost) position and velocity of the cloud. Since one stellar association, by the effects of its supernovae, may give rise to another, this mechanism is a particular example of sequential star formation processes (c.f. Miller, Prendergast, and Quirk[21]).

RESULTS: DYNAMICAL BEHAVIOR OF A SELF-GRAVITATING INTERSTELLAR MEDIUM (POP I MATTER)

The results of the computational studies based on this cloudy interstellar medium (ISM) model for the Pop I component reveal intriguing aspects of the dynamical behavior for the Pop I matter constituting cloudy galactic disks.[1] For example, we shall see that arm branchings, spurs, multiple armed structures, and flocculent patterns can occur as natural consequences of the dominant physical mechanisms and fundamental dynamical processes that are captured within the model.

Two-dimensional Physical Parameter Space of Spiral Morphologies

First, a framework is discovered for organizing various types of galactic spirals;[1] this framework is illustrated in FIGURE 1. The two principal controlling factors that

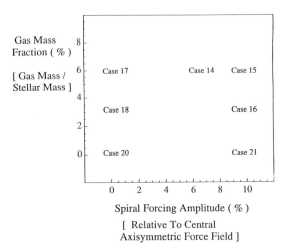

FIGURE 1. Framework for organizing various types of galactic spirals. In this two-dimensional parameter space, the two principal controlling factors that govern the spiral type are (1) the strength of the spiral driving, measured in terms of the ratio of the modal density wave's mean *spiral forcing amplitude* to the central axisymmetric force field, and (2) the strength of the Pop I self-gravity, measured in terms of *gas mass fraction*—the ratio of Pop I "gas and young stellar association" mass to the axisymmetric background Pop II stellar mass. These two factors largely determine (a) the magnitude of the global (large-scale) response, and (b) the magnitude of the local (small-scale) and mesoscale (intermediate-scale) responses, respectively.

govern the spiral arm structures and morphologies are (1) the strength of the spiral driving, and (2) the strength of the Pop I self-gravity. The first factor is measured in terms of the ratio of the modal density wave's mean *spiral forcing amplitude* to the central axisymmetric force field. The second factor is proportional to the Pop I surface mass density and is measured in terms of *gas mass fraction*—the ratio of Pop I "gas and young stellar association" mass to the axisymmetric background Pop II stellar mass that underlies the overall basic-state rotation of the system. Although there is some interrelation between these two factors, the principal effect is to determine separately: (a) the magnitude of the global (large-scale) spiral structure possible, and (b) the magnitude of the local (small-scale) and mesoscale (intermediate-scale) structures possible, respectively. Because of their rough independence, variations in the magnitudes of these two factors are found to produce a two-parameter family of general types of spiral structures and morphologies and gradations between the various general types.

We focus on prototypes from four categories of computed spiral structures (i.e., Cases 17, 14, 15, and 16), which are taken from a larger sample studied.[1] The gas mass fraction is *moderate* in Cases 17, 14, and 15 (upper row, FIG. 1) and *low* in Case 16 (middle row, FIG. 1). An $m = 2$ density wave mode is present to help drive the Pop I response in Cases 14, 15, and 16; its spiral forcing amplitude relative to the central axisymmetric force field is of *low-moderate* (7 percent) strength in Case 14 and *moderate* (10 percent) strength in Cases 15 and 16. In Case 17, no density wave mode is present. The computed spiral structures and morphologies in these four cases shed light on a new perception found for the Pop I matter in cloudy galactic disks. We shall view each of these cases individually.

Coexistence: Local, Intermediate, and Global Spiral Structures

Displayed in FIGURE 2 is a photographic intensity map of the Pop I response computed in Case 15 with *moderate* spiral driving and with Pop I matter of *moderate* gas mass fraction. Illustrated is the computed distribution of gas clouds, represented by blue patches, and the computed distribution of young stellar associations, that are in the process of forming from the gas clouds and evolving through their luminous stages, represented by white dots, at one representative time epoch (400 Myr) during the computations. Evident is a global $m = 2$ spiral pattern with frequent branching of spiral arms. It is produced by the dynamical behavior of the self-gravitating Pop I medium in the adopted cloudy ISM model under the influence of the density wave mode's regular two-armed spiral gravitational potential. This calculated mode is a growing mode, but we use the same pattern as an approximation to the stabilized mode after equilibration through nonlinear dissipative mechanisms are taken into account. The density wave mode's pattern does not extend all the way to the center of the system because of the presence of an inner wave barrier; and for this reason the Pop I response in the photographic intensity map in FIGURE 2 also does not extend all the way to the center.

There are significant differences (in Case 15, FIG. 2) between the ragged Pop I features and structures on *local* and *intermediate* scales and the invisible *global*-scale establishment behind the scenes constituted by the underlying $m = 2$ density wave mode. Local agglomerations and complexes of matter are seen to be assembled along

Case 15

FIGURE 2. Prototype for the *"moderate* spiral driving–*moderate* Pop I self-gravity" category of spiral structures [Case 15]. A global $m = 2$ spiral pattern is apparent with frequent branching of spiral arms. Gas clouds are represented by *blue patches* and young stellar associations, which are in the process of forming from the gas clouds and evolving through their luminous stages, are represented by *white dots.* Note the *coexistence* of spiral structures on *three* notable length scales: *local, intermediate,* and *global.* Numerous knots, aggregations, and agglomerations of cloud complexes and stellar associations are apparent on *local* scales; spurs, feathers, arm branchings, and other types of secondary spiral structures are evident on *intermediate* scales; and all of these coexist as manifestations within the grand design of *global $m = 2$* spiral structure.

the major spiral arms of the mode; the self-gravitational forces that lead to their formation are enhanced by the gravitational force field of these modal arms. After the assembling and formation stages, these agglomerations and complexes along the global spiral structure may undergo reverse shear for periods of time; many of these localized concentrations of matter exhibit outwardly protruding knots and spurs over considerable stretches of the major spiral arms. The spiral pattern obtained is similar in many respects to that observed in the external galaxy NGC 1232.

In evidence (in Case 15, FIG. 2) is actually a *coexistence* of spiral structures on *three* notable length scales: *local, intermediate,* and *global* scales. For example, an interarm bridge extending outward from the innermost major spiral arm to the next major arm can be seen spanning a location between 12 o'clock and 11 o'clock. A prominent spur in its formation stages can be seen extending outward from the other innermost major arm at a location near 1 o'clock. Other interarm bridges and spurs extending outward from the major arms are apparent at the locations of 3 o'clock, 6 o'clock, and 10 o'clock. Numerous knots, aggregations, and agglomerations of cloud complexes and stellar associations appear along both major spiral arms, such as the one apparent at the 7:30 location.

Particularly odd-looking structures that are frequently observed in galaxies also appear in our simulations as well. For example, "squared-off" straight arm sections are observed in the outer parts of M101, NGC 1232, and other external galaxies. Two such "squared-off" relatively straight arm sections appear in the outer parts of the computed distribution in FIGURE 2. Note the "squared off" relatively straight section of the outermost arm between 12 o'clock and 10:30 and the "squared-off" relatively straight section of the other outermost arm between 7:30 and 6 o'clock. These and other sections also show similar knotty appearances to those in M101 and NGC 1232.

Well-organized Global Spiral Structure

Displayed in FIGURE 3 is a photographic intensity map of the Pop I response computed in Case 16. Here, Pop I matter of *low gas* mass fraction and low self-gravity, but with the same *moderate* spiral driving as in Case 15, is seen to

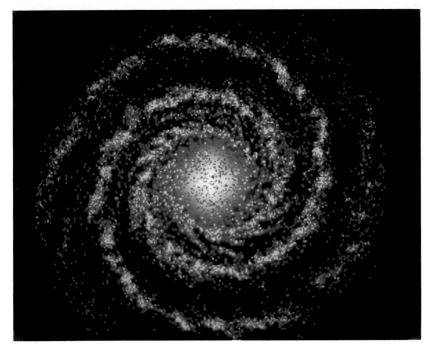

Case 16

FIGURE 3. Prototype for the "*moderate* spiral driving–*low* Pop I self-gravity" category of spiral structures [Case 16]. The modal $m = 2$ spiral driving of *moderate* strength is able to organize a coherent global Pop I response of this *low* gas mass fraction system. The *low* self-gravitational forces of the Pop I matter play a lesser role than those in Case 15. Consequently, the large-scale grand design of *global* $m = 2$ spiral structure dominates.

Case 14

FIGURE 4. Prototype for the "*low-moderate* spiral driving–*moderate* Pop I self-gravity" category of spiral structures [Case 14]. There are even more significant differences [than those in Case 15] between the ragged Pop I features and structures on *local* and *intermediate* scales and the invisible *global*-scale establishment behind the scenes constituted by the underlying $m = 2$ density wave mode. The numerous knots, aggregations, and agglomerations of cloud complexes and stellar associations on local scales and the spurs, feathers, arm branchings, and other types of secondary spiral structures on intermediate scales coexist as dominant manifestations within the grand design of *global m* = 2 spiral structure.

respond with a *globally coherent* grand design of spiral structure. It is the modal driving that organizes the coherent global Pop I response of this *low* gas mass fraction system in Case 16. The *low* self-gravitational forces of the Pop I matter play a much lesser role than in Case 15 and do not form as many features on *intermediate* scales, although numerous "knots" and agglomerations of matter are evident on *local* scales along the major spiral arms.

Coexistence: Dominant Arm Branchings and Spurs

Displayed in FIGURE 4 is a photographic intensity map of the Pop I response computed in Case 14. Here, Pop I matter of *moderate* gas mass fraction and *moderate* self-gravity, but with *low-moderate* spiral driving, is seen to respond in a somewhat less organized fashion. With *low-moderate* spiral driving force, the cloudy aggregations and complexes of matter that are assembled on local scales are somewhat less constrained in their stages of formation to locations of origin along the major spiral arms. Thus, the grand design in Case 14 does not stand out as prominently as that in Case 15 (or that in Case 16). Nevertheless, clearly evident is the *coexistence* of spiral structures on the *three* notable length scales: *local, intermediate,* and *global* scales. The numerous knots, aggregations, and agglomerations of cloud complexes and stellar associations on *local* scales and the spurs, feathers, arm branchings, and other types of secondary spiral structures on *intermediate* scales are seen to coexist as dominant manifestations within the grand design of *global m* = 2 spiral structure.

Multiarmed Structures without Global Organization

Displayed in FIGURE 5 is a photographic intensity map of the Pop I response computed in Case 17. Here, Pop I matter of *moderate* gas mass fraction and *moderate* self-gravity, but with *no* modal spiral density wave present [i.e., *zero* spiral driving], is seen to respond without any global organization. The resultant local and mesoscale features form entirely as a result of the self-gravity of the Pop I "gas and young stellar association" matter. We define the dynamical length scale δ as

$$\delta = \pi G \sigma / \kappa^2,$$

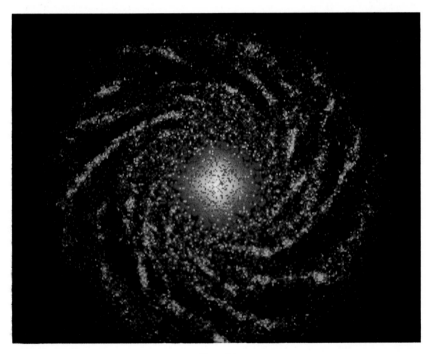

Case 17

FIGURE 5. Prototype for the *"zero* spiral driving–*moderate* Pop I self-gravity" category of spiral structures [Case 17]. Numerous patchy aggregations of cloud complexes and stellar associations on *local* scales and multiple arm structures on *intermediate* scales are entirely dominant over the full angular extent of the disk. There is *no* organized grand design of *global m* = 2 spiral structure. The local and mesoscale features and spiral structures form entirely as a result of the self-gravitational effects of the Pop I matter.

where $\sigma(r)$ is the local surface mass density for the *Pop I component*, and $\kappa(r)$ is the local epicyclic frequency appropriate for the basic-state rotation of the system. Despite the fact that the dynamical length scale δ is small ($\approx$ several hundred parsecs), patchy spiral arcs of 5–10 kpc length are seen to form purely through local self-gravitational Pop I processes. This result implies that the appearance of long spiral arms in multiarmed galaxies is *not necessarily* an indication of *any* spiral structure in the Pop II stellar component. Indeed, the dispersion speed for the Pop II stellar component could be so high as to render that component completely stable. Such a situation as that in Case 17 could arise in real systems if the Pop I matter constitutes a low-density, cool medium, thereby providing for a local wavelength that can be short (and an arm number that can be high). Of course, no overall symmetry is to be expected when the structures are produced completely locally as in Case 17.

There is a sharp contrast in appearances between modal spiral-driven cases, such as Case 15, and nondriven cases, such as Case 17. The "knots" and spurs that are prevalent in Case 15 are much less in evidence in Case 17, and the latter also shows very little, if any, tendency toward producing "squared-off" structures. The multiple arm structures that form in Case 17 also experience *no* predominant reverse shear that would be present if there were major spiral arms, and therefore undergo *no* tendency to be reoriented obliquely outward. We reiterate that the spiral structure in Case 17 is *entirely* due to self-organization by the Pop I matter. There is *no* underlying modal spiral gravitational field because the Pop II stellar component has only an axisymmetric distribution and is therefore completely inactive in regard to any possible $m = 2$ spiral driving. Nevertheless, the features that form on local and intermediate scales evidently conspire to give the appearance of patchy and multiple-armed structures (Case 17) and flocculent patterns (Case 18).

The flocculent spiral structure observed in galaxies such as NGC 2841 may be the result of the Pop I matter acting on its own within the axisymmetric field of a largely stable and featureless Pop II stellar component. Actually, the observed features in NGC 2841 give the appearance of features more like those in Case 18 than those in Case 17.[1] The features and structures that form in Case 18 are made up of somewhat more patchy constituents with somewhat lower density concentrations; their delineation is not nearly so marked and their extents are considerably less impressive than those in Case 17. The computed patchy spiral structures in Case 18 can be followed for no more than about 20° to 30° in azimuth without the patchiness of the features interfering with their continuity.

Nonlinear Gas Dynamics; Galactic Shocks

Characteristics of the self-gravitating Pop I response and the resultant prototype spiral structures exhibited are found to change dramatically along the sequence of increasing modal spiral driving (i.e., from Case 17, through Case 14, to Case 15). For the same fixed gas mass fraction in these three cases, stronger modal spiral driving is seen to better organize a coherent grand design, with the origins of the spurs, arm branchings, and interarm bridges largely within the confines of the major global spiral arms. It has been known for more than two decades that Pop I galactic matter—constituted by a cold, low-dispersion, dissipative gaseous component—in response to a spiral driving field of low to moderate perturbation force amplitude (e.g., 7–10 percent, as in Cases 14 and 15) has the tendency to pile up into strong nonlinear ridges of density enhancement and form galactic shocks along the major spiral arms.[6-8,22] The current work illustrates the extent to which such *nonlinear effects* of the Pop I component can dominate self-gravitating cloudy galactic disks. For example, displayed in FIGURE 6 at one sample time epoch (760–780 Myr) are

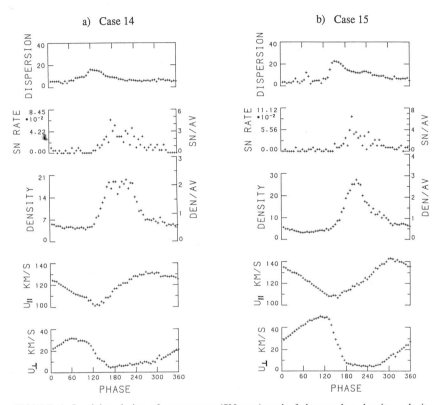

FIGURE 6. Spatial variation of supernovae (SN rate) and of the number density, velocity dispersion, and velocity components $u_\perp$ and $u_\parallel$, perpendicular and parallel to spiral equipotential contours, for the gas cloud system, plotted versus spiral phase about a representative half-annulus (1000 pc wide) at 6 kpc in Case 14 (**a**) and Case 15 (**b**). The distributions span a representative epoch (760–780 Myr) during the evolution, with the (+) values at each phase time-averaged over twenty intervals, each of 1-Myr width. Particularly in Case 15 for "*moderate* spiral driving," the sharp peak and broad interarm trough in the density profile characterizes the *nonlinear* nature of the cloud density distribution. Both $u_\perp$ and $u_\parallel$ velocity profiles in Case 15 exhibit strong *nonlinear* systematic motions. The $u_\perp$ velocity component undergoes a sharp deceleration from supersonic to subsonic near 180° spiral phase, characteristic of a *galactic shock*. In Case 15, peak-to-mean enhancements in the *postshock* region of 3:1 and 6:1 are evident in the cloud and supernova distributions, respectively. The corresponding nonlinear characteristics in Case 14 for "*low-moderate* spiral driving" are substantially less marked.

selected physical quantities computed in Case 14 [FIG. 6(a)] and Case 15 [FIG.6(b)]. Plotted with respect to spiral phase around a representative half-annulus (at 6 kpc) in the model galactic disk are cloud number density, components of velocity perpendicular and parallel to spiral equipotential loci, computed velocity dispersion among gas clouds, and computed distribution of young stellar associations currently active in supernovae explosions (SN rate).

The somewhat greater (but still moderate 10 percent) modal spiral driving in Case 15 gives rise to stronger nonlinear density contrasts and greater systematic velocity motions. The density distribution of the self-gravitating cloud system (in Case 15) is strongly peaked with peak-to-mean values on the order of 3:1 and arm-to-interarm contrasts typically 6:1, with arm thicknesses on the order of a kiloparsec. The sharp deceleration, just preceding 180° spiral phase, reflected in the $u_\perp$ velocity component from supersonic to subsonic is a striking manifestation, in these self-gravitating computations, with much-more-gradual-characteristic-rise downstream. This characteristic skewness in the $u_\perp$ velocity component as well as the characteristic asymmetry in the parallel velocity component $u_\parallel$ together delineate the galactic shock structure formed. Such skewness is less apparent in the density distribution, with the density rise occurring over the broad shock width of a number of collisional mean free paths.

This modal spiral-driven "pileup" of cold, low dispersion gas along the major spiral arms in Case 15 (and also in Case 16) thus underlies the organized large-scale distribution of Pop I galactic matter along a coherent global pattern. Self-gravitational effects of the Pop I matter itself provide for the localized partitioning of the overall distribution into smaller scale pockets of clumpy concentrations and agglomerations that can thereby form as localized entities within the overall large-scale distribution along major global spiral arms. In contrast for Case 17, these structures span radii that are shifted toward the outer parts of the disk; only there is the criterion for local instability achieved. In Case 15 the criterion for local instability is attained not only at these outer radii but also at radii further inward because of the high gas densities attained in the strong density ridges along the global spiral arms. The global spiral arms (in Case 15) thereby provide "fertile beds" for the onset of the localized self-gravity effects and the origination of the local structures.

ACKNOWLEDGMENTS

Special thanks go to C. C. Lin, S. A. Lowe, and D. S. Adler in their collaborations as coauthors on the work[1] recently submitted to the *Astrophysical Journal,* from which this paper constitutes an offspring. Thanks also go to R. H. Miller, B. F. Smith, B. G. Elmegreen, D. M. Elmegreen, and F. H. Shu for stimulating discussions. R. H. Miller and B. F. Smith kindly provided their two-dimensional polar-grid potential solver, which we modified for incorporation into the gas dynamics code used in this work.

REFERENCES

1. ROBERTS, W. W., D. S. ADLER, S. A. LOWE & C. C. LIN. 1992. Submitted for publication in Astrophys. J.
2. ROBERTS, W. W., S. A. LOWE & D. S. ADLER. 1990. *In* Galactic Models. J. R. Buchler, S. T. Gottesman, and J. H. Hunter, Eds., Vol. 596: 130–144. New York Academy of Sciences. New York.
3. ROBERTS, W. W. 1992. *In* The Reference Encyclopedia of Astronomy and Astrophysics. S. P. Maran, Ed.: 218–221. Van Nostrand Reinhold. New York.

4. BERTIN, G., C. C. LIN, S. A. LOWE & R. P. THURSTANS. 1989. Astrophys. J. **338:** 78.
5. ————. 1989. Astrophys. J. **338:** 104.
6. ROBERTS, W. W. & M. A. HAUSMAN. 1984. Astrophys. J. **277:** 744.
7. HAUSMAN, M. A. & W. W. ROBERTS. 1984. Astrophys. J. **282:** 106.
8. ROBERTS, W. W. & G. R. STEWART. 1987. Astrophys. J. **314:** 10.
9. PANNATONI, R. F. 1979. Ph. D. thesis, MIT, Cambridge, Mass.
10. THURSTANS, R. P. 1987. Ph. D. thesis, MIT, Cambridge, Mass.
11. LOWE, S. A. 1988. Ph. D. thesis, MIT, Cambridge, Mass.
12. MILLER, R. H. 1976. J. Comput. Phys. **21:** 400.
13. MILLER, R. H. & B. F. SMITH. 1979. Astrophys. J. **227:** 407.
14. ————. 1979. Astrophys. J. **227:** 785.
15. KALNAJS, A. J. 1972. Astrophys. Lett. **11:** 41.
16. ROBERTS, W. W. & F. H. SHU. 1972. Astrophys. Lett. **12:** 49.
17. LUBOW, S. H. 1986. Astrophys. J., Lett. **307:** L39.
18. LIN, C. C. & S. A. LOWE. 1990. *In* Galactic Models. J. R. Buchler, S. T. Gottesman, and J. H. Hunter, Eds., Vol. 596: 80–100. New York Academy of Sciences. New York.
19. BERTIN, G. & A. B. ROMEO. 1988. Astron. Astrophys. **195:** 105.
20. LEVINSON, F. H. & W. W. ROBERTS. 1981. Astrophys. J. **245:** 465.
21. MILLER, R. H., K. H. PRENDERGAST & W. J. QUIRK. 1970. Astrophys. J. **161:** 903.
22. ROBERTS, W. W. 1969. Astrophys. J. **158:** 123.

Observations and Models of a Selected Group of Barred Spiral Galaxies[a]

S. T. GOTTESMAN

Department of Astronomy
University of Florida
Gainesville, Florida 32611

INTRODUCTION

The galaxy program at the University of Florida received its initial support from the National Science Foundation in 1981. Essentially we have been concerned with barred spiral systems. The purpose of the program is to study the dynamics and distribution of matter in these systems. We have attempted to make this an observationally driven program for which the observations are used to constrain the parameters of our theoretical models.

Primarily, we employ the Very Large Array (VLA) Telescope of the National Radio Astronomy Observatory to obtain high-resolution data on the kinematics and distribution of atomic hydrogen. Our selection criteria emphasize isolation, angular size, HI surface brightness, structural symmetry, and the availability of photometry. Typically, our angular resolution is about 20″, and our velocity resolution about 25 km/sec (for NGC 1073 it was 13 km/sec). This material is combined with infrared (IR) data (graciously given to us by D. and B. Elmegreen, P. Grosbol, and R. Buta), which are used to obtain the underlying stellar (mass) distribution. We have published the observations[1-4] and theoretical analyses[5-7] of NGC 1073, 1300, 3359, 3992, and 4731 (observations only of NGC 4731).

Our approach has been to gather high-quality observations at radio, IR, and optical wavelengths. Then for each system we specify mass distributions for the background disk and bar, etc., that are consistent with these data. The model bar is rotated at a specified pattern velocity (regarded as a free parameter) and we calculate the response of the massless, gaseous disk. If successful, a model would have the same gaseous surface density and radial velocity pattern as the observed galaxy, when viewed at the same orientation. In this review, I will briefly outline some of our findings and then note the current extension of the project.

PHASE 1: OBSERVATIONS AND MODELS

NGC 1073: The gas distribution in this system is dominated by a broad ring and does not show any grand design, although bright optical features are associated with HI counterparts. Unlike most of the other galaxies in this study, NGC 1073 does reveal a significant gas bar.

[a]This research was supported by the National Science Foundation under Grants AST 81-16312 and AST 90-22827.

Velocity irregularities are seen, especially where the line of sight crosses the ring. The rotation rises in the bar region, flattens in the disk, and then falls at the edge of the disk. This is seen in both halves of the galaxy and may indicate that the mass of the disk is truncated. This "signature" is less pronounced than for NGC 3992.

In the models, a disk and triaxial bar were sufficient to produce the ring but not the velocity irregularities. However, the mass of the bar could not be greater than about 7 percent of the disk or its kinematic effects would be seen in the rotation law. To perturb the velocity field a mild oval distortion had to be employed, but it could not be very large or else it produced spiral features. The pattern speed of the bar was well constrained and put the corotation radius at or just beyond the end of the bar. No halo was required to model this system successfully.

NGC 1300: Strong spiral arms are observed in the atomic gas. These arms correspond very well with their optical counterparts. However, they are somewhat asymmetrical, and are offset slightly from the peak of the HI features. Also, the arms show a break in their structure; they are more open at larger than at smaller radii. This kink may be caused by resonances in the stellar orbits. Another prominent feature is the deep central hole in the atomic gas. This depleted zone is elliptical in shape with a semimajor axis length close to that of the bar. This shape may indicate a dynamical origin for the deficit (as in the case of NGC 3992). Alternatively, gas in the bar region may be in molecular form.

In the velocity field, irregularities are noted where the line of sight crosses the spiral arms and are probably the result of associated streaming effects. Outside the bar region a rotation curve can be constructed.

A reasonably successful model was produced for this system. Based on the rotation curve, the axisymmetric mass distribution was represented by a Toomre, $n = 1$ disk. A triaxial bar, constrained by the IR data was added, but was unsuccessful in generating spiral structure, because its forces are small in the spiral arm region; but a supermassive bar is not indicated by the rotation law. The mass of this feature cannot be more than about 9 percent of the disk. However, the large-scale effects were well reproduced by employing an $l = 2$ oval distortion. Halos were added to the model, but had little effect, beyond altering the total mass of the disk and the magnitude of the oval distortion required. Thus, halos are not necessary in the models. The model was not totally successful in reproducing the noncircular effects observed, and the pitch angle of the model arms was too large. However, the pattern velocity was well determined and placed the corotation radius just beyond the end of the bar.

NGC 3359: This galaxy is well resolved in HI. The gas and optical arms correlate strongly, and very significant velocity perturbations are associated with these features. In addition, patchy, low-density, armlike extensions exist well beyond the optical disk of the system, which may lie in the fundamental plane. The central zone is not significantly reduced in HI, although the bar is not observed in the atomic gas. The effect of the bar is seen, however, as a feature in the rotation law.

Our model of this system was the most successful of all of our program galaxies. The underlying axisymmetric component was a Toomre disk of index $n = 0$ [also called a generalized Mestel disk (GMD)]. A triaxial ellipsoid bar, constrained by the IR data, was employed. However, no combination of bar mass and pattern speed was able to generate the grand design spirals that are observed. The nonaxisymmetric bar forces fall off too quickly. They have to be supplemented by an oval distortion of the disk. Indeed, such a massless bar is all that is required to produce a successful model. However, for completeness, a hybrid model was used, combining a bar (with a mass of 3.6 percent of the disk and a mass/luminosity (M/L) of 0.6 that of the disk) with an $l = 2$ oval distortion. The pattern speed was well determined and set the corotation radius at or just beyond the end of the bar. No halo was required or incorporated in this model.

NGC 3992: The gas distribution shows a sharply defined edge with some distant low-density extensions at radii greater than that of the disk. Except near the edge of the disk, the spiral features are poorly resolved. There is a substantial deficit of gas (atomic and molecular) in the center of the system. This depleted region is elongated along the bar axis and has the same dimensions as the bar, and may be dynamically generated by the bar.

Owing to the relatively low resolution, the velocity field shows only mild perturbations (not as strong as in NGC 3359). However, there is a strong discontinuity in the "isovels" as the line of sight crosses the bar, an associated streaming effect. A pronounced drop is observed in the rotation velocity at the radius of the disk (greater than found for NGC 1073). It is observed on both sides of the galaxy and plausibly may be attributed to a truncation in the distribution of mass in the disk.

The models constructed for the galaxy consisted of four components: (a) an axisymmetric GMD; (b) a spherical halo, constrained by the observed kinematics; (c) a triaxial stellar bar constrained by the IR data; and (d) an $l = 2$ oval distortion of the disk.

Within the radius of the disk, a halo with a mass equal to that of the disk must exist. A triaxial bar and an associated oval distortion to the disk must coexist. Neither one alone can excite the observed gas response. The mass of the bar must lie between 18 and 30 percent of the disk. A less massive bar will not evacuate the gas from the center of the galaxy and a more massive one produces kinematic effects that are not observed. The pattern speed of the bar is well established, and places the corotation radius at just beyond the end of the bar. The mass to luminosity ratio of this bar is 4–7 times that of the disk. Were the two about equal, the bar would be unable to simulate the dynamics in the inner part of the galaxy.

NGC 4731: The spiral arms of this system are very well defined optically as well as in HI. However, they are not symmetric. Unlike several of our other galaxies, there is little or no central depression in the gas, and the bar is a notable HI feature. The velocity field shows significant noncircular perturbations, but the rotation is almost linear across the disk. Unfortunately, there is significant evidence that the disk of this system is warped (there is a nearby companion) and we have not been able to model it with any success.

PHASE 1: CONCLUSIONS

Our most successful models were for NGC 1073 and NGC 3359. However, these were the least interesting, since they required only an oval distortion to be added to the axisymmetric disk. One aspect of the problems we encountered was related to the gas code used, a two-dimensional "beam scheme."[8] The components employed, although constrained by the observations, were *ad hoc,* since there was no gravitational feedback; the models were not self-consistent. (A detailed review of the models and procedures is given by Hunter.[9]) Hence, the difficulties are associated with material bars and oval distortions, as well as the apparent inconsistency concerning halos. Bars in these models produce substantial effects in the central regions, but not far out in the disks. Ball[7] and Contopoulos *et al.*[10] have considered more realistic alternatives to an oval distortion, such as a spiral potential. Moreover, within the reference frame of these models, halos have little effect and probably are not massive.

In contrast, however, the pattern velocity appears to be a very well-determined parameter, and our models consistently place corotation at or near the end of the bar, in agreement with predictions of stellar dynamics.[10,11] The models, also, are successful in generating shocks at locations where narrow dust lanes are observed.

Furthermore, it was apparent that we had not chosen an ideal set of galaxies to observe and model. NGC 4731, while bright and open in structure, had a warped disk. NGC 3992, for which we had a wealth of material, had arms that were too tightly wound to be resolved by these observations. In addition, there were problems associated with NGC 1300 because its gas distribution is patchy and not symmetric.

PHASE 2: THE EXTENDED PROGRAM

In order to remedy the theoretical shortcomings we have been collaborating with G. Contopoulos toward building self-consistent models of barred spiral galaxies that we intend to compare with our observations. We have developed computer codes for applying the Contopoulos–Grosbol[12,13] method to the calculation of self-consistent model stellar disks and bars. Also, we have brought up in our computer environment several particle codes that will form (by definition) self-consistent simulations of gas and star mixtures. (See Hunter and Drimmel[14] and Hunter, Moore and England[15] for additional and more detailed discussions.)

Furthermore, based on the initial observations, we have chosen four supplementary systems that satisfy our selection criteria and should overcome the lacunae of our first set. We believe that these nine galaxies (the original five plus the four new ones) will be conclusive. The full panoply of phenomena associated with bars is displayed by these systems

NGC 1398: This is a large early type spiral with a bar length of 1.6 arcmin. The system displays an inner ring and an outer pseudoring. It is very symmetric with thin, tightly wound arms. The ends of the bar show small lobes that are probably caused by a substantial population of stars in the 2:1 orbital family. This galaxy exhibits the most conspicuous bulge of any object in our sample.

NGC 1530: This is a type 3 galaxy with two prominent open and symmetric arms with no confusing spurs. It is slightly smaller than NGC 1398, with a bar of length 1.2 arcmin. This bar exhibits strong, offset, dust lanes and lies within a ring and lens. The ring shows enhanced "hammerhead" structures that lead the bar. These features, as well as the dust lanes, undoubtedly have a dynamical cause.

(a)

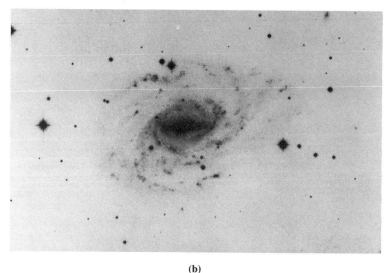

(b)

FIGURE 1. (a) NGC 1398. (b) NGC 1784. Observations of these two galaxies have been completed at the VLA telescope. (c) NCG 1530. (d) NGC 3319. Data Concerning the properties of these four, phase-2 systems are shown in TABLE 1.

NGC 1784: This is a late type system with structure that is similar to NGC 3992, particularly in the bar region, but with more open arms that will be easier to resolve and to model. The system has a narrow bar and ring with systematic dust lanes.

NGC 3319: This is a large, fairly late system with a pronounced, bright but narrow bar. The galaxy shows much evidence of star formation activity. The structure of the arms may indicate the location of several important dynamical resonances.

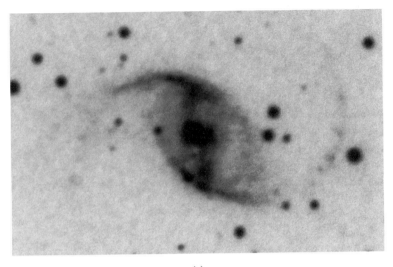

(c)

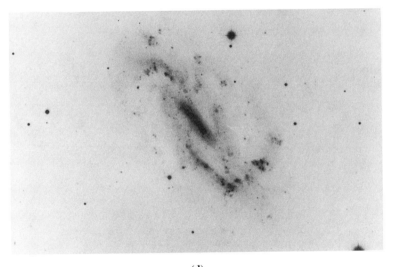

(d)

Photographs of these galaxies are shown in FIGURE 1(a)–(d), and several important characteristics are reported in TABLE 1. The additional new galaxies will allow us to study systems of an earlier type, with a more continuous sampling of luminosity class, as well as to investigate inner and outer rings and pseudorings. We have a more continuous distribution of galaxy type and shape in our expanded data base, and we will be able to investigate the properties of these galaxies in a more ordered and systematic fashion. We have illustrations of barred galaxies in all their structural variety (pure spirals, mixed rings and spirals, inner rings, and outer rings), and the older set (reanalyzed using modern algorithms) supplemented by the new

TABLE 1. Properties of Program Galaxies

Galaxy	Type	Lumin Class	Shape[b]	$D_{25}(')^c$	Bar Length (')	
N1398[a]	SBab	I	(r), [r] [R]	6.6	1.2 × 0.2	[R] = 4.8 × 3.3
N3992	SBb	I	(rs), [rs]	7.6	1.7 × 0.5	
N1300	SBb	I.2	(S), [rs]	6.5	2.3 × 0.5	
N1530[a]	SBb		[rs], [R]	4.9	1.2 × 0.5	
N1784[a]	SBbc	I–II	(rs), [r]	4.2	1.3 × 0.7	
N3359	SBc	I.8	(s), [rs] [lens]	6.3	1.7 × 0.6	
N1073	SBc	II	(rs), [rs]	4.9	1.2 × 0.2	
N3319[a]	SBcd	II.4	(s), [rs]	6.7	0.86 × 0.08	
N4731	SBcd	III	(s), [s]	6.5	1.1 × 0.2	

[a] Galaxies in Phase 2.
[b] ( ) Shape parameters from reference 16; [ ] shape parameters from reference 17.
[c] Diameter at twenty-fifth mag/$('')^2$.

material will provide a definitive data base for studying systematically the dynamics of isolated barred spirals. We will be able to study barred spirals as a function of structural and/or kinematical characteristics, as well as luminosity class. Observations commenced at the VLA telescope in the spring of 1991.

ACKNOWLEDGMENT

Throughout this project, I have benefitted from many stimulating discussions with Jim Hunter, George Contopoulos, and our students past and present.

REFERENCES

1. GOTTESMAN, S. T., R. BALL, J. H. HUNTER, JR. & J. M. HUNTLEY. 1984. Astrophys. J. 286: 471–490.
2. BALL, R. 1986. Astrophys. J. 307: 453–471.
3. ENGLAND, M. N. 1989. Astrophys. J. 337: 191.
4. ENGLAND, M. N., S. T. GOTTESMAN & J. H. HUNTER, JR. 1990. Astrophys. J. 348: 456–466.
5. HUNTER, JR., J. H., R. BALL, J. M. HUNTLEY, M. N. ENGLAND & S. T. GOTTESMAN. 1988. Astrophys. J. 324: 721–740.
6. ENGLAND, M. N. 1989. Astrophys. J. 344: 669–684.
7. BALL, R. 1992. Astrophys. J. To be published.
8. SANDERS, R. H. & K. H. PRENDERGAST. 1974. Astrophys. J. 188: 489–500.
9. HUNTER, JR., J. H. 1990. Ann. N.Y. Acad. Sci. 596: 174–180.
10. CONTOPOULOS, G., S. T. GOTTESMAN, J. H. HUNTER, JR. & M. N. ENGLAND. 1989. Astrophys. J. 343: 608–616.
11. CONTOPOULOS, G. 1990. Ann. N.Y. Acad. Sci. 596: 101–113.
12. CONTOPOULOS, G. & P. GROSBOL. 1986. Astron. Astrophys. 155: 11–23.
13. ———. 1988. Astron. Astrophys. 197: 83.
14. DRIMMEL, R. E. & J. H. HUNTER, JR. 1992. Instabilities in rigidly rotating disks. This issue.
15. HUNTER, J. H., JR., E. MOORE & M. N. ENGLAND. 1992. Numerical studies of disks. This issue.
16. SANDAGE, A. & G. TAMMANN. 1981. In A Revised Shapley-Ames Catalog of Bright Galaxies. Washington, D.C.: Carnegie Institution of Washington.
17. VAUCOULEURS, G. DE., A. DE VAUCOULEURS & H. J. CORWIN. 1976. In Second Reference Catalog of Bright Galaxies. Austin and London: Univ. of Texas Press.

Velocity Fields of Gas in Inclined Disks[a]

MARY ELAINE MAHON

Department of Astronomy
University of Florida
Gainesville, Florida 32611

INTRODUCTION

Polar ring galaxies exhibit luminous disks or rings of stars and gas that are nearly perpendicular to the central stellar disk of the galaxy. In most cases these rings deviate from a strictly polar orientation by roughly 5°–35°. If the gas in the inclined disks or rings of these galaxies is in a stable equilibrium configuration, then the gas clouds must follow trajectories defined by noncrossing, stable periodic orbits in the gravitational potential of the galaxy. In a stationary axisymmetric gravitational potential, stable closed periodic orbits are confined to the symmetry planes of the potential. Therefore, an inclined configuration of orbiting gas clouds cannot be stable in an oblate or prolate potential. Differential precession and viscous dissipation will act to align the angular momentum vectors of the gas rings with either the short axis of the potential if it is oblate, or the long axis if it is prolate.[1] However, if the gravitational potential of the galaxy is both nonaxisymmetric (triaxial) *and* rotating, a stable inclined configuration of gas clouds is possible due to the presence of the stable anomalous family of inclined orbits (*SAO's*). Of particular importance is the fact that, if a triaxial potential is rotating about its *long* axis, orbits in the stable anomalous family will be *prograde* in a reference frame corotating with the potential.

This paper presents the results of a systematic study of the *prograde* family of stable anomalous orbits in a nearly spherical, triaxial logarithmic potential that is rotating about its *long* axis. In particular, the construction of a simple model of the "spindle" galaxy, NGC 2685, from an ensemble of stable periodic orbits calculated in such a potential is described. If the orbits are suitably projected and weighted, this model yields velocity and surface density maps similar to those obtained from HI observations obtained with the Very Large Array (VLA).[2] This model includes *prograde* orbits from both the inclined family of stable anomalous orbits and a family of elliptical orbits in the equatorial plane.

The form of the triaxial potential employed in this study is given in the next section, as well as a brief description of the orbit and stability calculations. In the third section, the bifurcation sequence containing the *prograde* family of stable anomalous orbits is described as a function of the tumble speed of the potential (Ω). Also, various properties of the stable anomalous orbits in a nearly spherical triaxial potential are explored as functions of Ω. The fourth section describes the construction of an ensemble of orbits for a given model, projection of these orbits into an

[a]This work was supported in part through a summer research assistantship provided by the Florida Space Grant Consortium Space Assistance Enhancement Program (FSGC), and in part by NASA Grant NGT-40015. In addition, travel expenses to the Very Large Array (VLA) for observations of NGC 2685 were covered by a NASA–FSGC travel grant.

appropriate viewing orientation (for comparison with VLA HI observations), and weighting of the orbits by the observed HI flux. This paper concludes with a preliminary model of the distribution and velocity of neutral hydrogen gas in the galaxy NGC 2685.

ORBIT CALCULATIONS IN A ROTATING TRIAXIAL LOGARITHMIC POTENTIAL

The triaxial gravitational potential employed in this study is logarithmic and of the form

$$\Phi = \frac{v_c^2}{2} \ln \left[1 + \frac{x^2}{q_a^2} + \frac{y^2}{q_b^2} + \frac{z^2}{q_c^2} \right], \tag{1}$$

where x, y, and z are given in units of core radii, v_c is the limiting circular velocity at infinity, and q_a, q_b, and q_c are parameters that specify the shape of the gravitational potential. If (x, y, z) are the Cartesian coordinates, (p_x, p_y, p_z) the canonically conjugate momenta, and the z-axis is the tumble axis of the potential, then the Hamiltonian governing the motion of a unit mass test particle is given by

$$H = \frac{1}{2} (p_x^2 + p_y^2 + p_z^2) + \Phi(x, y, z) - \Omega(xp_y - yp_x). \tag{2}$$

For this study, orbits are integrated for fixed time steps in the corotating reference frame of the potential using a fourth-order Runge–Kutta routine. In the models considered here, $v_c = 160$ km s^{-1} and $R_{core} = 1$ kpc. These values were chosen to be a compromise between those derived from published rotation curve data for the polar ring galaxies NGC 2685[3] and NGC 660.[4] Even though the orbit calculations were performed using a specific set of model units, distances here are given in units of kpc, velocities in km s^{-1}, the numerical value of the Hamiltonian (H) in km^2 s^{-2}, and the rotation speed of the potential (Ω) in km s^{-1} kpc^{-1}.

The locations and stability of the periodic orbits are found by numerical integration of the equations of motion following the method of Magnenat[5] and Contopoulos and Magnenat.[6] The linear stability of each periodic orbit is given in terms of three quantities, b_1, b_2, and Δ, that are combinations of the elements of the linearized transformation T connecting a point in a surface of section with its first consequent.[5] Linear stability requires that $|b_1| < 2$, $|b_2| < 2$, and $\Delta > 0$. An orbit is simply unstable (U) whenever either $|b_1|$ or $|b_2| > 2$, doubly unstable (D) whenever both $|b_1| > 2$ and $|b_2| > 2$, and complex unstable (C) whenever $\Delta < 0$.[5]

THE BIFURCATION SEQUENCE

The results of a systematic study of the periodic orbits in a rotating triaxial gravitational potential that is rotating about its *long* axis are presented in this section. In particular, the bifurcation sequence, which contains the inclined family of *prograde*, stable anomalous orbits is explored as a function of Ω. The simplest periodic orbits and their bifurcations are found, as has been done for potentials tumbling about the short axis.[5,7–9]

In a triaxial potential rotating about its *short* axis the stable anomalous orbits (*SAO*'s) are *retrograde* in the corotating reference frame of the potential. If Ω is below a certain critical value, Ω_{crit}, the *retrograde* family of *SAO*'s arises by bifurcation from the z-axis family of radial orbits as H increases from zero.[7] However, if the potential rotates with Ω above Ω_{crit}, the *retrograde* family of *SAO*'s arises instead by bifurcation from the family of normal retrograde orbits in the equatorial plane.[8] For both of the preceding cases, the *retrograde* family of *SAO*'s terminates at higher values of H with the bifurcation of the stable branch of the family of retrograde orbits in the equatorial plane.[7–9]

Just as for a triaxial potential rotating about its *short* axis, there is, for a triaxial potential rotating about its *long* axis, a certain critical value of Ω (Ω_{crit}), above which a qualitative change occurs in the bifurcation sequence containing the *prograde* family of *SAO*'s. For the following discussion of this bifurcation sequence, all stability transitions are given in terms of increasing values of H.

If a potential is rotating about its *long* axis with Ω below Ω_{crit}, then the *prograde* family of *SAO*'s originates by bifurcation from the family of *prograde* elliptical orbits

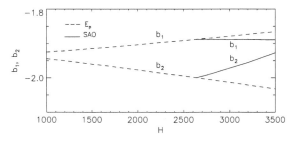

FIGURE 1. Stability diagram showing the bifurcation of the *prograde* family of *SAO*'s from the E_p family of *prograde* elliptical orbits in a rotating triaxial potential with shape parameters $(q_a, q_b, q_c) = (0.95, 0.92, 1.00)$ and $\Omega = 2.0$ km s^{-1} kpc^{-1}.

(E_p) in the equatorial plane at its transition from stable to unstable ($S \rightarrow U$). However, if the potential is rotating instead, with $\Omega_{crit} < \Omega < \Omega_{coll}$, then the *prograde* family of *SAO*'s originates by bifurcation from the z-axis family of radial orbits at its transition from S to U. The upper limit on the rotation speed, Ω_{coll}, is set by a collision of bifurcations that occurs in both the *SAO* and E_p–a orbit families.[b] For values of Ω satisfying $0 < \Omega < \Omega_{coll}$, the *prograde* family of *SAO*'s terminates with the bifurcation of the stable branch of the E_p–a family of *prograde* elliptical orbits in the equatorial plane.

In this paper, only orbits in potentials rotating with $\Omega < \Omega_{crit}$ are considered. Thus, the bifurcation sequence, $E_p \rightarrow$ *prograde SAO*'s $\rightarrow E_p$–a, is of particular interest. FIGURE 1 shows the bifurcation of the *prograde* family of *SAO*'s from the E_p

[b]A collision of bifurcations occurs whenever the stability parameters for an orbit satisfy $b_1 = b_2 = \pm 2$. For values of Ω above Ω_{coll}, the bifurcation sequence undergoes significant qualitative changes. This phenomenon was first noted by Contopoulos and Magnenat,[6] and is characteristic of three-dimensional Hamiltonian systems. It is beyond the scope of this paper to discuss the bifurcation sequence for $\Omega > \Omega_{coll}$.

family for low values of H in a potential with $(q_a, q_b, q_c) = (0.95, 0.92, 1.00)$ and $\Omega = 2.0 \text{ km s}^{-1} \text{ kpc}^{-1}$. For this potential, $\Omega_{\text{crit}} \approx 10.8 \text{ km s}^{-1} \text{ kpc}^{-1}$. The bifurcation of the SAO family occurs when the stability parameter for the E_p family, b_2, crosses the $b = -2$ axis. Note that, following its bifurcation from the E_p family, the stability parameters for the SAO family appear to converge toward one another. For slightly higher values of H than shown in FIGURE 1, there is a narrow interval in H for which the SAO's are complex unstable C. The onset of complex instability in this region occurs when the stability parameters satisfy $b_1 = b_2$. For the values of Ω considered in the models described below, the complex instability strip is so narrow that it can be safely ignored. However, for larger values of Ω near Ω_{crit}, the complex instability strip is much wider and its effects on the orbits may need to be considered if one is modeling the trajectories of gas clouds in or near this region.

    In FIGURE 2(a), the stability parameters for both the SAO and E_p–a families, in the same potential as for FIGURE 1, are shown as functions of H. Note the termination of the family of prograde SAO's at the bifurcation of the stable branch of the E_p–a family near $H \approx 6.2 \times 10^4$. FIGURE 2(b) gives a plot of the stability parameters as a function of the distance from the center of the galaxy at which each orbit crosses the intermediate axis (x-axis) of the potential. Note that for high values of H, orbits in the E_p–a family cross orbits of lower H on the intermediate axis of the potential. Orbits that cross orbits of lower H cannot be included in any ensemble of orbits used to model gas clouds. Thus, this property of the E_p–a family provides a

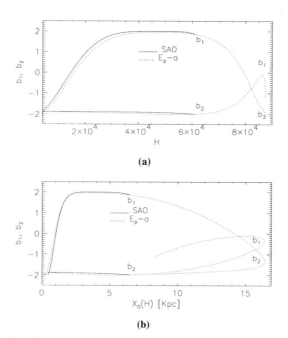

(a)

(b)

FIGURE 2. Stability diagrams showing the bifurcation of the E_p–a family of prograde elliptical orbits from the family of prograde SAO's. (a) Stability indices, b_1 and b_2, as a function of the value of the Hamiltonian (H). (b) Stability indices, b_1 and b_2, as a function of the distance from the origin that the orbits cross the intermediate axis (x-axis) of the potential $X_0(H)$.

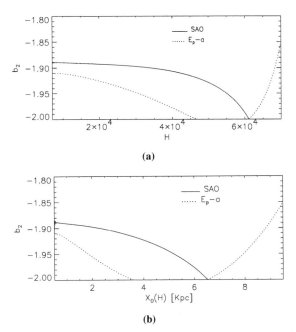

(a)

(b)

FIGURE 3. Blowup of stability diagrams in FIGURE 2 near the $b = -2$ axis to show the coexistence of stable branches of the SAO and E_p–a families. (a) b_2 versus H. Note the interval in H where $|b_2| < 2$ for both the E_p–a and SAO families of orbits. (b) b_2 versus X_0. Note the interval, $X_0 < 3.7$ kpc, where stable branches of the SAO and E_p–a families coexist.

natural high H cutoff for an ensemble of orbits used to model surface density and velocity fields of gas. A blowup of the region near the $b = -2$ axis in FIGURE 2(a) and (b) is given in FIGURE 3(a) and (b) to show the coexistence of stable branches ($|b_2| < 2$) of both the E_p–a and SAO families between $4125 < H < 46,696$. In the modeling procedure described below, only one orbit can correspond to a given value of H. Thus orbits from only one of these families can be included in the ensemble for this interval of H. For the model of NGC 2685 discussed in this paper, orbits from the E_p–a family are excluded over this range of H.

The major axes of orbits in the E_p family are aligned with the *intermediate* axis of the potential, while the major axes of orbits in the E_p–a family are aligned with the *short* axis of the potential. Orbits in the *prograde* family of SAO's, at their bifurcation from the E_p family, have their major axes aligned with the *intermediate* axis of the potential. However, at higher values of H, the direction of elongation of the orbits changes, so that upon joining the E_p–a family in the equatorial plane, the major axes of the SAO's are aligned with the *short* axis of the potential. A three-dimensional perspective plot of an ensemble of noncrossing orbits, including entries from both *prograde* families, SAO and E_p–a, is given in FIGURE 4(a). These orbits, computed in a potential with $(q_a, q_b, q_c) = (0.95, 0.92, 1.00)$ and $\Omega = 2.0$ are plotted over equal intervals in H. FIGURE 4(b) shows the orbits from E_p–a family, as they would appear in the equatorial plane.

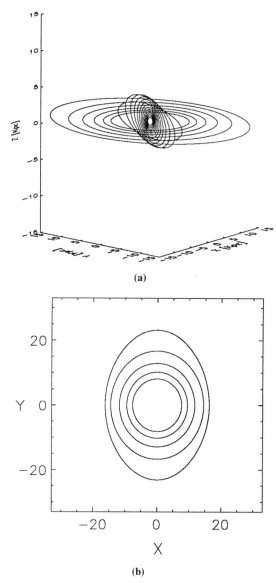

(a)

(b)

FIGURE 4. (a) Three-dimensional perspective plot of selected orbits from an ensemble including contributions from both the *prograde SAO* and E_p–a families, which were calculated in a reference frame corotating with the potential of FIGURE 1. (b) The E_p–a orbits of (a) as they would appear in the equatorial plane.

In FIGURE 5(a)–(d), for a potential with shape parameters (q_a, q_b, q_c) = (0.95, 0.92, 1.00), the maximum radial extent (R_{MAX}) of each orbit in the *prograde* anomalous family is plotted against the following quantities for six different values of Ω: the inclination (Θ), in degrees, of the orbit above the equatorial plane; the maximum extent, in kpc, of an orbit above the equatorial plane (Z_{MAX}); the maximum velocity component in the z-axis direction (VZ_{MAX}); and the orbital axis ratio (R_{MIN}/R_{MAX}). The legend in FIGURE 5(d) applies to all of the plots in FIGURE 5,

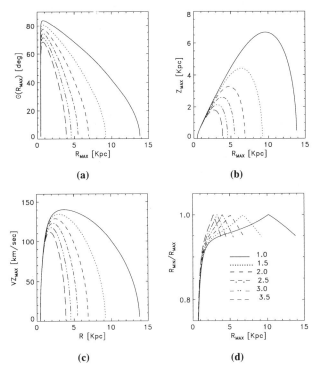

(a)   (b)

(c)   (d)

FIGURE 5. Properties of orbits in a potential with shape parameters (q_a, q_b, q_c) = (0.95, 0.92, 1.00) for six values of Ω as given by the legend in **(d)**. **(a)** The inclination of the orbits to the equatorial plane, Θ[degrees], as a function of the maximum radial extent of the orbit R_{MAX} [kpc]. **(b)** The maximum extent of the orbits above the equatorial plane, Z_{MAX} [kpc], versus R_{MAX}. **(c)** The maximum velocity in the direction of the rotation axis, VZ_{MAX} [km/sec] versus R_{MAX}. **(d)** The minor to major axis ratio (R_{MIN}/R_{MAX}) for the orbits versus R_{MAX}.

where Ω is in units of km s^{-1} kpc^{-1}. In FIGURE 5(a), one sees that, for the values of Ω considered and for increasing values of R_{MAX}, there is a steep initial rise in Θ to a maximum inclination above the equatorial plane. Beyond this maximum, Θ decreases gradually, with increasing R_{MAX}, until the *prograde SAO's* join the stable branch of the E_p–a family in the equatorial plane. Both the maxium inclination above the plane, as well as the maximum radial extent of these orbits at the point where they join the equatorial plane are *decreasing* functions of Ω. FIGURE 5(b) and (c) show that, for any orbit in an ensemble of *prograde SAO*'s, the maximum possible height above the plane, as well as the maximum possible velocity in the z direction, is also a *decreasing* function of Ω. Changes in the shapes of the orbits in each ensemble as a function of R_{MAX} are shown in FIGURE 5(d) in terms of the axis ratios (R_{MIN}/R_{MAX}). For small values of R_{MAX}, these orbits are extremely elongated, but their axis ratios increase sharply with small increases in R_{MAX}. For larger values of R_{MAX} the increase is more gradual and the axis ratios approach a maximum value of 1, which corresponds to a circular orbit. Beyond this circular orbit the directions of the major and minor axes are reversed and the axis ratios decrease, in an approximately linear fashion, with increasing R_{MAX}. Hence, the *prograde SAO*'s are elongated in the direction of the *short* axis of the potential when they join the E_p–a family in the equatorial plane.

CONSTRUCTION OF MODEL DENSITY AND VELOCITY MAPS

In order to quantitatively compare VLA HI surface density and radial velocity maps to similar maps constructed from an ensemble of orbits, the following approach is taken. First, for a potential with shape parameters (q_a, q_b, q_c) and rotation speed Ω, the locations of the periodic orbits in a given orbit family are determined, at equal intervals of H, over a specified range in H. In the models discussed below, only orbits in the SAO and E_p–a families are considered. Thus, the lower limit to H is set by the bifurcation of the SAO family of orbits from the E_p family inside the core radius. The upper limit to H is set by either the constraint that no orbits in an ensemble can cross (here, this applies to the high H orbits of the E_p–a family), or by observationally imposed constraints (such as the maximum observed radial velocity). And, since these orbits will later be weighted according to a polynomial in H, the ensemble must be further constrained so that there is only one orbit associated with each value of H. This constraint must be explicitly imposed whenever stable branches of both the E_p–a and SAO families exist over the same interval in H.

Second, each orbit in the ensemble is integrated, with equal time steps, over exactly one orbital period. For every Nth time step during the integration, where N is fixed for the ensemble, the corresponding position and velocity vectors for the orbit are transformed to an inertial coordinate frame, projected into an appropriate viewing orientation and binned in position and velocity. The projection, effected through three rotations and a reflection, puts the coordinates in the left-handed reference frame of a hypothetical observer in which the positive x-, y-, and z-axes point west, north, and along the observer's line of sight to the galaxy, respectively. This is in keeping with the observer's convention that positive radial velocities (with respect to the central systemic velocity of the galaxy) are to be interpreted as recessional. Each projected point is then binned into a cell in a three-dimensional array, or model map cube, $M(x, y, v_z)$. Since this analysis entails a quantitative comparison of moment maps derived from M, to moments derived from a similar VLA map cube, the linear cell sizes and channel velocity widths for M are set by the angular cell size and velocity resolution of the VLA maps. During the projection and binning process, if any projected position or velocity falls outside of the range of the map cube as defined by the cube of observed maps, this orbit and all of its projected points are eliminated from the ensemble.

Third, the number of points in each model map cell must be weighted by the observations. To do this, it is assumed that the number of points in each cell from a given orbit is some function of the value of the Hamiltonian, H. For simplicity, this weighting function is assumed to take the form of a polynomial. Therefore, if N_k is defined as the total number of points calculated for the kth orbit, n_{ijkl} as the number of points in the cell $M(i, j, l)$ due to the kth orbit, w as the polynomial weighting function of order m, and N_{orb} as the total number of orbits in the ensemble, then the total number of points in each cell summed over all of the orbits in the ensemble, F_{ijl}, is given by

$$F_{ijl} = \sum_{k=1}^{N_{orb}} w_k \cdot \frac{n_{ijkl}}{N_k}, \tag{3}$$

where $w_k = a_0 + a_1 \cdot H_k + a_2 \cdot H_k^2 + \cdots + a_m \cdot H_k^m$. Consider the matrix F, where

$$F_{ij} = \Delta v_{ch} \sum_{l=1}^{nch} F_{ijl}, \tag{4}$$

and Δv_{ch} is the channel width in velocity. The coefficients of w are determined by a least squares fit of the basis functions of F to the zeroth moment of the VLA cube (the integrated intensity map). Given the coefficients of w, the weighted flux in each element in the model map cube is obtained from (3).

Prior to calculating the moments of the model radiation field, the model maps in the weighted cube are corrected for the response of the VLA antenna beam. Therefore, each map in the cube is convolved with a synthesized elliptical Gaussian "beam" derived from a least squares fit of an elliptical Gaussian to the response of the VLA to a point source. The zeroth and first moments of the model radiation field, $M0$ and $M1$ are then computed as defined below.

$$M0 = \Delta v \cdot \sum_{l=1}^{nch} M(i, j, l), \tag{5}$$

and

$$M1 = \frac{\sum_{l=1}^{nch} v_l \cdot M(i, j, l)}{\sum_{l=1}^{nch} M(i, j, l)}. \tag{6}$$

The zeroth moment gives a map of the integrated intensity, while the first moment gives a map of the intensity weighted mean velocity along the observer's line of sight. These maps can be subtracted from their observed counterparts for examination of the residuals to help determine which parameters (projection angles, shape parameters, or rotation speed) need to be adjusted to improve the model.

RESULTS AND CONCLUSION

Integrated intensity and intensity weighted, mean velocity maps of NGC 2685, derived from VLA observations are presented in FIGURE 6(a) and (c), respectively.[2]

These VLA maps were produced from naturally weighted channel maps with a spatial resolution (or half-power beam width) of 34.3″ × 33.6″, and a velocity resolution of 20.7 km s^{-1}. FIGURE 6(b) and (c) give maps derived from an ensemble of orbits calculated in the potential of (1) with $(q_a, q_b, q_c) = (0.95, 0.92, 1.00)$ and $\Omega =$

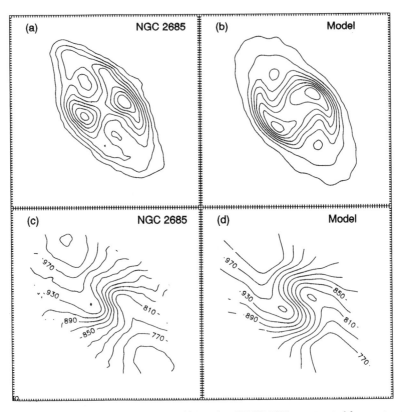

FIGURE 6. (a) VLA map of the integrated intensity of NGC 2685, constructed from naturally weighted channel maps with a spatial resolution of 34.3″ × 33.6″. Contour levels are for (0.2, 0.3, 0.4, 0.6, 0.8, 1.0) × (map maximum). (b) Model of the integrated intensity constructed from projected orbits in a triaxial potential rotating about its long axis. Contour levels are for (0.2, 0.3, 0.4, 0.6, 0.8, 1.0) × (map maximum). The shape and rotation parameters for this potential are $(q_a, q_b, q_c) = (0.96, 0.94, 1.00)$ and $\Omega = 2.0$. (c) VLA map of the intensity weighted mean velocity for NGC 2685. The velocity resolution of the observations is 20.7 km s^{-1}. (d) The intensity weighted mean velocity derived from the model. Axes for maps in (a)–(d) are marked at intervals of 9 arcsec/cell, or 0.5 kpc/cell for $H_0 = 75$ km s^{-1} kpc^{-1}.

2.0. The orbits have been projected on the sky and weighted by the map in FIGURE 6(a) with a fifth-order polynomial weighting function in H. The maps in these figures demonstrate that it is possible to reproduce the principal features of both the integrated intensity and intensity weighted, mean velocity maps, with a simple model constructed from orbits in a nearly spherical triaxial potential that is rotating about its *long* axis. One of the main advantages to the model presented here is that it allows for the stars and gas in the plane of the central stellar disk to rotate in the same sense. If the density and velocity of HI in polar ring galaxies can be accounted for by models of orbits in such potentials, such models could provide important constraints on the overall distribution of matter around these galaxies.

ACKNOWLEDGMENTS

In developing the ideas presented here I have benefited from very helpful interactions with Professors George Contopoulos and Henry Kandrup.

REFERENCES

1. TOHLINE, J. E., G. F. SIMONSON & N. CALDWELL. 1982. Astrophys. J. **252:** 92.
2. MAHON, M. E. 1991. In preparation.
3. SCHECHTER, P. L. & J. E. GUNN. 1978. Astronomical. J. **83:** 1360.
4. BENVENUTI, P., M. CAPACCIOLI & S. D'ODORICO. 1976. Astron. Astrophys. **53:** 141.
5. MAGNENAT, P. 1982. Astron. Astrophys. **108:** 89.
6. CONTOPOULOS, G. & P. MAGNENAT. 1985. Celestial Mech. **37:** 38.
7. HEISLER, J., D. MERRITT & M. SCHWARZSCHILD. 1982. Astrophys. J. **258:** 490.
8. MARTINET, L. & D. PFENNIGER. 1987. Astron. Astrophys. **173:** 81.
9. MARTINET, L. & T. DE ZEEUW. 1988. Astron. Astrophys. **206:** 269.

Nonlinear Self-consistent Models of Barred Galaxies[a]

G. CONTOPOULOS[b, c] AND D. E. KAUFMANN[b]

[b]*Department of Astronomy*
University of Florida
Gainesville, Florida 32611

[c]*Department of Astronomy*
University of Athens
Athens, Greece

INTRODUCTION

The problem of nonlinear self-consistent models of *spiral* galaxies has been considered already.[1–3] A review of this problem and its relation with the *linear* problem, and the problem of *barred* galaxies was given in a previous Florida Workshop.[4]

In the nonlinear case we assume that the amplitude of the spirals is strong; therefore, the nonlinear effects are important. Such effects are the gaps near the 2/1, 4/1, −4/1, and −2/1 resonances, leading to different orientations of the orbits on the two sides of each gap. Another nonlinear effect is the stochasticity of the orbits, which is important near corotation.

Our study is based on a numerical calculation of periodic orbits at different distances *r* from the center. Then a number of nonperiodic orbits with a given velocity dispersion are superimposed to derive the response density.

A Fourier analysis gives the amplitude and the phase of the response density as functions of *r*. These are compared with the corresponding quantities of the imposed density. This procedure is repeated with different sets of parameter values until the best agreement is found.

The main conclusions of our study are the following.

1. The response spiral agrees well with the imposed spiral between the inner Lindblad resonance (ILR, or 2/1 resonance) and the 4/1 resonance. A similar agreement exists between the outer −4/1 resonance and the outer Lindblad resonance (OLR, or −2/1 resonance).[5]
2. Beyond the 4/1 resonance the orbits give an out of phase response with respect to the imposed spiral. Furthermore, the orbits near corotation are mostly stochastic.
3. On the other hand, in weak spirals the phase difference is less important, and the stochasticity is also reduced considerably.

[a]This research was supported in part by National Science Foundation Grant 9022827. One of the authors (D. E. K.) received the support of NASA through the Florida Space Grant Consortium.

4. Therefore strong spirals must terminate near the 4/1 resonance. However, weak spirals can extend all the way to corotation and may reach the OLR. Beyond the −4/1 resonance and up to the OLR we can again have strong spirals.

5. Gas plays an important role in supporting the spirals near corotation, especially if there is a weak stellar spiral substratum.[5]

A study of the role of gas near and beyond the 4/1 resonance has been given recently by Artymowicz and Lubow.[6]

In the present paper we apply the preceding methods in the case of strong barred galaxies, with spiral arms beyond the end of the bar, and find some models that are approximately self-consistent.

One special question is to find the role of stochasticity of the orbits near corotation. In order to understand this problem we study the behavior of stochastic orbits in a simple model with different degrees of perturbation.

BARRED MODELS

We have considered several models of bars followed by an outer spiral. As a guide we have used the barred galaxy NGC 3992 that we have already studied,[5] but with a wide variation of the parameters of its models.

We employed the type of model used by Contopoulos and Grosbøl,[1] consisting of an axisymmetric background that produces a flat rotation curve

$$v = v_{max} [1 - \exp{(-\epsilon_d r)}]^{1/2}, \tag{1}$$

where ϵ_d is an inverse scale factor, and a bar component

$$V_1 = V_B \cos 2\theta, \tag{2}$$

where

$$V_B = Ar \exp{(-\epsilon_s r)}, \tag{3}$$

which is continued beyond the end of the bar r_{bar}, by a spiral in which 2θ is replaced by

$$2\theta - \frac{2 \ln{(r/r_{bar})}}{\tan i}, \tag{4}$$

where i is the pitch angle. The value of $\epsilon_s = 0.4$ kpc^{-1}.

The axisymmetric potential is

$$V_0 = v_{max}^2 [\ln r + E_1 (\epsilon_d r)], \tag{5}$$

where E_1 is the exponential integral. The value of v_{max} is 275.3 km s^{-1} and $\epsilon_d = 0.258$ kpc^{-1}.

The pattern velocity Ω_s is taken as 51.2 km s^{-1} kpc^{-1} (constant). Thus the various resonances appear at the following distances: ILR (very near the center), 4/1 (2.0 kpc), corotation (4.4 kpc), −4/1 (6.8 kpc), OLR (9 kpc).

We have used values of i of the order of $i = -10°$, and $A = 5400$ km^2 s^{-2} kpc^{-1} or $A = 4000$ km^2 s^{-2} kpc^{-1}. The present value of $A = 5400$ gives roughly the same maximum amplitude as the Florida model[5] (with $A = 97,422$).[d]

In most models the bar potential was continued as a spiral of the form (4) beyond r_{bar}, and in general $r_{bar} = r_{cor} = 4.4$ kpc. Only in a few cases we considered both a bar and spiral potential beyond corotation. Also in a few cases we considered $r_{bar} < r_{cor}$.

We used the usual criteria[1] for self-consistency, namely the agreement between the response and the imposed amplitude and phase. In particular, we used the quantities

$$R^* = \frac{(\sigma_2/\sigma_0)_{resp}}{(\sigma_2/\sigma_0)_{imp}} \tag{6}$$

and

$$\Delta\theta = \theta_{resp} - \theta_{imp}, \tag{7}$$

where σ_2 is the 2θ-component and σ_0 the axisymmetric component of the density amplitude at distance r, and θ is the azimuth of the 2θ maximum. Details about the method of calculation will be given in another paper. Here we only remark that the axisymmetric density σ_0 is not equal to the observed density, because of the existence of dark matter. Furthermore, the effects of thickness have to be taken into account.[2] Because of these two factors, $\sigma_{0,resp}$ is not necessarily equal to $\sigma_{0,imp}$. Following Contopoulos and Grosbøl we have taken

$$\sigma_{0,imp} = c_0 \exp(-\epsilon_0 r), \tag{8}$$

where $\epsilon_0 = 0.1$ kpc^{-1} and c_0 can vary within rather wide limits. If we choose a value for c_0, we only require R^* to be roughly constant, because then we can scale c_0 so that $R^* = 1$. On the other hand, we require $\Delta\theta$ to be as close to zero as possible.

As regards the initial conditions of the orbit, we found, first, the stable periodic orbits corresponding to the circular periodic orbits of the unperturbed potential. Then we added eight more orbits with a given velocity dispersion d, of the order of 40 km s^{-1}, representing a Gaussian distribution. In cases near corotation, where all the periodic orbits are unstable, we used the initial conditions of circular periodic orbits, r_c, at different azimuths around the center, and then we also added orbits with a dispersion of velocities.

Some representative results from the calculations are given in FIGURES 1–10.

In FIGURES 1 and 2 we give the response density of a bar with $A = 4000$, followed, beyond corotation, by a spiral with $i = -10°$. The dispersion of velocities is $d = 40$ km s^{-1}. The circles in FIGURE 1 represent the $4/1$ resonance, corotation, the $-4/1$ resonance, and the OLR. In FIGURE 2 we superimpose on the response figure the imposed spiral. We remark that in the outer parts the response systematically deviates inward from the imposed spiral. Such a deviation was common also in normal spirals,[2,7] and indicates that logarithmic spirals may not be the best models for the outer parts of the spiral arms.

---

[d]There is a typing error of the form of V_B for $r > r^*$ in the Florida model.[5] The correct expression, which was used in the numerical calculations of that paper, is $V_B = [A \exp(-0.4r)/r^2] (q_3 r - 1)$.

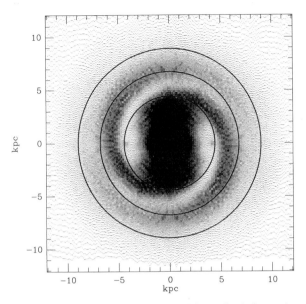

FIGURE 1. The response density in a barred galaxy with amplitude factor $A = 4000$ km^2 s^{-2} kpc^{-1}, pitch angle $i = -10°$, $r_{bar} = r_{cor}$, and dispersion of velocities $d = 40$ km s^{-1}. The four circles are: 4/1 resonance, corotation, −4/1 resonance, and the OLR (−2/1 resonance).

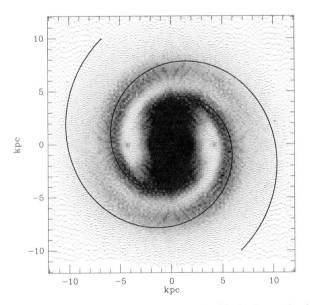

FIGURE 2. The same response density as in FIGURE 1, with the imposed spiral $V_1 = V_B$ $|\cos [2\theta - 2 \ln (r/r_{bar})]/\tan i|$ superimposed.

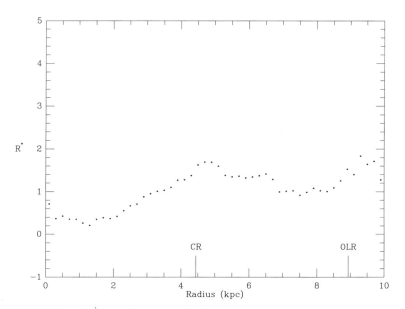

FIGURE 3. The ratio $\dot{R}^*$ as a function of r in the model of FIGURE 1. CR = corotation, OLR - outer Lindblad resonance.

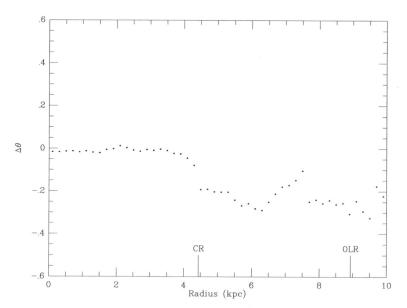

FIGURE 4. The azimuth difference $\Delta\theta = \theta_{resp} - \theta_{imp}$ as a function of r (in radians) in the model of FIGURE 1.

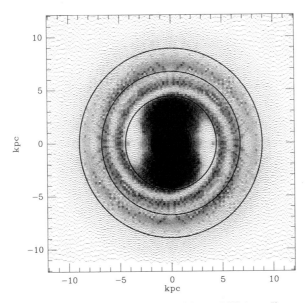

FIGURE 5. The response density in a barred galaxy with $A = 5400$, $i = -5°$, $r_{bar} = r_{cor}$, and $d = 40$. Symbols as in FIGURE 1.

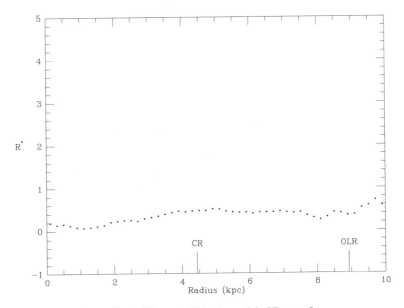

FIGURE 6. The ratio R^* in the model of FIGURE 5.

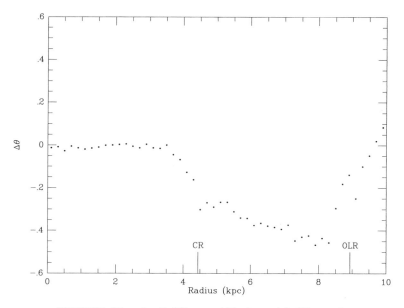

FIGURE 7. The azimuth difference $\Delta\theta$ in the model of FIGURE 5.

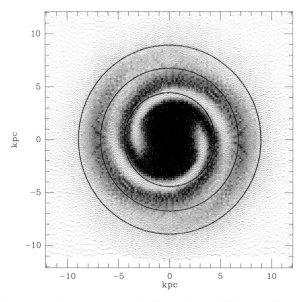

FIGURE 8. The response density in a barred galaxy with $A = 5400$, $i = -10°$, $r_{\text{bar}} = \frac{3}{4}\,r_{\text{cor}}$, $d = 40$. Symbols as in FIGURE 1.

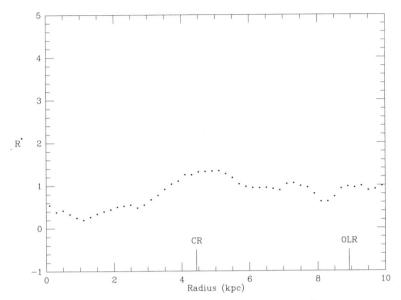

FIGURE 9. The ratio R^* in the model of FIGURE 8.

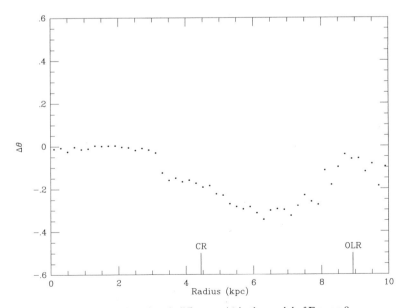

FIGURE 10. The azimuth difference $\Delta\theta$ in the model of FIGURE 8.

The corresponding values of the response to imposed ratio R^* are given in FIGURE 3, and the phase difference $\Delta\theta$ in FIGURE 4.

We notice that the value of R^* is fairly constant between corotation (CR) and the OLR. The agreement is not so good inside the bar. The reason is that in our present model we use only the 2θ-component, omitting the 4θ- and higher order components. In this way the role of the imposed 2θ-component is overemphasized with respect to the 2θ-component response and the value of R^* is reduced near the center. At any rate, our main aim was not to find the best model for the bar, but the the the spiral outside the bar.

As regards the angle deviation, this is practially zero inside the bar (as it should be because of the symmetry of the orbits around the bar), and a rather small negative deviation outside the bar of the order of -0.2 rad, that is, $-10°$ to $-15°$. In view of the fact that the spirals are rather tight, the deviation in radial distance from the imposed spiral arms is small.

Similar results are found if the dispersion of velocities is $d = 80$ km s^{-1}, but the agreement is worse if $d = 20$ km s^{-1}.

Similar results are also found when $A = 5400$, keeping $i = -10°$. But if we change i to $i = -5°$, we find the following changes. The spiral is very tight (FIG. 5), the response/imposed ratio is almost constant, but at rather low values (FIG. 6), while the azimuth difference $\Delta\theta$ varies considerably (FIG. 7). We cannot consider this model as acceptable.

An (absolute) increase of the pitch angle to $i = -30°$ gives also unsatisfactory results. Thus it seems that the pitch angle cannot vary appreciably in a model with given Ω_s and A.

Another change refers to the position of the end of the bar. By taking $r_{bar} = \frac{3}{4} r_{cor}$ we find FIGURE 8. The corresponding R^* is fairly constant between corotation and the OLR (FIGURE 9), but the deviation of $\Delta\theta$ (FIG. 10) is somewhat larger than in FIGURE 4.

We also explored the variation of A, Ω_s, and the other parameters of the model. An important decrease or increase of these parameters gave worse results. Further details of this study will be given elsewhere.

Our conclusion from this study is that our method can exclude certain ranges of parameters in constructing self-consistent models. On the other hand, some parameter values give rather good models, that we can call "approximately self-consistent." Further improvement may be realized by a better adjustment of the parameters of the models. In seems that there is not much freedom in the choice of each model if we have the main characteristics of a galaxy determined from observations.

THE ROLE OF STOCHASTIC ORBITS

A detailed study of the stochastic orbits near corotation is given by Kaufmann.[8] Here we only distinguish between weakly stochastic orbits [FIG. 11(a)] and strongly stochastic orbits [FIG. 11(b)]. Weakly stochastic orbits fill rings with fuzzy boundaries and may support in part the spiral stucture, while strongly stochastic orbits fill a large region and do not seem to be influenced by the spiral arms. In fact, a weakly stochastic orbit tends to stay longer near the spiral arms because there we have the

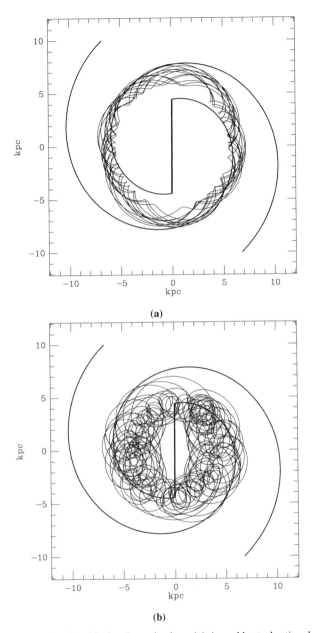

(a)

(b)

FIGURE 11. Two stochastic orbits in a barred galaxy. (**a**) A weakly stochastic orbit ($A = 1000$ km^2 s^{-2} kpc^{-1}, $r_c = 6$ kpc, initial $r = 7.08$ kpc). (**b**) A strongly stochastic orbit ($A = 4000$ km^2 s^{-2} kpc^{-1}, h (Jacobi constant) $= 105,000$ km^2 s^{-2}, initial $r = 4.06215$ kpc.).

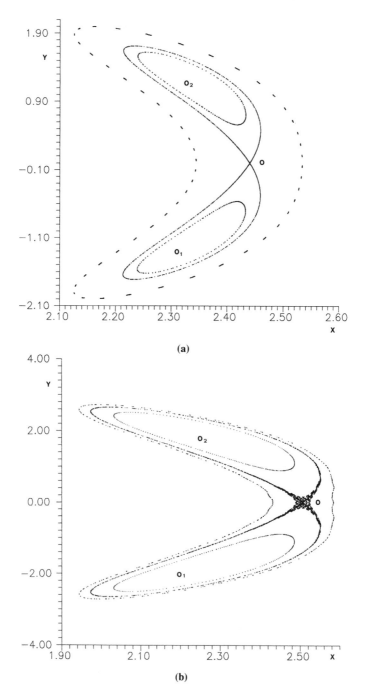

(a)

(b)

FIGURE 12. Asymptotic curves from an unstable periodic orbit O, together with some invariant curves, surrounding either of the stable periodic orbits O_1, O_2, or both. (a) An (almost) integrable case. (b) A nonintegrable case with a relatively small perturbation ($h = 23.2$).

minima of the potential. But strongly stochastic orbits pass through the spiral arms so fast that they cannot change their behavior.

In order to better understand the transition from weak to strong stochasticity Contopoulos and Polymilis[9] have studied the orbits near the "separatrix" of the main unstable periodic orbit in the simple Hamiltonian system

$$H \equiv \tfrac{1}{2}(\dot{x}^2 + \dot{y}^2 + 1.6x^2 + 0.9y^2) - \epsilon xy^2 = h \qquad (9)$$

for various values of h, and $\epsilon = 0.08$.

For $\epsilon = 0$ system (9) is integrable and the "central" periodic orbit $x = \dot{x} = 0$ is stable. This orbit is also stable for $\epsilon \neq 0$ and small values of h. But for $h \geq 22.17$ this

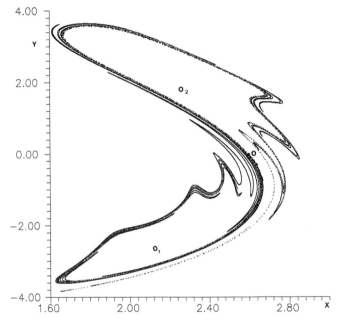

FIGURE 13. An asymptotic curve from an unstable periodic orbit O, with a perturbation larger than in FIGURE 12(b) ($h = 24$). The oscillations of the asymptotic curve (tongues) make a number of turns around both stable periodic orbits O_1 and O_2, before going to large distances in the stochastic region.

orbit becomes unstable. An unstable orbit is represented on a Poincaré surface of section by one point (or a finite number of points); from such a point emanate 4 eigenvectors in 2 different directions and 4 corresponding asymptotic curves (2 outgoing, or unstable, and 2 ingoing, or stable). If an unstable orbit exists in an integrable system, the outgoing and ingoing asymptotic curves form a single curve called a *separatrix* [FIG. 12(a)]. Orbits starting inside the separatrix form islands around two stable invariant points, O_1 and O_2, while orbits outside it form invariant curves surrounding the whole separatrix. But in a nonintegrable case the outgoing and ingoing curves intersect each other along an infinity of homoclinic points and make an infinity of oscillations that constitute the "homoclinic tangle" [FIG. 12(b)]. This homoclinic tangle produces the stochastic regions filled by nonperiodic orbits starting close to the unstable periodic orbit.

If the deviation from an integrable case is small, the area filled by the homoclinic tangle is small. Therefore the stochastic region is also small [FIG. 12(b)]. Inside the tangle there are still islands of stability, and outside it there are regions of ordered motion defining closed invariant curves on the surface of section. But if the perturbation increases, the oscillations of the asymptotic curves become very large

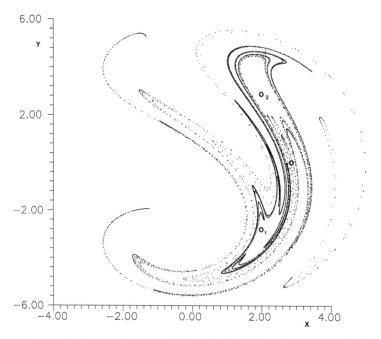

FIGURE 14. An asymptotic curve from an unstable periodic orbit O, with a perturbation larger than in FIGURE 13 ($h = 25$). Its oscillations (tongues) go faster into the stochastic region (left and right).

and may extend to large distances on the surface of the section, and also eliminate the main islands inside the tangle.

This behavior is well known. What is new in our study[9] is the form of the tongues produced by the asymptotic curves. When the perturbation is not very small (FIG. 13), the stochastic region is relatively large. But the tongues become more and more elongated as we calculate them over longer and longer intervals of time, and surround the regions of islands several times before going to a relatively large distance outward. Only when the perturbation becomes even larger do the tongues extend to large distances without first going several times around the islands (FIG. 14).

This behavior implies that even when a stable periodic orbit becomes unstable the orbits of its neighborhood behave for a long time as if they follow a separatrix, that is, as if the motion is ordered. Only later in time do such orbits deviate considerably and appear as strongly stochastic. Therefore, systems that are formed by perturbation of integrable systems not only have small stochastic regions (for small perturbations), but even if they have relatively large stochastic regions the behavior or the orbits close to the unstable periodic orbits is rather regular over long periods of time.

This phenomenon explains the behavior of slightly stochastic orbits in galactic models that follow almost regular patterns for several periods before coming very stochastic. In this way we also explain the fact that such orbits do not escape to infinity for an extremely long time, when their energy is somewhat larger than the escape energy and there is no other integral of motion to restrict their motions.

REFERENCES

1. CONTOPOULOS, G. & P. GROSBØL. 1986. Astron. Astrophys. **155**: 11.
2. CONTOPOULOS, G. & P GROSBØL. 1988. Astron. Astrophys. **197**: 83.
3. PATSIS, P. A., G. CONTOPOULOS & P. GROSBØL. 1991. Astron. Astrophys. **243**: 373.
4. CONTOPOULOS, G. 1990. Ann. N.Y. Acad. Sci. **596**: 101.
5. CONTOPOULOS, G., S. T. GOTTESMAN, J. H. HUNTER & M. N. ENGLAND. 1989. Astrophys. J. **343**: 608.
6. ARTYMOWICZ, P. & S. H. LUBOW. 1992. Astrophys. J. **389**: 129.
7. GROSBØL, P. 1990. Ann. N.Y. Acad. Sci. **596**: 114.
8. KAUFMANN, D. E. 1992. Orbits in barred spiral galaxies. This issue.
9. CONTOPOULOS, G. & C. POLYMILIS. 1992. Phys. Rev. A. In press.

Orbits in Barred Spiral Galaxies[a]

DAVID E. KAUFMANN

Department of Astronomy
University of Florida
Gainesville, Florida 32611

INTRODUCTION

Our approach to the problem of nonlinear self-consistent models of barred spiral galaxies is discussed by Contopoulos and Kaufmann[1] in this volume. Previous studies by Contopoulos and Grosbøl[2,3] and Patsis, Contopoulos, and Grosbøl[4] have employed the same technique to produce self-consistent models of normal spirals. In all of these investigations primary emphasis is placed upon the role of the resonant periodic orbits in determining the basic structural characteristics of galaxies.

Periodic orbits are of special importance because they trap quasi-periodic orbits around them if they are stable, and induce stochasticity in nearby orbits if they are unstable (FIGS. 1 and 2). Indeed, Sparke and Sellwood[5] found that most of the particles that make up a rapidly tumbling, two-dimensional N-body bar are on orbits trapped around the main family of prograde periodic orbits. In the present paper we briefly summarize the periodic orbit families that are important in our models.

In the region near corotation, stochastic orbits assume primary importance (FIG. 2). If the perturbation is large, then this stochastic region can also be quite large and extend well inside and outside of corotation. In our models the imposed perturbation was rather large, thus the stochastic region was substantial. Since this created a dearth of stable, periodic orbits with which to build self-consistent bar and spiral structure near corotation, we sought to investigate the response of the stochastic orbits to this strong imposed perturbing potential.

PERIODIC ORBITS

The dynamically important periodic orbits in our models are those derived from the "central" or, in the notation of Contopoulos,[6] x_1 family. These are the orbits that reduce to circles in the purely axisymmetric case. The introduction of a bar or spiral perturbation breaks this central family into an infinity of families by gaps at all even resonances between the epicyclic frequency κ and the angular velocity in the frame corotating with the barred spiral pattern $\Omega - \Omega_s$. That is, where

$$\frac{\kappa}{\Omega - \Omega_s} = 2n, \quad n = 1, 2, \ldots.$$

[a]The author was supported by the Florida Space Grant Consortium with a NASA Space Grant fellowship.

140

Also, regions of instability are produced in the central family near the odd resonances, where

$$\frac{\kappa}{\Omega - \Omega_s} = 2n - 1, \qquad n = 1, 2, \ldots .$$

From these regions we have the bifurcations of the odd resonant families. Hence, the
most important information about a model galaxy is provided by the positions and
properties of the main resonances.

Contopoulos[7] found that in the case of a barred galaxy with a unique inner
Lindblad resonance (ILR), the bar tends to be enhanced by orbits between the ILR

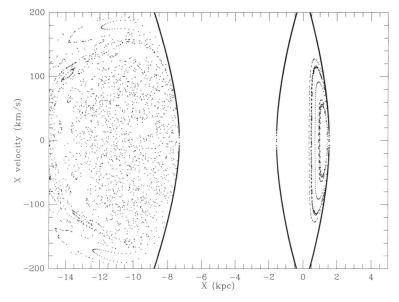

FIGURE 1. Surface of section for the case $A = 4000$ km^2 s^{-2} kpc^{-1} of Contopoulos and
Kaufmann,[1] for a value of the Jacobi constant of 86,385 km^2 s^{-2}. Consequents are taken to be
the points $(x, \dot{x})$ where an orbit crosses the bar minor axis ($y = 0$) upward ($\dot{y} > 0$). One hundred
consequents are plotted for each orbit. In the bar, essentially all of the orbits are trapped
around the x_1 family. Outside corotation the orbits are predominantly stochastic.

and corotation, and by orbits beyond the outer Lindblad resonance (OLR) (FIG. 3).
In contrast, orbits inside the ILR and between corotation and the OLR are generally
oriented perpendicularly to the bar and tend to destroy the bar. Beyond the OLR the
orbits are only modestly elongated along the bar because the perturbation is small at
these large distances. Also, these orbits are rather sparsely populated compared to
orbits closer to the galactic center where the matter density is greater. These facts,
together with the observed termination of bars near corotation in numerical simulations,[8-12] suggest that the orbit families of importance in a self-consistent bar exist
between the ILR and corotation.

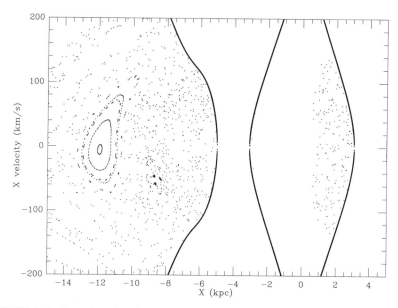

FIGURE 2. Surface of section for the model of FIGURE 1, but with a value of the Jacobi constant of 100,230 km^2 s^{-2}. Orbits in the bar as well as those outside corotation are predominantly stochastic. The invariant curves near $x = -12$ kpc, $\dot{x} = 0$ km s^{-1} represent orbits trapped around the 2/1 resonant family outside the outer Lindblad resonance. This family is dynamically insignificant in our models.

We find that the most important periodic families in the bar are the 2/1 resonant, or x_1, family (FIG. 4) and the 4/1 resonant, or $x_1(2)$, family (FIG. 5). Only these families are stable over a large enough energy range and trap enough quasi-periodic orbits around them (FIGS. 6 and 7) to be dynamically important in our models.

Outside corotation we find only one periodic family that is significant in supporting the spiral structure. It is the outer $x_1(2)$ family that exists between the $-4/1$ and outer Lindblad resonances (FIG. 8). This family, however, supports the spiral only for a rather short span between these two resonances. This leaves the problem of the existence of significant stellar spiral structure from the end of the bar, near corotation, out to and perhaps a little beyond the $-4/1$ resonance.

STOCHASTIC ORBITS

Given the rather large amount of stochasticity in our models, we sought to investigate whether these orbits would support the imposed bar and spiral structure. We first looked at various individual orbits to find their long-term behavior. Stochastic orbits with relatively small Jacobi integrals trapped inside the bar tend to fill elliptical regions defined by the corresponding curves of zero velocity (CZVs). Orbits with similarly low Jacobi integrals outside corotation are not restricted, in general, by any boundary and they may escape. Our model, however, has an asymptotically flat rotation curve, so its infinite mass precludes escapes. Typically, orbits of this type fairly uniformly fill rings and do not support the outer spiral structure (FIG. 9).

Interesting changes in behavior occur when the value of the Jacobi integral nears and exceeds the value at the Lagrange point L_1. At this point communication between the bar and the outer spiral is established. Orbits of this type form many loops near the spiral potential minima as they approach or recede from the L_1 and L_2 points (FIGS. 10 and 11). They may or may not pass through L_1 or L_2 into the bar on these approaches. Orbits that do enter the bar may be trapped there for very long times. Inside the bar these orbits again fill elliptical regions defined by the corresponding CZVs. Such orbits are oriented along the bar, but they do not support strong thin bar structure. These migrating orbits, then, can generate quite different-looking density responses over long times, depending on whether (and how many times) they cross over from the outside spiral to the bar and vice versa. This type of behavior generally ceases when the value of the Jacobi integral exceeds the value at L_4. In this case, the orbit is unconstrained energetically and it tends to fill, more or less uniformly, a rather circular region (see [1, fig. 14(b)]).

We sought to understand how this interesting behavior of the individual stochastic orbits would manifest itself in a statistical sense. In order to address this problem we started approximately 1500 orbits on 16 radial segments, equally spaced in azimuth, extending from 2.5 kpc to 8.28 kpc (FIG. 12). These orbits were each assigned a value of the Jacobi integral identical to the circular orbit of the same radius in the axisymmetric background. Some orbits were excluded because their

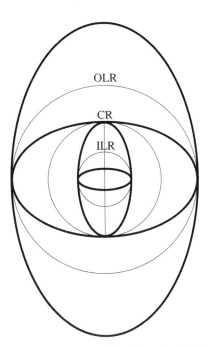

FIGURE 3. Orientation of orbits in a bar potential with a unique ILR, where the bar is oriented vertically. Orbits between the ILR and corotation (CR) and outside the OLR are oriented along the bar. Orbits inside the ILR and between CR and the OLR are oriented perpendicularly to the bar.

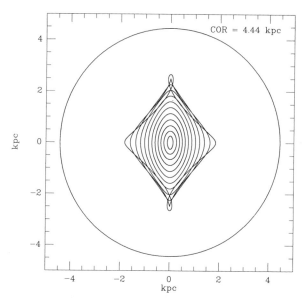

FIGURE 4. The x_1 family of periodic orbits in the case A = 4000 km^2 s^{-2} kpc^{-1}. The *circle* represents corotation at 4.44 kpc.

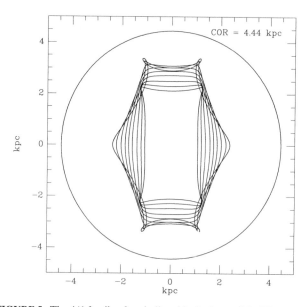

FIGURE 5. The 4/1 family of periodic orbits in the model of FIGURE 4.

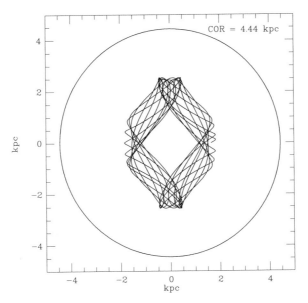

FIGURE 6. Quasi-periodic orbit trapped around the x_1 family.

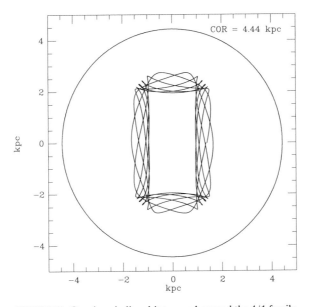

FIGURE 7. Quasi-periodic orbit trapped around the 4/1 family.

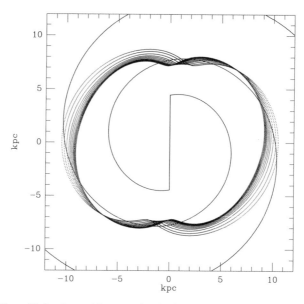

FIGURE 8. The $x_1(2)$ family outside corotation in the model of FIGURE 4. The bar and spiral potential minima are drawn for reference.

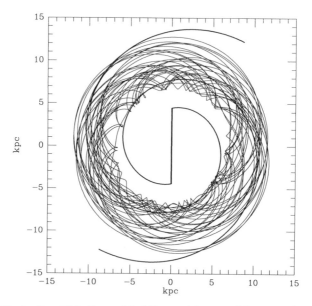

FIGURE 9. Stochastic orbit in the model of FIGURE 4 integrated for approximately 6 billion years. The value of the Jacobi constant is 91,404 km^2 s^{-2}, less than the value at the Lagrange point L_1 of 97,264 km^2 s^{-2}. The orbit generally fills a ring and does not support the spiral structure.

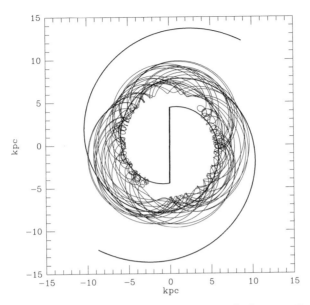

FIGURE 10. Stochastic orbit with a Jacobi constant of 97,652 $km^2\,s^{-2}$, marginally above that of L_1. The orbit does not enter the bar but enhances the spiral somewhat.

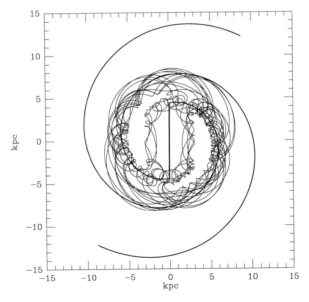

FIGURE 11. Stochastic orbit with a Jacobi constant of 100,230 $km^2\,s^{-2}$. This orbit enters and exits the bar and enhances the outer spiral structure. It does not, however, support a strong thin bar.

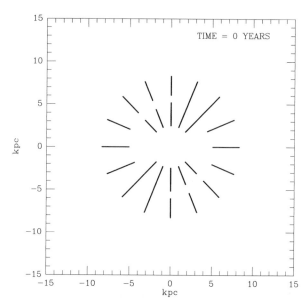

FIGURE 12. Initial positions of approximately 1500 stochastic orbits in the case $A = 4000$ km^2 s^{-2} kpc^{-1}.

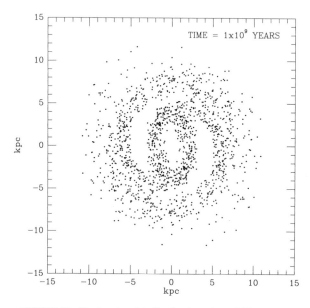

FIGURE 13. Stochastic orbit distribution after 1 billion years.

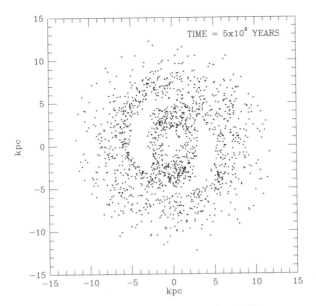

FIGURE 14. Stochastic orbit distribution after 5 billion years.

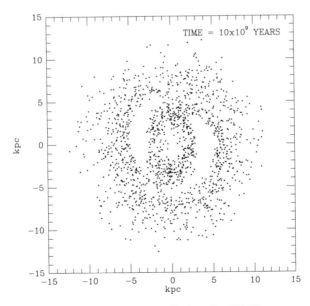

FIGURE 15. Stochastic orbit distribution after 10 billion years.

initial conditions were outside their CZVs after the bar and spiral perturbations were added. The remaining orbits were integrated in the imposed potential for roughly 10 billion years. The integrations were stopped every billion years and the positions logged. FIGURES 13–15 show the particle distributions after 1, 5, and 10 billion years, respectively. There are several features of note. First, we see that the spiral structure is clearly delineated and enhanced by these orbits in all three snapshots. The enhancement extends from the end of the bar at 4.4 kpc out until the spiral arms diffuse into a fuzzy ringlike distibution in the outer disk. Secondly, particles in the bar tend to stay near the outer parts of the elliptical regions defined by their CZVs, thus these particles do not support a strong, *thin* bar perturbation. Lastly, we note the similarity of all three snapshots. We see no tendency for these stochastic orbits to segregate into separate bar and outer ring populations. A significant proportion seem to be continuously entering and exiting the bar, lingering near the spiral potential minima along the way, and thereby enhancing them.

CONCLUSIONS

The major role in stellar dynamical models of barred spiral galaxies is played by the families of periodic orbits. These, in turn, are determined by the placement and properties of the major resonances. Self-consistent bar structure can be explained by orbits trapped around the stable x_1 and 4/1 families between the ILR and corotation.

Stochastic orbits, while tending to weaken strong thin bars, may be quite important in enhancing spiral structure outside the bar all the way from corotation to the OLR. The stochastic orbits found to exhibit this enhancing behavior all have Jacobi integrals within or near the range defined by the values of the Jacobi integral at the Lagrange points L_1 and L_4. Stochastic orbits outside this range do not support spiral or thin bar structure.

ACKNOWLEDGMENT

I would like to thank Professor G. Contopoulos for many useful discussions on the properties of orbits in galactic models and on self-consistent models of spiral and barred spiral galaxies.

REFERENCES

1. CONTOPOULOS, G. & D. E. KAUFMANN. 1992. Nonlinear self-consistent models of barred galaxies. This issue.
2. CONTOPOULOS, G. & P. GROSBØL.1986. Astron. Astrophys. **155:** 11.
3. ———. 1988. Astron. Astrophys. **197:** 83.
4. PATSIS, P. A., G. CONTOPOULOS & P. GROSBØL. 1991. Astron. Astrophys. **243:** 373.
5. SPARKE, L. S. & J. A. SELLWOOD. 1987. Mon. Not. R. Astron. Soc. **225:** 653.
6. CONTOPOULOS, G. 1975. Astrophys. J. **201:** 566.
7. ———. 1980. Astron. Astrophys. **81:** 198.
8. SELLWOOD, J. A. 1980. Astron. Astrophys. **89:** 296.
9. ———. 1981. Astron. Astrophys. **99:** 362.
10. SCHWARZ, M. P. 1981. Astrophys. J. **247:** 77.
11. THIELHEIM, K. O. & H. WOLFF. 1981. Astrophys. J. **245:** 39.
12. ———. 1984. Astrophys. J. **276:** 135.

The Disk of the Milky Way

LEO BLITZ

Astronomy Department
University of Maryland
College Park, Maryland 20742

INTRODUCTION

Of all astrophysical disks, the one about which the most is known is the Milky Way. Nevertheless, much new has been learned about the large-scale structure of the disk in the last decade. The stellar and gaseous disks comprise high and low temperature components. The atomic and ionized phases of the interstellar medium have both been shown to consist of distinct components that have different scale heights, and the same seems to be true for the stars. The evidence for large amounts of dark matter in the disk, while not ruled out, no longer appears to be compelling. New work on the large-scale structure of the Milky Way provides a quantitative analysis of the large-scale noncircular motions of the gas in the disk, and a dynamical model to explain them. Ongoing work by several groups has found direct evidence for a bar at the center of the Galaxy; the agreement between the groups about the properties of the bar is quite good.

THE THICK GALACTIC DISKS

The Stars

One of the most significant new realizations about the disk of the Milky Way in the last decade is that the stars and the gas have components with two different scale heights. Gilmore and Reid[1] determined the space distribution of K dwarfs toward the south galactic pole, and showed that the space density of the stars could not be fit with a single distribution. Instead, the data were fit with two exponentials, one with a scale height of about 300 pc, and the other with a scale height of about 1300 pc (see FIG. 1). The larger scale height material has been called the *thick disk,* and its reality seems to be reasonably well established.

Because these stars are found so far from the plane, their scale height and velocity dispersion measure the total surface density of the disk, and the best numbers so far[2-4] suggest that the surface density in the solar vicinity is 50–70 $M_\odot pc^{-2}$. The smaller number is consistent with the total census of matter in the disk and does not require an additional dark matter component as postulated by Bahcall.[5] However, the number has a large enough uncertainty that the disk may, in fact, contain a significant dark component. Such a component might come, for example, from large numbers of condensed objects below the hydrogen burning limit, the "brown dwarfs."

The thickness of the thin disk has been explained by a combination of scattering by molecular clouds and diffusion of stellar orbits,[6-8] but the observations are not yet fully explained by theory.[9] Nevertheless, the large scale height of the thick disk cannot be explained by such mechanisms and is presumably a fossil of the formation history of the Galaxy. If that is indeed the case, there should be some record of it in the metallicity of the stars in the disk. That is, is it possible, from a kinematically derived sample, to distinguish two distinct metallicity classes that correspond to the thin and thick disk populations? Latham[10] has carried out such a study and finds that while there is clear evidence for metallicity differences in the kinematically derived thin and thick disk populations, it is unclear from the metallicity data whether the

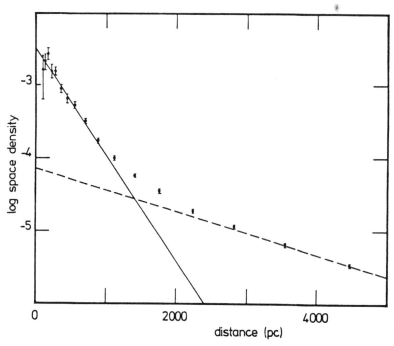

FIGURE 1. Plot of the space density of K dwarf stars toward the south galactic pole showing the two scale height distributions that constitute the thin and thick disk populations.[1]

stars fall into two distinct groups, or whether the thick disk is just the tail of the thin disk population. Data of this type are very difficult to obtain in other galaxies, so it is important to resolve the issue of how distinct the two populations are.

The Gas

Nearly contemporaneous with the discovery of the thick stellar disk in the Milky Way, was the discovery of the thick HI and HII layers in the disk. Perhaps best established is the Reynolds layer, the layer of ionized hydrogen with a scale height of about 1500 pc. Reynolds,[11] using his own measurements of the column density of diffuse HII solar vicinity combined with column density measurements of the ionized component from pulsar dispersion measures, showed that the HII must lie in a two-component system. The smaller scale height component is associated with ordinary HII regions in the thin disk of the Galaxy. The thick HII layer accounts for about 25 percent of the total column density of atomic hydrogen in the solar vicinity.

Evidence for an atomic layer with two different scale heights goes back at least as far as Falgarone and Lequeux.[12] Lockman[13] has similarly shown that the atomic gas appears to consist of two distinct components. In a recent review, Dickey and Lockman[14] argue that the cold HI has a central density of 0.4 cm^{-3} and a scale height of about 200 pc, and the warm HI has a density of about 0.1 cm^{-3} and a scale height of about 500 pc. The temperature of each component is determined from emission/absorption observations against background continuum sources. Of all the gas phases, only the molecular component has not shown any evidence for a warmer or thicker phase.[15] The largest excursions of gas from the plane are all within 3 standard deviations of the local scale height, which for the molecular gas, is about 70 pc in the solar vicinity.

Measurements of the scale height of the gas in the outer Galaxy show that the scale height increases monotonically with distance from the galactic center with local variations that are probably related to spiral arm features. Estimates of the gas velocity dispersion are now obtainable to distances of at least $2 R_0$, and the results suggest that the velocity dispersion of the gas in the outer regions of the Galaxy are similar to what is measured locally.[16] Kulkarni, Blitz, and Heiles[17] used the measurements of the gas scale height to show that the dark matter implied by the flat rotation curve of the Galaxy could not reside in the disk. A more recent determination of the variation of the scale height with galactic radius was undertaken by Merrifield,[18] who developed a new method to measure both the scale height of the gas and the rotation curve of the Milky Way using HI observations alone. By assuming that the orbits of the gas about the galactic center are axisymmetric, one can use the variation of the scale height with radius to measure the distance of gas with a constant $v/\sin l$. Merrifield showed that, within the accuracy limits imposed by his assumptions, the rotation curve remains approximately flat, and the scale height increases approximately as described by Blitz, Kulkarni, and Heiles.[17]

THE SHAPE OF THE DISK

One of the enduring assumptions that has gone into the analysis of the large-scale structure of the Milky Way from the observations of the gas is that the gravitational potential of the disk is axially symmetric. Indeed, to first order, the motions of the gas are axisymmetric, as can be seen from FIGURE 2, a longitude–velocity diagram of the atomic gas in the plane of the Milky Way excluding the 10° on either side of the center. Nevertheless, persistent evidence for nonaxisymmetric motions has appeared in the literature from the systematic deviations of the inner Galaxy rotation curves,[19] and the systematic negative velocities of the gas motions toward the galactic anticenter in both HI and CO.[20]

Using the latitude averaged HI survey data shown in FIGURE 2, Blitz and

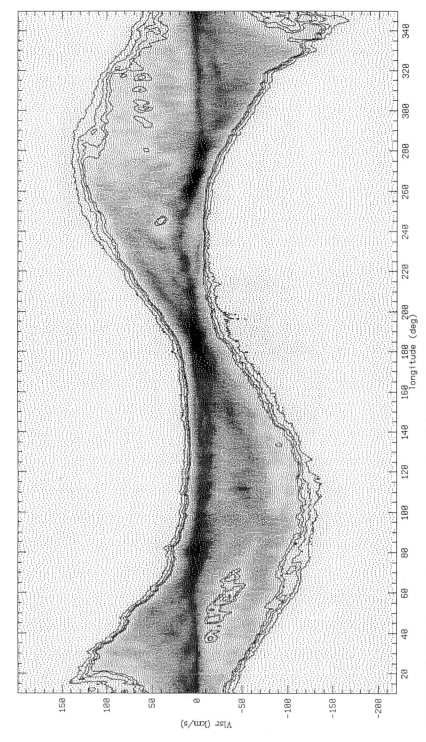

FIGURE 2. The latitude averaged antenna temperature of atomic hydrogen shown in a plot of radial velocity vs. galactic longitude. Only the lowest contours are plotted; the higher contours are shown in gray scale. The symmetry of the plot with respect to the galactic anticenter shows that the Milky Way is, to first order, axially symmetric.

Spergel[16] found a new way to systematize the deivations from axisymmetry. Because contours of constant antenna temperature within a fixed velocity interval are proportional to surface density of atomic hydrogen, one can subtract the velocity at which a particular contour is observed at a particular longitude from that at its colongitude to find the deviation in the velocity of the gas from its mean or expected value. The colongitude is defined as $360° - l$; gas at a given longitude should have the same observed radial velocity as equivalent gas at the colongitude in an axisymmetric galaxy. Care must be taken to consider gas far enough from the center to minimize perturbations from spiral arms. Blitz and Spergel found that the difference velocities so constructed, which they called v_{diff}, have a characteristic shape that requires a large-scale deviation from axisymmetry of the HI orbits. FIGURE 3 shows the 2 K

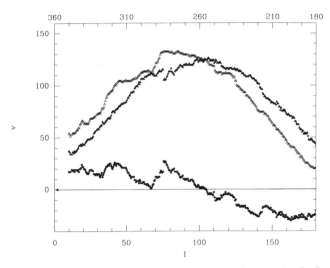

FIGURE 3. A plot of the 2 K contour of antenna temperature between longitudes of 10° and 180° (*solid triangles*) and between 180° and 350° (*open triangles*). In an axisymmetric galaxy, the two curves should be indistinguishable. The *solid squares* indicate the quantity v_{diff}. Small-scale structure in the plot of v_{diff} is presumably due to local perturbations.

contour of latitude averaged HI emission at $10° < l < 180°$ and $180° < l < 350°$. The bottom part of the figure shows v_{diff}. The overall shape of the v_{diff} curve does not change with contour level, and is best explained if there is a large scale outward component of motion of the local standard of rest (LSR) relative to the distant HI of about 15 km s^{-1}. FIGURE 4 shows a plot of the v_{diff} curve of FIGURE 3 with outward components of the LSR of 10, 15, and 20 km s^{-1} superimposed on the plots.

Blitz and Spergel first attempted to explain the detailed shape of the v_{diff} curves with a dynamical model that had the sun moving on a nearly circular orbit about the center and the outer Galaxy gas moving on increasingly elliptical orbits resulting from a triaxial halo potential. However, no amount of tinkering with the parameters of the model, including adding rotation to the halo, could reproduce the data in

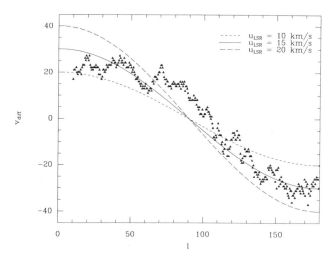

FIGURE 4. The v_{diff} curve of FIGURE 3 and the expected v_{diff} curves from galaxy models with different values of the outward motion of the local standard of rest.

detail. It is important to remember that the HI data are very good, and using the latitude averaged HI data brings the noise level down so low that it is possible to differentiate clearly between different classes of dynamical models.

The v_{diff} curves could be reproduced if instead the sun is moving on an elliptical orbit, and the ellipticity of the orbits decreases with increasing distance from the center. Such a model is produced when the disk responds to a triaxial spheroid potential. To get good agreement with the observations, it was necessary to have the pattern of the potential revolve at about 5 km s^{-1} kpc^{-1}. One major hurdle for the model is that although the sun must have an outward motion with respect to the galactic center of 15 km s^{-1}, the HI absorption line feature observed toward the center which samples most of the line-of-sight HI has a nearly zero velocity relative to the LSR.[21] After having fixed all of the free parameters of the model, however, Blitz and Spergel showed that most of the HI inward of the solar circle moves on *similar ellipses,* and therefore the HI in the disk along the sun-center line will have no net radial velocity.

If this is the explanation, however, it is necessary to show that the gas that is not subject to the triaxial potential, and that is independent of the gas from which the model is constructed, exhibits evidence for the outwardly moving LSR. There is, in fact, such gas orbiting very close to the galactic center. The molecular disk within 300 pc of the center is too close to the center to be affected by the triaxial potential of the spheroid; the kinematics of this gas clearly show the signature of a net positive velocity of about 18 km s^{-1} with respect to the LSR. Furthermore, the Liszt and Burton[22] models of the HI that lies very close to the galactic center also show signs of the outward motion of the LSR.

Kuijken[23] has argued that the v_{diff} curves can be produced by an $m = 1$ perturbation to the velocity field of the HI similar to that seen in "lopsided" galaxies. A way to test for an $m = 1$ or an $m = 2$ mode is by examining the differences in the column densities for gas at a given longitude and colongitude. An $m = 1$ mode that produces the required sign of the systematic HI motions toward the galactic anticenter requires most of the disk mass to be in the third or fourth galactic quadrants. Gas will preferentially pile up at these longitudes and differences made between column densities of gas at various longitudes and colongitudes should find a systematic excess in the third and fourth quadrants. For an $m = 2$ mode, however, the gas should pile up in the second and fourth quadrants.

A plot of the quantity $N_{diff}\%$, which is the fractional column density difference between gas in the third and fourth quadrants and that in the second and first, respectively, is shown in FIGURE 5. The plot shows a clear excess in the fourth quadrant and a deficiency in the third as required by the model with the $m = 2$ perturbation. Also shown in the figure are curves using different values of the LSR velocity from which the column densities are integrated. Higher values of the LSR velocity include only gas at larger distance from the solar circle. By taking integrals of the column density starting at larger velocities, one excludes local gas that may contaminate the analysis.[23] Since the overall shape of the $N_{diff}\%$ curves are invariant to the choice of distance from the solar circle, the overall shape must be a global property of the HI distribution, and therefore indicates that the perturbation to the potential is an even rather than an odd function.

Perhaps the definitive test of the triaxial spheroid model will be possible when the

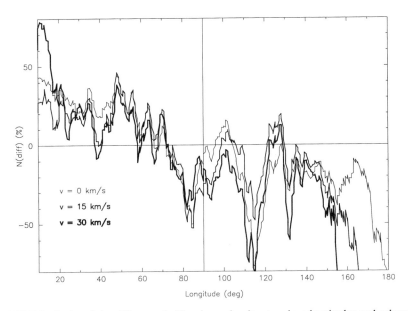

FIGURE 5. A plot of the difference in HI column density at various longitudes and colongitudes plotted as a percentage. That the curves are odd functions implies that the underlying potential of the galaxy has an $m = 2$ mode. An $m = 1$ mode would show an even function. An axisymmetric galaxy would have all of the curves centered at 0 percent. The *increasing pen thickness* implies increasingly large distances from the solar circle from which the integrations begin, in turn implying smaller effects of local spiral features.

COBE data from the DIRBE experiment become available. These data are high-sensitivity well-calibrated near-infrared data that are dominated by the emission from the evolved stars in the disk. Qualitative data presented at various scientific meetings by the COBE group show that emission is seen at large angles from the galactic midplane; the signature of a triaxial spheroid should be evident in the data.

EVIDENCE FOR THE BAR

Photometric Evidence

The question of whether the center of the Milky Way contains a stellar bar has been in the air since de Vaucoulerus[24] first suggested it. His suggestion was based on the similar magnitude of HI noncircular velocities observed toward the galactic center and observations of the gas velocities in barred spirals. Analyses of the motions of the HI kinematics within about 12° of the galactic center have shown that the noncircular velocities could be understood in terms of closed elliptical orbits that are the presumed response to a strongly triaxial potential.

Direct evidence for the bar at the center became available only last year when Blitz and Spergel[25] showed that the near-infrared emission measured by a Japanese balloon borne experiment[26] implied that the distribution of stars in the center is not axisymmetric. Blitz and Spergel[25] showed that if there is a bar at the center, and its long axis is oriented obliquely to the line of sight, several effects should be observable. (1) The near side of the bar should be systematically bighter than the far side. The reason for this is that most lines of sight through equal angles on either side of the center will traverse regions of higher stellar density on the near side because of perspective effects. In an axsymmetric bulge, there should be no systematic brightness difference on either side of the sun-center line. (2) The near side of the bar (as determined by the surface brightness) should have a systematically higher angular scale height than the far side. Again, there should be no systematic difference in an axisymmetric bulge. (3) Close to the center, there should be a sign change in the surface brightness difference between the near and the far sides of the bar. That is, the side that exhibits a larger surface brightness should actually become less bright close to the center than the portion on the other side of the sun-center line. The reason for this is that lines of sight that are close to the center probe nearly the same density of stars, but perspective effects cause lines of sight on the far side close to the center to traverse longer paths, and thus appear to be brighter. This counterintuitive results suggests that there should be a hole in the differential surface brightness of the near and far sides of the bar. If the Milky Way has a bar, it must pass all three tests.

Blitz and Spergel[25] used the Matsumoto et al.[26] data to test whether there was any evidence for a bar, and difference maps produced positive results for all of the effects just mentioned. Furthermore, they found that the bar has a slight misalignment with the galactic plane. The orientation of the bar is such that the near side is observed in the first galactic quadrant and the far side in the fourth. In the first quadrant the bar is tiled slightly below the galactic plane. Extinction cannot account for their results, and therefore the bulge of the Galaxy is in fact a bar, and is presumably rapidly rotating.

Subsequently, three other studies, all using the Infrared Astronomical Satellite (IRAS) data base of point sources confirmed the asymmetries for various different populations of bulge stars, and all showed the asymmetries in the same sense at the Blitz and Spergel work. Weinberg,[27] using a clever new analytical technique, found that the distribution of evolved stars that show evidence for variability is not axisymmetrically distributed in the galactic center. Nakada[28] measured IRAS bulge stars, and Whitelock[29] looked at the distribution of Miras in the bulge, and both found evidence for an asymmetric barlike distribution.

Dynamical Evidence

Simultaneous with and independent of the Blitz and Spergel[25] analysis, Binney *et al.*[30] examined the kinematics of the HI and the CO in the central regions of the Milky Way. They devised a dynamical model of the inner regions and found that a natural way to explain the gross features of the kinematics is with a rapidly rotating triaxial central potential, that is, a bar. They argued that near the corotation resonance of a bar, gas orbits become chaotic and self-intersecting. Gas near this point would rapidly lose angular momentum and fall toward the center. There are two sets of closed orbits inside the corotation resonance, termed the x_1 and x_2 orbits after Contopoulos. Gas would settle on the closed x_1 orbits after falling through corotation, and slowly drift toward the center as a result of viscous effects. Closer to the center, the x_1 orbits become cusped and then self-intersecting. Since the gas cannot exist on such orbits, it can only exist on the last nonintersecting orbit outside the inner Lindblad resonance, and then it must fall through that resonance until it winds up on the x_2 orbits, which are perpendicular to the x_1 orbits.

Binney *et al.*[30] produced triaxial models for both the HI and the CO in the inner galaxy and argued that the extent of the CO is consistent with it being only on the x_2 orbits. The inner edge of the molecular ring at $0.5 R_0$, has a location consistent with the last nonintersecting orbit outside the corotation resonance of the bar. Furthermore, the kinematic envelopes of the HI and CO are consistent with the predictions of the barred models. In fact, the *shape* of the envelope strongly constrains the position angle of the bar to be within about $16° \pm 2°$ to the line of sight, at an orientation similar to that required by the Blitz and Spergel analysis.

It is rather remarkable that in the space of about 18 months there have been a number of independent analyses that all have argued for the presence of a stellar bar, and that the analyses seem to be pretty much consistent with one another. As is the case for the spheroid, the definitive test for the reality of the bar will come from the COBE data. If it is confirmed, the next task will be to see how tightly the COBE data can constrain the mass distribution of the bar, and whether it confirms the position angle determined by the Binney *et al.* analysis.

REFERENCES

1. GILMORE, G. & N. REID. 1983. Mon. Not. R. Astron. Soc. **202:** 33.
2. BOULD, A. 1990. Mon. Not. R. Astron. Soc. **244:** 25.
3. BAHCALL, J., C. FLYNN & A. GOULD. 1992. Astrophys. J. **389:** 234.
4. KIUJKEN, K. 1991. Astrophys. J. **372:** 125.

5. BAHCALL, J. 1984. Astrophys. J. **287:** 926
6. SPITZER, L. & M. SCHWARZSCHILD. 1951. Astrophys. J. **114:** 385.
7. ———. 1953. Astrophys. J. **118:** 106.
8. WIELEN, R. 1977. Astron. Astrophys. **60:** 263.
9. BINNEY, J. & C. LACEY. 1988. Mon. Not. R. Astron. Soc. **230:** 597.
10. LATHAM, D. 1992. *In* Large Scale Structure of the Milky Way: Recent Progress, L. Blitz, Ed. Kluwer. Dordrecht, the Netherlands. In press.
11. REYNOLDS, R. 1989. Astrophys. J., Lett. **339:** L29.
12. FALGARONE, E. & J. LEQUEUX. 1973. Astron. Astrophys. **25:** 253.
13. LOCKMAN, F. J. 1984. Astrophys. J. **283:** 90.
14. DICKEY, J. M. & F. J. LOCKMAN. 1990. Annu. Rev. Astron. Astrophys. **28:** 215.
15. BLITZ, L. 1990. *In* The Disk–Halo Connection in Galaxies, H. Bloemen, Ed.: 41. Kluwer. Dordrecht, the Netherlands.
16. BLITZ, L. & D. SPERGEL. 1991. Astrophys. J. **370:** 205.
17. KULKARNI, S., L. BLITZ, & C. HEILES. 1982. Astrophys. J., Lett. **259:** L63.
18. MERRIFIELD, M. 1992. Astron. J. In press.
19. KERR, F. J. 1962. Mon. Not. R. Astron. Soc. **123:** 327.
20. BLITZ, L., M. FICH & A. A. STARK. 1979. *In* Instellar Molecules, B. Andrew, Ed.: 213. Reidel: Dordrecht, the Netherlands.
21. RADHAKRISHNAN, V & N. V. G. SARMA. 1980. Astron. Astrophys. **85:** 249.
22. LISZT, H. S. & W. B. BURTON. 1980. Astrophys. J. **236:** 779.
23. KIUJKEN, K. 1991. *In* Warped Disks and Inclined Rings around Galaxies, Casertano, Sackett, and Briggs Eds.: 159. Cambridge Univ. Press. Cambridge, England.
24. DE VAUCOULEURS, G. 1964. *In* The Galaxy and the Magellanic Clouds, F. J. Kerr and A. W. Rogers, Eds.: 195. Australian Academy of Science. Sydney.
25. BLITZ, L. & D. SPERGEL. 1991. Astrophys. J. **379:** 631.
26. MATSUMOTO, T., *et al.* 1982. *In* The Galactic Center, G. Reigler and R. Blanford, Eds.: 48. American Institute of Physics: New York.
27. WEINBERG, M. 1992. Astrophys. J. In press.
28. NAKADA, Y., S. DEGUCHI, O. HASHIMOTO, H. IZUMIURA, T. ONAKA, K. SEKIGUCHI & I. YAMAMURA. 1991. Nature **353:** 140.
29. WHITELOCK, P. & R. CATCHPOLE. *In* Large Scale Structure of the Milky Way: Recent Progress, L. Blitz, Ed. Kluwer: Dordrecht, the Netherlands. In press.
30. BINNEY, J., O. GERHARD, A. A. STARK, J. BALLY & K. I. UCHIDA. 1991. Mon. Not. R. Astron. Soc. **252:** 210.

Numerical Studies of Disks[a]

J. H. HUNTER, JR.,[b] E. MOORE,[b] AND M. N. ENGLAND[c]

b Department of Astronomy
University of Florida
Gainesville, Florida 32611
and
c Astronomy Program
Computer Sciences Corporation
10000 A. Aerospace Road
Lanham, Maryland 20706

INTRODUCTION

In the present communication, two distinct problems will be considered, one in more detail than the other. The bulk of the paper will be devoted to summarizing an efficient method, developed by two of the authors (J. H. H. and E. M.), for constructing self-consistant models of flat, truncated disks with specified rotation curves. In the final section of the paper, two of the authors (J. H. H. and M. N. E.) outline a theory, developed in collaboration with G. Contopoulos, that may account for large-scale vortices in the gas that often are found in the neighborhood of the $L_{4,5}$ points of the bar in models of barred galaxies.

SELF-CONSISTENT, FLAT DISKS

A major objective of our research program at the University of Florida has been to model particular galaxies that have been observed at the Very Large Array (VLA) in 21 cm, as well as at infrared and other wavelengths. Consequently, we require that our model rotation curves be in rough accord with observations. Having built a marginally stable model (in a global sense), bar and spiral arm formation can be induced, and controlled, at each radius by reducing the stabilizing velocity dispersions while increasing the velocity of the local standard of rest (LSR). Following the approach of Jeans,[1] our method of calculating velocity dispersions is developed by taking moments of the collisionless Boltzmann equation. For any steady axisymmetric disk, the results may be combined to yield an ordinary differential equation for the radial velocity dispersion as a function of the radius. Model results on a variety of disks show that they become stable when the ratio of the total rotational kinetic energy to the absolute value of the gravitational energy is roughly 0.14–0.16, in reasonable agreement with the conjecture of Ostriker and Peebles.[2]

We confine our attention to arbitrarily flat disks in which particle motions are restricted to the radial (r) and tangential (ϕ) directions. It should be emphasized at the outset that we make no attempt to deduce the correct distribution function f for a

[a] This research was supported in part by National Science Foundation Grant AST-9022827.

realistic galactic disk. (Of course, f is known[3,4] for rigidly rotating Kalnajs/Hohl disks, designated hereafter K/H, but these are unsuitable for modeling disks with significant velocity shear.) In initializing our calculations, we assume axial symmetry, divide each model into a large number of concentric rings, and restrict the distribution function for each annulus by imposing the following constraints.

1. With respect to the LSR (which is assumed known for time-independent models, as discussed below), the distribution of peculiar radial velocities u_r is symmetric and may be characterized by radial velocity dispersion σ_r.
2. At each value of u_r, the initial distribution of peculiar tangential velocities u_ϕ is symmetric about the mean, $\overline{V}_\phi$; the corresponding initial tangential velocity dispersion is σ_ϕ. Consequently, for each annulus one of the axes of the initial velocity ellipsoid is oriented parallel to the tangential direction, and the initial stress tensor is diagonal, possessing only the radial and tangential "pressures," $p_{rr} = \nu\sigma_r^2$ and $p_{\phi\phi} = \nu\sigma_\phi^2$, where ν is the surface density in the ring. The distribution function is defined so that $\int mf\,d\tau_\nu = \nu(r, t) \equiv \nu$, where m is the mass of each individual particle.

We wish to guarantee global stability and yet avoid the assumption that the heating "corrections" are small. Using standard notation in cylindrical coordinates and assuming axial symmetry $[(\partial/\partial\phi) = 0]$, we multiply the collisionless Boltzmann equation by a velocity-dependent quantity Q and integrate over velocity space. If $Q = mV_r$, we arrive at the conservation of radial momentum. In the time-independent case with only bulk azimuthal motion allowed (no bulk radial motion), the resulting equation is

$$\frac{d}{dr}(\nu\sigma_r^2) + \frac{\nu}{r}(\sigma_r^2 - \sigma_\varphi^2) = -\nu\frac{d\Phi}{dr} + \frac{\nu}{r}\overline{V}_\phi^2 = -\frac{\nu}{r}(V_0^2 - \overline{V}_\phi^2), \tag{1}$$

where $V_0(r)$ is the local circular velocity of a cold (unstable) disk having surface density $\nu(r)$, Φ is the gravitational potential, and $\overline{V}_\phi$ the average (hydrodynamic) azimuthal velocity. By letting $Q = mV_rV_\phi$, we form the cross moment equation. Subject to the assumptions stated previously, this expression becomes

$$\frac{\partial}{\partial r}(\nu\overline{V}_\phi\sigma_r^2) - \frac{\nu V_\phi}{r}(\overline{V}_\phi^2 + 3\sigma_\phi^2) + \nu\overline{V}_\phi\frac{V_0^2}{r} + \frac{2\nu\overline{V}_\phi}{r}\sigma_r^2 = 0. \tag{2}$$

Excellent reviews of this stellar "hydrodynamic" approach may be found in Binney and Tremaine[5] (1987) and references therein.

Equations (1) and (2) may be combined to yield

$$\sigma_r^2\left(\frac{d\overline{V}_\phi}{dr} + \frac{\overline{V}_\phi}{r}\right) - \frac{2}{r}\overline{V}_\phi\sigma_\phi^2 = 0, \tag{3a}$$

or

$$\sigma_\phi^2 = \frac{\sigma_r^2}{2}\left(1 + \frac{d\ln\overline{V}}{d\ln r}\right). \tag{3b}$$

(Equation (3a) is identical with [5, eq. (4-51)].) Finally, we assume that $\overline{V}_\phi(r)$, the

LSR velocity, is proportional to $V_0(r)$, but of smaller amplitude; $\overline{V}_\phi = kV_0$, where constant k ($0 \leq k \leq 1$) parameterizes the heating. If $k = 1$, the disk is cold with no velocity dispersions, whereas $k = 0$ corresponds to a disk supported entirely by internal pressure. Consequently,

$$\frac{d \ln \overline{V}}{d \ln r} = \frac{d \ln V_0}{d \ln r}.$$

With this substitution, **(3)** reduces to the well-known result from epicyclic theory. However, in the present context, where the initial "hydrodynamic" orbits are constrained to be circular, it is important to recognize that the velocity dispersions need not be small, as is the case in linear theory. In particular, the asymmetric drift is known and equals $(1 - k)V_0$.

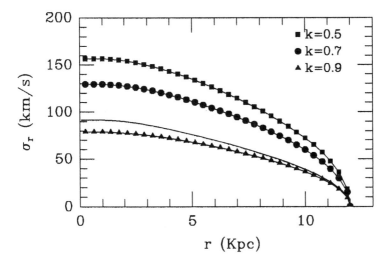

FIGURE 1. The radial peculiar velocity as a function of radius for three values of k for a correctly truncated Toomre $n = 0$ disk. The *solid curve* is the Toomre dispersion minimum for the same disk.

Upon combining **(1)** and **(3)** we arrive at a single first-order ordinary differential equation for σ_r^2

$$\frac{d}{dr}(v\sigma_r^2) + \frac{v}{2r}\sigma_r^2\left(1 - \frac{d \ln V_0}{d \ln r}\right) = -\frac{v(1 - k^2)V_0^2}{r}. \tag{4}$$

Having specified k and exact forms for the surface density and cold rotation field, this equation can be solved for the initial radial velocity dispersions. As a boundary condition, we require that σ_r^2 approach zero at $r = R$, the edge of the initial disk. In most cases, **(4)** must be solved numerically. The result is shown graphically in FIGURE 1 for a Toomre $n = 0$ disk of radius R for which the surface density and local circular velocity are given exactly by

$$
v(b, r) = \frac{C_1^2}{\pi^2 G} \left(\frac{1}{\sqrt{r^2 + b^2}} \right) \tan^{-1} \left(\frac{\sqrt{R^2 - r^2}}{\sqrt{r^2 + b^2}} \right), \qquad r \leq R
$$

$$
= 0, \qquad\qquad\qquad\qquad\qquad\qquad r > R \qquad (5)
$$

and

$$
V_0^2(b, r) = C_1^2 \left[1 - \frac{b}{\sqrt{r^2 + b^2}} \right], \qquad r \leq R \qquad (6)
$$

where b is a shape parameter, and C_1 is the asymptotic rotational velocity of the corresponding infinite disk (Hunter, Ball, and Gottesman,[6] referred to hereafter as HBG). Also shown in the figure is the minimum radial velocity dispersion necessary to suppress local axisymmetric instabilities, calculated using Toomre's criterion.[7]

In practice we often found it expedient to impose isotropic heating, $\sigma_r = \sigma_\phi$, thereby simplifying (1) to the form

$$
\frac{d}{dr}(v\sigma_r^2) = -\frac{v}{r}(V_0^2 - \overline{V}^2) = -\frac{v}{r}V_0^2(1 - k^2). \qquad (7)
$$

Analytical solutions of this equation may be obtained for several cases of interest. When **k** is varied, we find global stability against bar formation occurs for $k \leq 0.50$. This result agrees well with the empirical results of Ostriker and Peebles,[2] who find that **t**, the ratio of the total rotational kinetic energy to the absolute value of the gravitational energy, must be less than 0.14 for global stability. This particular value of **t** corresponds to a value of 0.53 for k. (From the Virial theorem, $\mathbf{t} = k^2/2$.)

NUMERICAL EXAMPLES

In this section, we illustrate the utility of our method by examining several models, having varying amounts of differential rotation, for which exact solutions to the cold disk are known. The calculations described herein were carried out using a grid code, developed by one of the authors (E. M.). Our standard simulations consisted of $2 \times 10^4 - 5 \times 10^4$ identical particles, distributed upon either a 64×64 or 128×128 mesh. First we consider Kalnajs/Hohl (K/H) disks, for which exact time-independent solutions of the Boltzmann equation exist (Kalnajs,[3] Hohl[4]). Interior to disk radius R, the local circular velocities and surface density are given by

$$
V_0(r) = \frac{Cr}{R} = \Omega_0 r, \qquad (8)
$$

and

$$
v(r) = \frac{2C^2}{\pi^2 GR} \left(\sqrt{1 - \frac{r^2}{R^2}} \right), \qquad (9)
$$

where C is the local circular velocity at $r = R$ and Ω_0 is the angular velocity. For solid body rotation, it is apparent from **(3)** that the radial and azimuthal velocity dispersions are equal. Upon solving **(7)** for σ_r, we recover the well-known result ([4, eq. (19)])

$$\sigma_r(r) = \sqrt{\frac{\Omega_0^2(1 - k^2)(R^2 - r^2)}{3}}. \tag{10}$$

Consequently, the total velocity dispersion, $\sigma(r) = \sqrt{2}\sigma_r(r)$. We found such disks to be macroscopically stable for $k \leq 0.50$, which implies $t \leq 0.13$, a result in reasonable agreement with Kalnajs's stability analysis of the bar mode, which yields $k < \sqrt{125/486} = 0.5072$, or $t < 0.1286$.

Although of considerable formal interest, K/H disks are not suitable starting points for modeling real galaxies. Consequently, we have used our method to simulate the evolution of a wide variety of stable truncated Toomre disks, for which the distribution functions are unknown. Exact solutions for the cold disks of this family were developed by HBG.[6] For the most part, we have confined our attention to the $n = 0$ and $n = 1$ Toomre disks, which have been used extensively in modeling gas flows in real galaxies (Hunter *et al.*,[8] England,[9] England, Gottesman, and Hunter[10]). While we do not discuss the matter in our present communication, it is a straightforward procedure to form a linear combination (or combinations) of truncated Toomre disks [6, p. 78] in order to initialize a model with a suitable rotation curve.

For an infinite $n = 0$ disk, the local circular velocity is given by **(6)** and the surface density is of the form

$$v(r, b) = \frac{C_1^2}{2\pi G} \frac{1}{\sqrt{r^2 + b^2}}. \tag{11}$$

It is a useful approximation to truncate this distribution at $r = R$, whereupon **(11)** then may be integrated analytically to yield the result

$$\sigma_r^2(r) = C_1^2(1 - k^2)\frac{\sqrt{b^2 + r^2}}{b}\left[\ln\left|\frac{(b + \sqrt{b^2 + r^2}/\sqrt{b^2 + r^2})}{(b + \sqrt{b^2 + R^2}/\sqrt{b^2 + R^2})}\right|\right]. \tag{12}$$

We have developed similar approximate solutions for the radial velocity dispersions in $n = 1$, and other, Toomre disks.

We find that these closed forms are similar in appearance to the exact solutions and work well in practice. After some experimentation, we found that the simple procedure of assigning a peculiar speed for each particle equal to the total velocity dispersion within a thin annulus at radius r works quite well. Irrespective of our initial choice of distribution function, the peculiar velocities relax to a near Gaussian appearance after roughly one rotation period. Thus, the magnitude of the total initial velocity dispersion ($\sigma = \sqrt{2}\sigma_r$) of each particle in a ring was calculated and its initial direction was selected at random. Using **(16)** to initialize the velocity dispersions,

FIGURE 2 shows the surface density distributions after four rotation periods of an $n =$ 0 disk for different values of k. The disk characteristics are: $M = 10^{11} M_\odot$, $R = 12$ kpc, and $b = 2$ kpc. It is clear that the model becomes less unstable as k diminishes; even so, a bar (or oval) structure forms when $k = 0.6$. FIGURE 3 illustrates the evolution of the surface density of a model for which $k = 0.5$. We consider this model to be marginally stable against bar formation. The evolution of the radial velocity dispersions at selected radii are shown in FIGURE 4. FIGURE 5 displays the rotation curve of the model after 12 rotations, along with the initial rotation curve. Statistical fluctuations, due to the random heating and the finite number of particles in each annulus, are apparent in FIGURE 5. The rotational velocities of the relatively few particles at larger radii, which are discussed in the next section, are excluded from this figure.

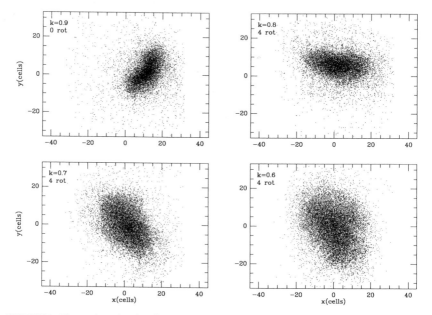

FIGURE 2. The surface density of a Toomre $n = 0$ disk after four rotations for four values of k. As k decreases, the disk stabilizes.

We find that, for $k \leq 0.50$, stable disks can be generated and maintained for many rotation periods. As such values of k correspond to heating in excess of what we believe actually exists in disk galaxies, we have experimented with reducing the heating by adding spherical halos. Thus, for example, we have successfully created a stable disk with $k = 0.7$ by including a halo having a mass equal to that of the disk interior to radius R. The halo models we have used have constant density cores and their densities at larger radii diminish as r^{-2} (see [6, eq. (23)]). In order to reduce the ratio of the average velocity dispersions to the rotational velocity down to a value close to that observed, we found that the halo mass interior to the disk radius must exceed that of the disk by roughly a factor of 2. Results were sensitive mainly to the

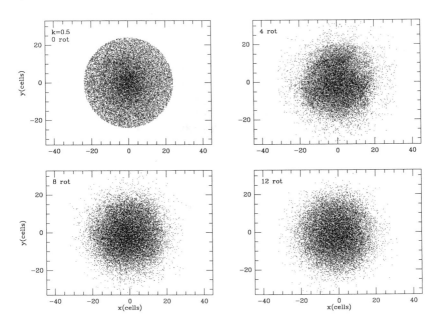

FIGURE 3. The surface density of a stable ($k = 0.5$) Toomre $n = 0$ disk initially and after 4, 8, and 12 rotation periods.

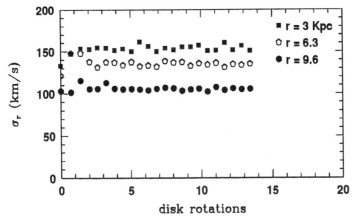

FIGURE 4. σ_r (km/s), found by averaging over annuli one-half kpc wide, plotted vs. disk rotations for various values of r (kpc).

halo mass interior to the disk radius, but also depended upon the value of r_0, stabilizing as r_0 increased. HBG have shown that all truncated Toomre disks have regimes, just beyond their truncation radii, that are epicyclically unstable,

$$\frac{d \ln V(r)}{d \ln r} < -1.$$

The less centrally condensed the disk, the greater the extent of the unstable region. K/H disks exhibit similar behavior, because they may be regarded as limiting cases of $n = 0$ Toomre disks for which r/b is small. Consequently, structural changes should take place during the early evolution of truncated disk models, even if their interiors are macroscopically stable. This behavior is apparent in time sequences of surface density plots published by many authors, and it is present in our models as well. However, this edge instability does not have catastrophic consequences. Instead, the disks adjust, and their rotation curves change somewhat. Typically, a model adjusts within a few rotation periods (4, say), after which it evolves only very slowly.

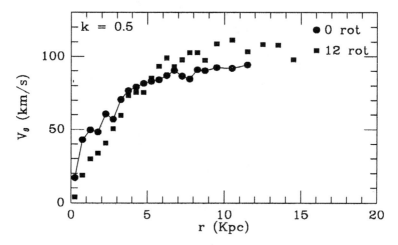

FIGURE 5. The initial and final (after 12 rotation periods) rotation curves for a Toomre $n = 0$ disk with $k = 0.5$.

GALACTIC VORTICES

During the course of our numerical studies of the past decade, we have been impressed with the fact that many models exhibit large-scale, stationary vortices in the vicinities of the $L_{4,5}$ libration points associated with the model bars. In some models, having relatively weak bars, the vortices are very nearly centered upon $L_{4,5}$, whereas in others the vortex centers have shifted either well in advance of, or behind, $L_{4,5}$ in the direction of bar rotation. Moreover, for strongly nonlinear bars, the vortex centers may be well within the corotation radius. These observations prompted G. Contopoulos and J. H. Hunter to carry out an analytical examination of the consequences of adding small amounts of shear viscosity to the equations of motion of test particles moving in the disk and bar potential. In view of the fact that the unperturbed velocities of short-period orbits near $L_{4,5}$ look like gas streamlines, we regarded the shear viscous acceleration as a small quantity and added the term to the equations of motion. Although our approach is limited to regarding the viscous accelerations as small, we anticipate that we will be able to predict both the directions and approximate magnitudes of the displacements of the vortex centers from $L_{4,5}$ in models. At the present time, M. N. England, J. H. Hunter, and G. Contopoulos are performing detailed numerical simulations to check the analytical predictions.

ACKNOWLEDGMENT

We thank R. Drimmel for running tree code simulations of a number of our models.

REFERENCES

1. JEANS, J. H. 1919. Philos. Trans. R. Soc. London, Ser. A **218:** 157.
2. OSTRIKER, J. P. & P. J. E. PEEBLES. 1973. Astrophys. J. **186:** 467.
3. KALNAJS, A. J. 1972. Astrophys. J. **175:** 63.
4. HOHL, F. 1972. J. Comput. Phys. **9:** 10.
5. BINNEY, J. J. & S. TREMAINE. 1987. Galactic Dynamics. Princeton Univ. Press. Princeton, N.J.
6. HUNTER, J. H., R. BALL & S. T. GOTTESMAN. 1984. Mon. Not. R. Astron. Soc. **208:** 1.
7. TOOMRE, A. 1964. Astrophys. J. **139:** 1217.
8. HUNTER, J. H., R. BALL, J. M. HUNTLEY, M. N. ENGLAND & S. T. GOTTESMAN. 1988. Astrophys. J. **324:** 721.
9. ENGLAND, M. N. 1989. Astrophys. J. **337:** 191.
10. ENGLAND, M. N., S. T. GOTTESMAN & J. H. HUNTER. 1990. Astrophys. J. **348:** 456.

Instabilities in Rigidly Rotating Disks[a]

RONALD E. DRIMMEL AND JAMES H. HUNTER, JR.

Department of Astronomy
University of Florida
Gainesville, Florida 32611

INTRODUCTION

In order to gain insight into the evolution of disks consisting of large numbers of self-gravitating masses, it is desirable first to acquire an understanding of the behavior of relatively simple models. Such idealizations often possess general characteristics that also are present in models of more realistic systems. Moreover, these models may serve as test cases to be used in conjunction with the development of numerical codes and/or for the comparison of the predictions of different codes. With this philosophy in mind, we have developed a two-dimensional version of Hernquist's TREECOD[1] for the purpose of modeling flat disks. In addition, we have available a two-dimensional grid code developed by E. Moore. Both codes employ an identical time-centered leapfrog algorithm to advance particles' trajectories in time.

Kalnajs[2] and Hohl[3] (designated hereafter K/H) have derived an exact solution to the collisionless Boltzmann equation for the distribution functions of self-gravitating, identical point masses in rigidly rotating flat disks. Although all such single-component systems are unstable,[2] they provide self-consistent initial conditions for numerical experiments. In the present communication we compare the predictions of both codes on identical problems: models having the same initial conditions. All models discussed here have the following properties: number of particles $N = 2 \times 10^4$, disk mass $M = 10^{11} M_\odot$, disk radius $R = 12$ kpc, and surface density

$$
\nu(r) = \begin{cases} \dfrac{2C^2}{\pi^2 GR} \sqrt{1 - \dfrac{r^2}{R^2}} & r \leq R, \\ 0 & r < R, \end{cases}
\tag{1}
$$

where C is the local circular (cold rotational) velocity at radius R, and G is the gravitational constant. Heating (velocity dispersion) has been introduced using the known distribution function for these disks.

THE MODELS

Cold and Cool Disks

Models of cold disks are initially supported entirely by rotation, and are known to be violently unstable to short wavelength disturbances. Although the rapidly develop-

[a]This work was supported in part by the University of Florida and the IBM Corporation through their Research Computing Initiative at the Northeast Regional Data Center. Additional support for one of the authors (J. H. H.) was provided by National Science Foundation Grant AST-9022827.

ing, small-scale structures are transient, they provide a means of calibrating parameters of the two numerical codes. Gravitational forces in our TREECOD simulations are strictly Newtonian unless particles approach within a critical separation $r = 2\epsilon$, where ϵ is a softening length. For smaller r the gravitational forces are softened and vanish as $r \rightarrow 0$; the softening is given by a continuous piecewise polynomial derived by Hernquist and Katz.[4] The softening parameter will determine the minimum scales of instabilities, as well as the maximum rates at which they grow. In grid codes, where the gravitational forces are evaluated on a mesh possessing a finite spacing, it is the cell length l that limits the scales of the smallest and most rapidly growing disturbances. FIGURE 1 shows typical results for the surface density distributions predicted by the two codes after 0.1 cold rotation periods of initially identical models. We find that similar structures will develop when $\epsilon/l \sim 2.2$.

A striking feature in these figures is the appearance of cell-like structures, which increase in size with time and eventually disappear. Filamentary structures, corresponding to the cell boundaries, persist for a longer time, especially in the outer regions of the disk where they evolve into thin, transient arms. Such cell structures and filaments also are seen in cosmological models of cold universes,[5] which are supported by expansion rather than by rotation. Very similar results have been reported by Monaghan and Lattanzio,[6] who used a grid code to evolve a gas disk with molecular cooling. This cell/filament structure is a consequence of gravitational instability in a cold medium, which has been discussed generically in some detail by Shandarin and Zeldovich.[7] The characteristic scales and growth rates of the initial cells are strongly dependent upon ϵ and l. This fact is illustrated in FIGURE 2, which is the same case shown in the previous figure, but with an ϵ set equal to the average interparticle distance (0.129 kpc).

In order to interpret these results, we use the well-known dispersion relation for local, small-amplitude disturbances in a rigidly rotating, flat sheet. Letting perturbed quantities develop as $e^{i(\mathbf{k \cdot r} - \omega t)}$, we have

$$\omega^2 - \left(k^2 \sigma^2 + 4\Omega^2 - 2\pi G k \nu\right) = 0, \tag{2}$$

where σ is the total velocity dispersion (thermal speed), and Ω the angular rotation rate. If $\sigma = 0$, ω is proportional to $\sqrt{k}$, implying that the shorter the wavelength the faster the growth. The softening length (or cell length) of a model effectively defines the shortest wavelength because it limits the size of instabilities that can be realized in that particular model. For cold K/H disks ($\sigma = 0$), the approximate e-folding time of a disturbance of wavelength λ is given by

$$t_e = \frac{P}{8\pi} \sqrt{\frac{2\lambda}{R}} = 0.0563 P \sqrt{\frac{\lambda}{R}}, \tag{3}$$

where P is the rotation period of the cold disk. If we assume the minimum wavelength $\lambda_m \sim 4\epsilon = 2.2$ kpc, $t_e \approx 0.02P$. Hence, the most rapidly growing disturbances in the model of FIGURE 1 have grown for about five e-folding times, which is consistent with the density contrasts seen here. Moreover, the size of the cells is roughly 2.2 kpc.

Cool models with relatively small velocity dispersion (or heating) behave differently from their cold counterparts. In FIGURE 3 we show a model with the same

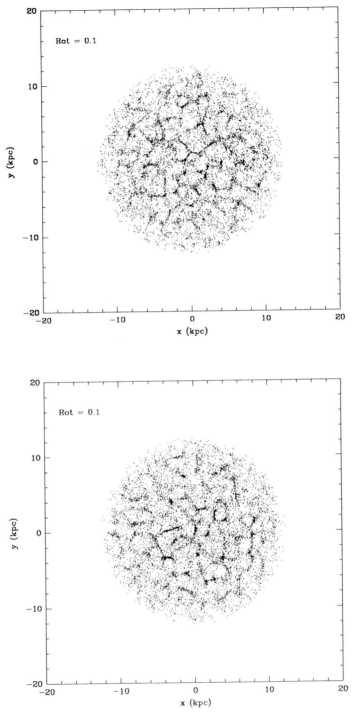

FIGURE 1. Cold K/H disk. Top figure shows TREECOD run with $\epsilon = 0.55$ kpc. Bottom figure refers to a grid code with 0.25 kpc as the grid spaceing. Ten thousand points from each model are plotted.

initial conditions as that of FIGURE 1, but with initial particle velocities assigned via the distribution function solution with $\sigma = 74$ km/s at $r = 0$. (The minimum velocity dispersion to stabalize a Kalnajs disk at our scale is $\sigma = 204$ km/s.) This velocity dispersion corresponds to a temperature of about 3 K when scaled down to the size of Monaghan and Lattanzio's disks (10^4 solar masses and 12.6 pc radius). When σ is not equal to zero, the wavelength of maximum growth,

$$\lambda_M = \pi^2 R \frac{\sigma^2}{C^2}, \tag{4}$$

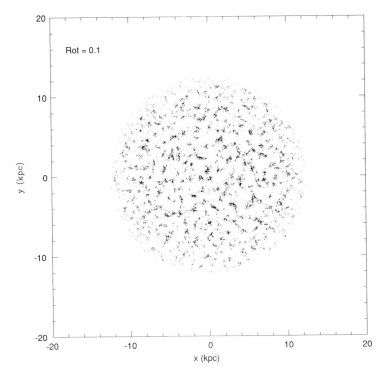

FIGURE 2. Cold K/H disk with $\epsilon = 0.129$ kpc. Note the lack of filaments and cell structure.

is approximately 7.7 kpc in this model. The corresponding e-folding time is given approximately by

$$t_e = \frac{P}{4\pi} \sqrt{\frac{\lambda_M}{R}} = 0.0796P \sqrt{\frac{\lambda_M}{R}}. \tag{5}$$

For this particular model $t_e \simeq 0.064P$, which is consistent with our numerical results.

The most noticable difference between this model and those with no heating is the lack of the sharply defined filaments, though the characteristic distance between clumps is about the same size as λ_M. This can be understood when one considers that the exponentially growing instabilities are limited by either thermal motions in, or the discreteness of, the system, which will limit the maximum density in a small region. In effect, the thermal motions blur out the filament structure and the clumps are found where the wavefronts of the rapidly growing Fourier components intersect. Similar cells and filaments develop in other cold and cool disk models, such as truncated Toomre disks, their development being only slightly modified by the velocity shear of the background material.

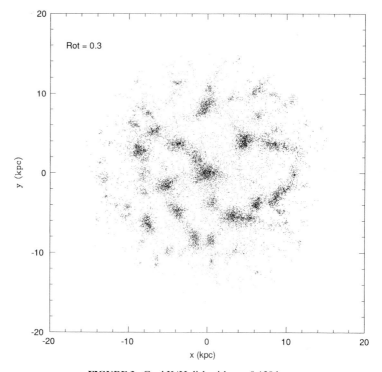

FIGURE 3. Cool K/H disk with $\epsilon = 0.129$ kpc.

As mentioned previously, the local structures described earlier are transient. By one rotation period, all cold and cool models we have studied fragment into numerous subunits. After about five rotations the largest fragments have coalesced, via dynamical friction, into a single condensed object. Though the detailed initial evolution differs from case to case, depending upon both the characteristics of the initial model and the softening length, the final end state is qualitatively the same.

WARM AND HOT DISKS

Using the method developed by Hunter and Moore, outlined in a separate communication appearing in these proceedings,[8] we have constructed hot, macroscopically stable K/H disks and truncated Toomre disks, as well as warm, globally unstable models, which evolve into bar configurations. Both TREECOD and the grid code predict essentially the same evolution for these models over many rotation periods, and the results are relatively insensitive to ϵ and l. The reason for this behavior is that the local Jeans lengths in such models are significantly larger than either ϵ or l. All single-component K/H disks are microscopically unstable; for hot models we find that their velocity distributions change rapidly from their initial unstable forms into roughly Gaussian distributions, relative to the local standard of rest, with high-velocity cutoffs. Models that are given an initial velocity distribution without an appropriate high-velocity cutoff, such as a true Gaussian, become noticably more extended than the models discussed previously.

CONCLUSION

We conclude that both tree and grid codes predict similar results for the evolution of the disks if the gravitational softening parameter ϵ and the cell length l are chosen carefully. In our experiments we found a good choice to be $\epsilon/l \sim 2.2$. The transient cells and filaments, which grow rapidly in cold and cool disks, are particularly sensitive to this ratio. Both codes lead to essentially the same results for warm and hot models, which possess relatively large initial velocity dispersions.

ACKNOWLEDGMENTS

We thank E. Moore for running the grid code models discussed in this paper, as well as Nikos Hiotelis for assisting in the development of the two-dimensional version of the TREECOD, and Lars Hernquist for making TREECOD accessible to us.

REFERENCES

1. HERNQUIST, L. 1987. Astrophys. J., Suppl. Ser. **64:** 715.
2. KALNAJS, A. 1972. Astrophys. J. **175:** 63.
3. HOHL, F. 1972. J. Comput. Phys. **9:** 10.
4. HERNQUIST, L. & N. KATZ. 1989. Astrophys. J., Suppl. Ser. **70:** 419.
5. BEACOM, J. F., et al. 1991. Astrophys. J. **372:** 351.
6. MONAGHAN, J. J. & J. C. LATTANZIO. 1991. Astrophys. J. **375:** 177.
7. SHANDARIN, S. F. & YA. B. ZELDOVICH. 1989. Rev. Mod. Phys. **61:** 185.
8. HUNTER, J. H., JR., E. MOORE & M. N. ENGLAND. 1992. Numerical studies of disks. This issue.

Numerical Models of Barred Spiral Galaxies[a]

E. M. MOORE

Department of Astronomy
University of Florida
Gainesville, Florida 32611

INTRODUCTION

In an earlier paper in these proceedings,[1] a method of constructing featureless, stable disks was presented. It was found that the heating parameter, **k**, which varies from 0 for a purely pressure supported disk, to 1 for a cold disk, must be $\lessgtr$ 0.5 to ensure macroscopic stability. As **k** increases above this value, the stabilizing effect of the noncircular velocities decreases, resulting in more and more unstable disks. These results were used to develop a new method of inducing and controlling bar and spiral arm formation by reducing the stabilizing stellar peculiar velocities in the center of the model, but maintaining them in the outer regions; that is, **k** is allowed to vary with radius across the disk. A bar forms in the interior and spiral structure is excited in the outer gas disk in response to this bar. By varying the central value of **k**, the rate at which dispersions increase outward, and the halo mass, the size and shape of the bar can be constrained. Spiral structure persists for many rotational periods in the gas disk that is initialized with little velocity dispersions, and because it is dissipative, remains cool.

THE NUMERICAL ALGORITHM

The numerical scheme models a stellar and gaseous disk and can include an imposed halo. The stellar disk responds only to gravitational forces, while the gas component feels gravitational and vicious forces. The gravitational forces are calculated using a fast Fourier transform on a 128×128 Cartesian grid. The viscous forces are computed by the method of smooth particle hydrodynamics, following Lucy[2] and Sanders.[3] The viscous force is a bulk viscosity, consisting of a single term, proportional to the velocity divergence squared. It provides the gas with a dissipative mechanism and affects the gas flow only in the case of compression, acting to prevent the crossing of orbits, and thus approximating gas streamlines. The viscous force acting on the jth particle is defined to be:

$$-\nabla q_j = \frac{1}{\rho_j} \sum_i^{n_\sigma} m \frac{q_i}{\rho_i} \nabla w(|\mathbf{r}_j - \mathbf{r}_i|),$$

[a]This research was supported by National Science Foundation Grant AST-9022827.

176

where

ρ_i, ρ_j the continuous densities at the ith and jth particle positions, $\rho_i = n_i m$, where n is the number/area.

m the mass of the particle, all gas particles are assumed to have the same mass.

w the weighting function.

q_i the viscous pressure at the location of particle i.

The summation is carried over all gas particles within a circular area of radius σ of particle j, n_σ. The viscous pressure introduced in the previous equation is specified as:

$$q_i = \alpha \sigma^2 \rho_i (\nabla \cdot \mathbf{V})^2,$$

where α is a dimensionless number parameterizing the strength of the viscous force.

The halo consists of a constant density core, which is usually made to be a small percent of the initial radius, and then falls off in a Keplerian fashion.[4] The total halo mass is an input parameter that greatly affects the final morphology of the model.

FIGURES 1 and 2 show results from two models. Stellar densities are presented above; the gas distribution at the same time step are just below. The stars are initially laid out in a Toomre $n = 0$ disk, while the gas is distributed uniformly, to increase the gas to stellar surface density in the outer regions of the disk.[5] In both models, the total disk mass is 10^{11} solar masses, and the initial radius is 36 cells (18 kpc).

Shown in FIGURE 1 is a model in which the heating varies linearly across the stellar disk from $\mathbf{k} = 0.99$ for $r < 12$ cells to $\mathbf{k} = 0.5$, for $r > 34$ cells. Gas makes up 10 percent of the disk mass. The gas parameters are $\alpha = 0.1$ and $\sigma = 0.7$ cells. A halo of mass equal to the disk mass, within the initial disk radius, is included. The initial gas dispersion is random and less than 7 km s^{-1}. The stellar heating changes by about a factor of 3, from ≈ 20 km s^{-1} in the center to a high of ≈ 60 km s^{-1} halfway across the disk. Early in the model, both components develop a hole at the center, with a radius slightly under 12 cells, the size of the area with reduced heating. By five rotations the stellar development seems to be complete. A dense bar has formed in the center of the disk, surrounded by an apparently featureless stellar disk. In the gas, spiral features begin to appear early in the model, and become more defined as the model progresses.

In the second model (FIG. 2) a more massive halo is imposed and the initial stellar disk is given more stabilizing peculiar velocities than the previous model. The stellar heating varies across the disk from $\mathbf{k} = 0.98$ for $r < 5$ cells to $\mathbf{k} = 0.55$, for $r > 28$. Ten percent of the disk mass is due to the gas component. Gas parameters are: $\alpha = 0.1$ and $\sigma = 0.6$ cells. The mass of the halo within the initial disk radius is 1.6 times the disk mass. The initial gas dispersion is random and less than 5 km s^{-1}. Density plots of this model are seen in FIGURE 2. The initial model development is similar to that of model one, but less violent. By 3 to 5 rotations, spiral structure appears in the gas component, but it is not as open as that in the previous model. Rather, the disk has spread out very little, forming dense spirals fairly close to the model center. The interarm region is densely populated. By five rotations a small bar is beginning to appear. Between five and nine rotations, the model expands slightly, and the ring feature found at three rotations begins to differentiate into narrow

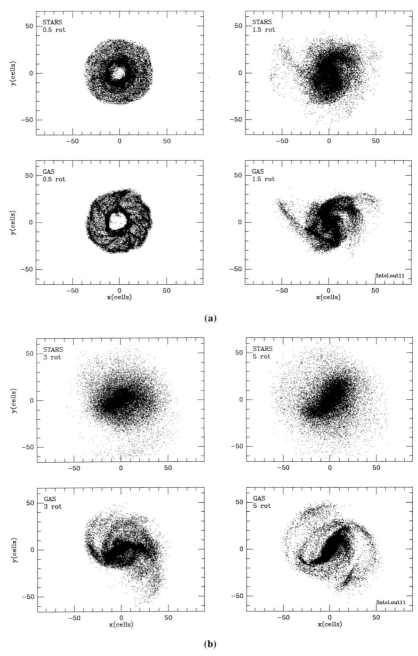

FIGURE 1. The first model described in the text. The stellar density is plotted on top, the gas below. The rotations are labeled in the *top left corner* of each plot.

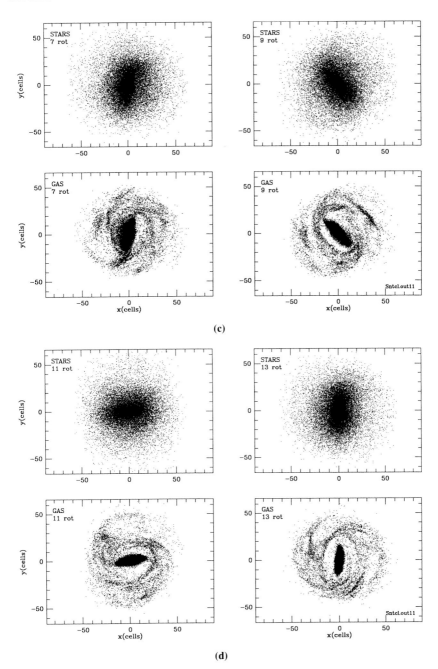

(c)

(d)

FIGURE 1.

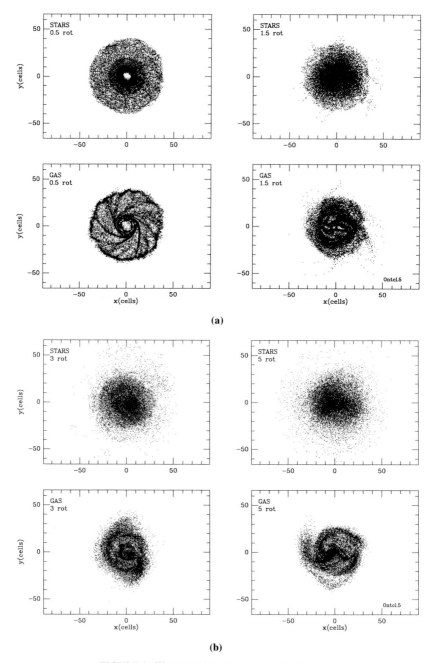

FIGURE 2. The second model described in the text.

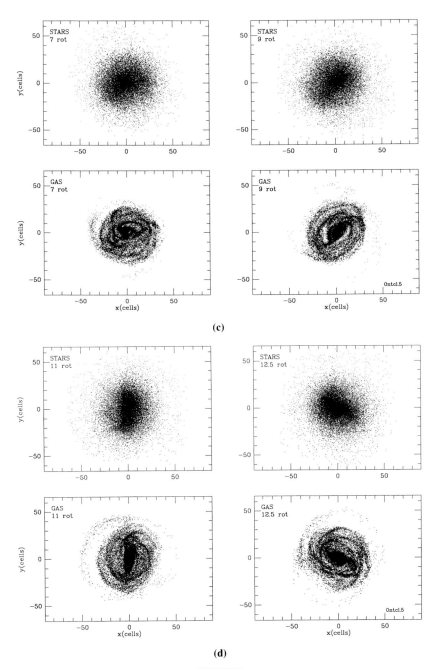

(c)

(d)

FIGURE 2.

spirals. These remain close to the bar, however, rather than displaying the open structure seen in FIGURE 1. The lower mass halo combined with the smaller stabilizing noncircular velocities of the first model lead to a more open spiral structure.

CONCLUSIONS

The models are sensitive to the size of the cool region in the center, the rate at which the heating is "turned on" over the disk, and the halo mass. These factors compete, resulting in a wide variety of realistic-looking spiral structures. If the halo mass is small compared to the disk mass, or the peculiar velocities are not very large, open spiral features are found. Conversely, if a massive halo is added, tight spiral arms develop. If too much heating is applied, the models tend to be featureless. Due to the large noncircular velocities in the stellar component, spiral features are smoothed out within two or three rotation periods.

REFERENCES

1. HUNTER, JR., J. H., E. MOORE & M. N. ENGLAND. Numerical studies of disks. This issue.
2. LUCY, L. B. 1977. Astron. J. 82: 1013.
3. SANDERS, R. H. 1977. Astrophys. J. 216: 916.
4. HUNTER, J. H., R. BALL & S. T. GOTTESMAN. 1984. Mon. Not. R. Astron. Soc. 208: 1.
5. BERTIN, G. 1989. In Galactic Models, J. R. Buchler and S. T. Gottesman, Eds. N.Y. Acad. Sci. 596.

Enhancement of Three-arm Spirals in Multiple-arm Galaxies

BRUCE G. ELMEGREEN

IBM Research Division
T. J. Watson Research Center
P.O. Box 218
Yorktown Heights, New York 10598

INTRODUCTION

The response of galactic stars and gas to spiral wave resonances can be strong enough to give observable effects, such as spurs midway between the arms at the 4:1 resonance,[1,2] endpoints to the arms at the outer 2:1 resonance,[3] and endpoints to bright star-formation ridges at the corotation resonance.[4] For some galaxies, a large number of these resonances can actually be seen, and the pattern speeds for the spirals can be estimated. This method to get pattern speeds was applied to 19 galaxies in three publications.[5–7] We discuss mostly the latter paper here. Another review including the results of the first two papers is in Elmegreen.[8]

The search for resonances using optical tracers is relatively straightforward for galaxies with symmetric two-arm spiral structures, but for galaxies with irregular or multiple-arm structures the procedure is less clear. Often there are many spurs and spiral arm termination points in such galaxies, giving the impression that there are several different radii for each type of resonance indicator. Then a unique solution for the pattern speed would seem to be impossible.

To overcome this problem, we use an image processing technique to display only the twofold or threefold symmetric parts of the enhanced galaxy images. This accentuates the resonance features that are most important for the main spiral waves, and it also removes the extraneous features that result from random star-formation or local spiral-like instabilities. We find that most galaxies contain both two- and three-arm spirals, and that the three-arm components lie almost exactly between the 3:1 resonances for the same pattern speeds as the two-arm components. One of the three arms is also consistently found to be at the position of the strongest of the two arms. These results suggest that multiple-arm galaxies generally contain three-arm spiral components, and that these components are driven out to their absorbing resonances by an interaction between the main two-arm spirals and an $m = 1$ asymmetry in these spirals. Many galaxies also contain a fourfold spiral structure resembling spurs at the inner 4:1 resonance.

IMAGE-ENHANCEMENT PROCEDURE

The procedure for the image enhancement is as follows. First the galaxy is deprojected to a face-on orientation. The position angles and inclinations for this deprojection are usually obtained from the literature, but these parameters are checked, or new ones determined if necessary, by examining the images in a coordinate system where the logarithm of the radius is plotted versus the inclination angle. If the galaxy center, position angle, or inclination are wrong, then obvious vertical stripes or asymmetries appear in this diagram. We make the usual assumptions that most of the optical part of the galaxy is in one plane and the isophotal contours are circular.

The second step in the enhancement is to remove the average radial light distribution. This is done so that the spirals and other nonaxisymmetric structures can be viewed throughout the disk in a single photograph, without requiring saturation in the center or unnecessary faintness in the outer parts. The average radial light distribution is found with a boxcar average using a box size equal to $R_{25}/4$ for radius R_{25} at 25 magnitudes per square arc second.

A third step is to normalize to a constant value the root-mean-square (rms) intensity fluctuations at each radius. This tends to enhance the spirals in the inner part of the galaxy relative to the outer part, because the relative spiral arm amplitude generally increases with radius in nonbarred galaxies. After these three steps, we have an enhanced image that shows the original spiral and star formation structures with great clarity.

To examine the symmetric structures in galactic spirals, we process these enhanced images again. For the two-arm symmetric part, we subtract from the original image a 180° rotated version of this image, making a new image that contains only the antisymmetric structure, truncated so that negative values are set equal to zero. Then we subtract this truncated image from the original to give an image with only the twofold symmetric features. Algebraically, this procedure can be written

$$S_2(r, \theta) = I(r, \theta) - [I(r, \theta) - I(r, \theta - 180°)]_T$$

for truncation symbol T. The threefold symmetric image is made in a similar fashion, using the original enhanced image and subtracting rotated versions of this image with rotation angles equal to 120° and 240°:

$$S_3(r, \theta) = 2I(r, \theta) - [I(r, \theta) - I(r, \theta - 120°)]_T - [I(r, \theta) - I(r, \theta + 120°)]_T.$$

Similar images are made for higher order symmetries too, following this same procedure. Note that the degree of symmetry of various features in the S_3 image is represented as a gray scale, with features that occur on three parts of an equilateral triangle appearing twice as bright in the S_3 image as features that appear on only two sides of the equilateral triangle.

An example of the results of this processing is shown in FIGURE 1, which contains the original, deprojected, and enhanced images of NGC 4321 (M100) in the top left, top right, and middle left boxes, respectively, and the twofold, threefold, and fourfold images in the middle right, lower left and lower right boxes, respectively. The S_2, S_3, and S_4 images have circles at the resonances found in this study: the inner 4:1, corotation and outer 2:1 resonances are on the S_2 image, the inner and outer 3:1 resonances are on the S_3 image, and the inner and outer 4:1 resonances on the S_4 image. The ratios of these radii are fixed by the slope of the rotation curve, which is taken to be 0.14 for this galaxy.[7] These resonances are discussed below.

FIGURE 1. The galaxy NGC 4321, with the original, deprojected, and enhanced images in the **top left, top right,** and **middle left,** and the two-, three-, and fourfold symmetric images in the **middle right, lower left,** and **lower right,** respectively. The symmetrized images have *circles* at the appropriate resonances for that symmetry, that is, at the inner and outer 3:1 and 4:1 resonances for the three- and fourfold symmetric images, and at the inner 4:1, corotation, and outer 2:1 resonances for the twofold symmetric image. The ratios of all of these resonances are fixed by the rotation curve. This galaxy has two symmetric star-formation ridges ending at corotation on each side, symmetric spurs at the inner 4:1 resonance, an end to the main two-arm spiral at the outer 2:1 resonance, and limits to the underlying three-arm spiral at the inner and outer 3:1 resonance. The *calibration bars* in each figure represent, on the **left** and **right,** 100 pixels and the isophotal radius R_{25}.

RESULTS

The enhanced images show evidence for spiral wave resonances. The ends of the two- and three-arm spirals are usually sharp and in the ratio of the outer 2:1 to outer 3:1 resonances for the appropriate rotation curves. The ratio of the outer to the inner extents of the three-arm spirals is also the same as the ratio of the outer to inner 3:1 resonance radii. These results imply that the twofold structure lies within the outer 2:1 resonance, and that the threefold structure lies precisely between the outer and inner 3:1 resonance limits, with the same pattern speed as the twofold structure.

The corotation resonance also shows up in about half of the galaxies studied as a clear termination point for bright ridges of star formation in the main two-arm spiral.

FIGURE 2. The galaxy NGC 5457, with the sky and enhanced images in the **upper left** and **right,** and the two-, three-, four-, and fivefold images in sequence. *Circles* are at the inner 4:1, corotation, and outer 2:1 resonances in the S_2 image, and at the inner and outer 3:1, 4:1, and 5:1 resonances in the other three images. The main symmetric arms end at the outer 2:1 resonance (although star-formation arms extend further out in the enhanced image), star formation ridges end at corotation, a prominent four-arm structure is at the inner 4:1 resonance, and the three-arm structure is limited by the inner and outer 3:1 resonances.

Star formation continues beyond this radius, but it is not so tightly confined to the arms. Corotation in NGC 4321 is also the location of a circle of star formation that goes all of the way around the galaxy, presumably as a result of wave-independent star formation.

The inner 4:1 resonance is usually close to the inner termination point of the main spirals and bright star-formation ridges, and in about one-quarter of the galaxies studied, including NGC 4321, it is also where there are faint spurs midway between the arms on each side. This four-arm structure can be seen in the lower right of FIGURE 1.

FIGURE 2 shows the results of the image and symmetry enhancements for NGC 5457 (M101). The sky view, enhanced, S_2, S_3, S_4, and S_5 images are in the top left, top right, middle left, middle right, lower left, and lower right, respectively. The S_2 image has circles at the inner 4:1, corotation, and outer 2:1 resonances, and the S_3, S_4, and S_5 images have circles at the inner and outer 3:1, 4:1, and 5:1 resonances, respectively. All of these circles are in the proportion given by the slope of the rotation curve (0.10), so once any one resonance radius is found, all of the others follow.

The results in FIGURE 2 are consistent with the more general results found for the other galaxies in our study: the outer 2:1 resonance marks the outer limit of the two-arm structure, the outer and inner 3:1 resonances limit the three-arm structure, and bright ridges of star formation end at the corotation resonance.

FIGURE 3 shows S_2 images of M81 (top) and M101 in a coordinate system where the logarithm of the radius is plotted on the vertical axis and the azimuthal angle is plotted on the horizontal axis. Tic marks are in units of $0.1R_{25}$ and π, respectively. What is important about these diagrams is that they illustrate how M81 and M101 have a similar segmented spiral structure, with spiral arm segments at a relatively large pitch angle midway and in the outer parts of the disk, and horizontal gaps (i.e., phase shifts) between these arm segments.

We connect the bright parts of the segments in FIGURE 3 with trailing and leading logarithmic spiral arms, as shown in FIGURE 4. This diagram illustrates what we interpret to be the interference pattern between trailing, inward-moving spiral waves and leading, outward-moving spiral waves. That is, the bright parts of the arms (triple lines in the figure) are located at the intersection points of two opposing wave trains. We believe that such interference patterns support the modal theory of spiral

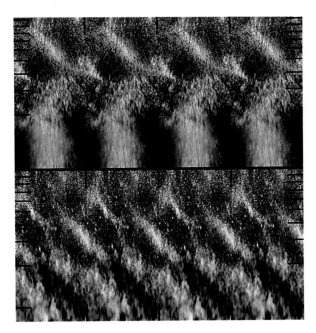

FIGURE 3. The twofold symmetric images of the galaxies NGC 3031 (M81) and NGC 5457 (M101) are shown in a log r-θ coordinate system. *Tic marks* on the vertical axis are in units of $0.1R_{25}$, and on the horizontal axis they are in units of π radians with two full cycles shown. Both galaxies have broken arm segments at a resonance, with a phase shift between the pieces. In M81, the break occurs at the inner 4:1 resonance and in M101, it occurs at the corotation resonance.

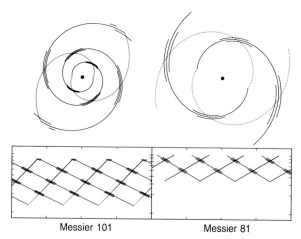

| Messier 101 | Messier 81 |

FIGURE 4. Schematic diagrams of the main spiral arms in M81 and M101, showing how the bright parts of the arms (*triple lines*) can be the result of an interference between inward-moving trailing waves and outward-moving leading waves. In M81, the leading waves have the same pitch angle as the trailing waves, but in M101, the leading waves are slightly more open than the trailing waves. These diagrams do not attempt to reproduce the phase shifts between the arm pieces at the break points.

structure, as developed by Bertin, Lin, and collaborators.[9] Only these two galaxies in our sample of 18 show such obvious phase shifts. In M81, the spiral arms drawn here have pitch angles of 14° for both the trailing and leading components. In M101, the pitch angles are 11.5° for the trailing component and 23.7° for the leading component.

CONCLUSIONS

We conclude from this study that many two-arm spirals can be wave modes between an inner reflecting barrier that lies slightly inside the inner 4:1 resonance, and the outer 2:1 resonance (i.e., outer Lindblad resonance). The three-arm spirals are driven out to their inner and outer resonance limits by asymmetries in this two-arm spiral, and at these resonance limits they Landau damp. Such damping is likely to be an important source of energy loss from the three-arm spiral, and if this spiral is driven by the two-arm spiral, then the whole three-arm system is an important source of energy loss from the two-arm system.

One implication of this three-arm driving is that the three-arm structure might appear after the two-arm structure forms, and so galaxies with very young two-arm spirals may not have prominent three-arm spirals yet. Galaxies M81 and M51, for example, are likely to have young two-arm spirals because of recent interactions with companion galaxies. These two galaxies also have the weakest three-arm components in our sample. It follows that galaxy interactions may trigger the two-arm spirals directly or as a wavemode, and then shortly after the interaction the structure will be dominated by two main arms. But after a while, the three-arm structure becomes strong, and then the arms become multiple.

Another result of this work is that star formation is occasionally compressed along a thin ridge that ends abruptly at corotation. This ridge is presumably the result of a shocklike structure in the interstellar medium, but it does not necessarily indicate that star formation is triggered along this ridge—only that the cold gas component is compressed more there than elsewhere in the galaxy.

ACKNOWLEDGMENTS

Most of the work discussed here was done in collaboration with Debra Meloy Elmegreen and Luis Montenegro. Luis also helped clean a watermark off the digitized I band image of M101, where it appeared far to the north, away from the main galaxy image.

REFERENCES

1. SHU, F. N., V. MILIONE & W. W. ROBERTS. 1973. Astrophys. J. **183:** 819.
2. ARTYMOWICZ, P. & S. LUBOW. 1991. Astrophys. J. In press.
3. LIN, C. C. & F. H. SHU. 1966. Proc. Nat. Acad. Sci. **55:** 229.
4. ROBERTS, W. W. 1969. Astrophys. J. **158:** 123.
5. ELMEGREEN, B. G., D. M. ELMEGREEN & P. E. SEIDEN. 1989. Astrophys. J. **343:** 602.
6. ELMEGREEN, B. G. & D. M. ELMEGREEN. 1990. Astrophys. J. **355:** 52.
7. ELMEGREEN, B. G., D. M. ELMEGREEN & L. MONTENEGRO. 1992. Astrophys. J., Suppl. Ser. **79:** 37.
8. ELMEGREEN, B. G. 1991. *In* Dynamics of Galaxies and Their Molecular Cloud Distributions, F. Combes and F. Casoli, Eds.: 113. Kluwer. Dordrecht, the Netherlands.
9. BERTIN, G., C. C. LIN, S. S. LOWE & R. P. THURSTANS. 1989. Astrophys. J. **338:** 78.

Dynamics of Polar Gas Disks

LINDA S. SPARKE

Washburn Observatory
University of Wisconsin-Madison
Madison, Wisconsin 53706-1582

INTRODUCTION

Some early-type galaxies show rings of gas, dust, and luminous material that appear to lie almost at right angles to the major axis of the central stellar body; the most famous example of this is the "Spindle galaxy," NGC 2685. It is generally assumed, and in some cases has been confirmed by observation,[1] that the inner galaxy is in rotation about its minor axis, consistent with the interpretation that it is a disk or flattened elliptical seen edge-on. The ring rotates about its own minor axis, highly inclined to that of the galaxy. The ring material sometimes forms a broad annulus; in A0136-0801, the outer edge of the luminous ring extends to about three times the radius of the inner edge,[2] while in UGC 7576 the kinematics of the neutral hydrogen suggests that the gas extends over a factor of 2 in radius.[3]

Whitmore *et al.*[1] have made a compilation of known polar rings, polar ring candidates, and related objects. They estimate that 1–2 percent of S0 galaxies currently have polar rings; the rings are neither common nor extremely rare. The rings are not exactly perpendicular to the galaxy, even allowing for projection effects,[4] but may be misaligned by up to 25°. All but one of the confirmed polar ring systems, for which the very different rotation axes of the ring and the galaxy have been observed directly, are S0 galaxies; only one, AM2020-504, is an elliptical. Polar rings around S0 galaxies are similar to the minor-axis gas disks observed in ellipticals,[5] but differ in that the stars and the ionized gas (as well as the neutral hydrogen) extend far beyond the body of the central galaxy.

The central galaxies of polar ring systems tend to be rather small, and the ring extends out to many scale lengths of the inner disk. Rotation speeds in the ring do not drop with radius[2,6] as they should do if all the mass of the galaxy were concentrated in the visible portion; as in spiral galaxies, a substantial dark halo must be present. Discussions of dark matter in spiral galaxies usually assume for simplicity that the halo is spherical.[7] This assumption can be tested in polar ring galaxies; in a flattened potential, polar orbits are elongated; velocities at the top of the orbit are lower than the circular speed at the same radius in the equatorial plane. Thus, comparing the rotation curve of the ring with the circular speed inferred (with difficulty) from velocity measurements of the stars in the central galaxy places limits on the flattening of the total mass distribution. On the basis of their measurements, Schweizer *et al.*[2] and Whitmore *et al.*[6] concluded that the total mass, including the dark halo, had a nearly round shape, in contrast to the obviously flattened stellar distribution. Sackett and Sparke[8] fitted a model consisting of disk, bulge, and oblate halo to velocity data for NGC 4650A, and found that an oblate halo with a shape between E0 and E6 could fit the observations; more recent measurements[9] appear to exclude a complete round halo.

Polar ring galaxies generally are gas-rich, often containing several billion solar masses of neutral hydrogen; synthesis mapping[10,11] shows that the gas is associated with the ring rather than with the central stellar body. The galaxy NGC 3998 appears to have an HI ring in polar orbit with no corresponding optical ring.[12] A single-dish survey currently in progress[13] shows typically a few billion solar masses of gas in or immediately around polar ring galaxies. The large masses are puzzling, since they are significantly greater than the HI content of a normal spiral.[14] The central galaxies of polar ring systems are usually small, low-mass systems; dynamical modeling for NGC 4650A[8] assigns a mass of $7 \times 10^9 \, M_\odot$ to the central stellar body, about equal to the measured mass of gas in the ring. How have these tiny galaxies managed to capture such huge amounts of gas?

Because the angular momentum of the polar ring material is so different from that of the underlying galaxy, it is usually that the ring has been acquired from outside, after the main stellar body had formed. One possibility is that the rings are the remains of a gas-rich dwarf irregular galaxy that has been captured into a high angular momentum orbit, and torn apart by differential rotation. This interpretation is supported by the continuity in appearance between polar ring galaxies and more disturbed systems such as the "X-shaped" galaxies[15] that seem to be in the process of merging, and by the fact that at least one polar ring galaxy (ESO 415 $-$ G26 $=$ MCG $-$ 5-7-1)[16] shows the faint shells and ripples that are usually taken as the signature of a merger. There is some uncertainty as to how the ring could actually form. Numerical simulations using the TREESPH scheme[17] indicate that a captured dwarf galaxy could be smeared out in angle and radius to form a polar ring; the process was not rapid, and substantial lopsidedness remained after several rotation periods. But Quinn,[18] using a different numerical technique but similar initial conditions, found a ring that remained narrow in radius, settling only very slowly into a plane. Another possibility is that polar rings represent the delayed infall of primordial or intragroup gas; if the incoming material did not share the rotation axis of the inner galaxy, a polar ring would result. The giant ring in Leo,[3] a 200-kpc-diameter structure in coherent rotation containing at least a billion solar masses of hydrogen, may be a larger scale example of such a phenomenon.

Once a polar ring is in place, it evolves under the influence of the gravitational potential of the central galaxy. Because of the width of the rings, simple estimates[16] imply that they would become severely twisted by differential precession in much less than a Hubble time. Two-dimensional mapping of the velocity field in some rings shows that they are indeed twisted; an example is the ring in NGC 4650A, mapped in the $H\alpha$ line by Nicholson[19,20] using the Taurus imaging Fabry–Perot device. But other rings, most notably those in A0136-0801[2] and in UGC 7576,[10] are extremely regular in appearance, and despite their high gas content, lack the blue colors associated with recent star formation. These apparently settled rings suggest that there may be a stabilizing mechanism.

Sparke[21] showed that a sufficiently massive polar ring around an oblate galaxy could be stabilized by its own gravity, so that it precesses coherently as a unit around the galaxy pole. The same set of equations, in which the ring is approximated as a series of massive concentric circular wires, free to tilt under the gravitational torques of each other and of the central galaxy, may be used to consider the time evolution of polar rings. This model takes into account differential precession in the potential of the central galaxy, and the self-gravity of the ring material, but not dissipative processes such as viscous settling or inflow.

EQUATIONS OF MOTION FOR A SELF-GRAVITATING POLAR RING

In what follows, the central galaxy of a polar ring system is assumed to consist of a disk and an axisymmetric (but not necessarily spherical) halo sharing the same equatorial plane. The path of any star or gas cloud in the polar ring can be considered as an orbit precessing about the symmetry axis z of the galaxy; if precession is slow compared to the time required to complete one orbit, then the change in the orbital elements due to that precession may be calculated by averaging over the rapid orbital motion. Further, the gravitational force exerted by that star on the rest of the material may be replaced by the force due to a torus of material spread over the orbit.[22] Ring particles feel both the gravitational influence of the central galaxy and torques induced by other ring material. Because the galaxy is flattened, the actual orbits will be somewhat elliptical rather than circular, and stars will not move on them with precisely uniform speed. But these effects are first order in the galactic oblateness, and change the precession-inducing torques only at second order; they are neglected in this work. Thus a set of concentric circular massive wires, rotating in the spherically averaged gravitational field of the galaxy, serves as a model for the polar ring.

Any one wire may be described by its radius r, which is constant since no dissipation occurs, by its mass m, the inclination $\theta(t)$ to the galactic equator, and the azimuth $\phi(t)$ at which the orbit cuts the (x, y) symmetry plane of the galaxy, in the ascending direction. Following the conventions of Goldstein [23, sec. 4.4] and using ψ to label the position of a point on the orbit, the energy E of the wire is given by

$$E = \frac{mr^2}{2}(\dot{\theta}^2 + \dot{\phi}^2 \sin^2 \theta) + \frac{mr^2}{4}(\dot{\psi} + \dot{\theta}\cos\theta)^2 + V(\theta, \phi), \qquad (1)$$

where $V(\theta, \phi)$ is the gravitational potential energy of the wire in the combined field of the galaxy and of the other ring material. The energy does not depend on the coordinate ψ, hence the conjugate momentum

$$p_\psi = \frac{mr^2}{2}(\dot{\psi} + \dot{\phi}\cos\theta) \qquad (2)$$

is conserved; this is just the angular momentum of the orbital motion, $p_\psi = mr^2\Omega(r)$. The other two momenta are p_ϕ, the z angular momentum, and p_θ, the angular momentum about the instantaneous line of nodes where the ring cuts the plane $z = 0$. They are given by

$$p_\phi = mr^2\dot{\phi}\sin^2\theta + p_\psi\cos\theta, \qquad \dot{p}_\phi = \partial V(\theta, \phi)/\partial\phi \qquad (3)$$

$$p_\theta = mr^2\dot{\theta}, \qquad \dot{p}_\theta = \frac{\partial V(\theta, \phi)}{\partial\theta} + \frac{(p_\phi - p_\psi\cos\theta)(p_\psi - p_\phi\cos\theta)}{mr^2\sin^3\theta}. \qquad (4)$$

The gravitational potential $V(\theta, \phi)$ has two components: that due to the central galaxy and that from the other wires making up the ring. Here the galactic potential itself is modeled using two components: disk and halo. The first component is taken to be a thin Kuzmin[24,25] disk that approximates the standard exponential disk within the first 4–5 scale lengths, but has a simple form for the potential Φ and surface density Σ:

$$\Sigma(R) = \frac{aM_D}{2\pi(r^2 + a^2)^{3/2}}, \qquad \Phi(x, y, z) = -\frac{GM_D}{\sqrt{R^2 + (a + |z|)^2}}, \tag{5}$$

where $R^2 = x^2 + y^2$, M_D is the mass of the disk, and a is a scale parameter. The dark halo is represented by a mass distribution stratified on concentric oblate spheroids of constant ellipticity e:

$$\rho(x, y, z) = \rho(m^2), \qquad m^2 = R^2 + \frac{z^2}{(1 - e)^2}. \tag{6}$$

The corresponding potential gradient at any point can be found as a one-dimensional integral [26, sec. 2.3]. The "pseudoisothermal" form

$$\rho(m^2) = \frac{\rho_0}{1 + m^2/r_H^2} \tag{7}$$

was used to represent a halo in which the circular velocity is asymptotically constant at a value V_H far beyond the core radius r_H. This density distribution corresponds to an infinite total mass, which is unphysical; it must be truncated at some outer surface. But since circular velocities are not observed to drop in real polar rings, the truncation appears to lie beyond their outer limits.

The torque due to the potential of the central galaxy is clearly zero in the azimuthal ϕ direction, while the θ torque on each wire is found by integrating around in angle. In practice the torque was approximated as

$$\partial V(\theta, \phi)/\partial \theta = \sin \theta \cos \theta [A_0 + A_2 P_2(\cos \theta) + \cdots], \tag{8}$$

omitting higher order terms; the coefficients A_0, A_2 were found at the beginning of the calculation for each radius r, and stored for use in evaluating expression (8) at any angle θ.

The polar ring is made up of a series of wires with radii r_i, masses m_i, and other quantities similarly labeled. The mutual potential energy of each pair of wires depends only on the angle α_{ij} between their planes, given by

$$\cos \alpha_{ij} = \cos \theta_i \cos \theta_j + \sin \theta_i \sin \theta_j \cos(\phi_i - \phi_j), \tag{9}$$

and can be found as follows. The gravitational potential due to a circular ring of mass m', radius r' lying in the (x, y) plane is [26, sec. 2.6.2]

$$\Phi(x, y, z) = -\frac{2Gm'}{\pi} \times \frac{K(k)\sqrt{(1 - k^2/2)}}{(r^2 + r'^2)^{1/2}}, \tag{10}$$

where

$$k^2 = \frac{4Rr'}{(r^2 + r'^2 + 2Rr')}. \tag{11}$$

Here $K(k)$ is the first complete elliptic integral, R is the cylindrical radius $R^2 = x^2 + y^2$, so that $r^2 = R^2 + z^2$. A second wire of radius r lying at an angle α to the first follows a curve $z = r \sin \eta \sin \alpha$, where η runs between 0 and 2π. The mutual potential energy is then

$$V_m(\alpha) = -\frac{Gmm'}{\pi^2(r^2 + r'^2)^{1/2}} \int_0^{2\pi} K(k)\sqrt{1 - k^2/2}\, d\eta, \tag{12}$$

where m is the mass of the second wire and k is given as a function of η via expression (11). The torque between the two wires follows by differentiating, and making use of the relation $E(k) = (1 - k^2)d[kK(k)]/dk$:

$$\partial V_m(\alpha)/\partial\alpha = -\frac{Gmm'rr' \sin 2\alpha}{\pi^2(r^2 + r'^2)^{3/2}}$$

$$\times \int_0^{2\pi} \left[\frac{E(k)\sqrt{(1 - k^2/2)}}{(1 - k^2)} - K(k)\right] \times \frac{(1 - k^2/2)^{3/2}}{k^2} \times \frac{\sin^2 \eta\, d\eta}{\sqrt{1 - \sin^2 \alpha \sin^2 \eta}}. \tag{13}$$

In practice the integral is evaluated on a grid of points between $0 > \eta > \pi/2$, for each pair of wires making up the ring. Since the integrand takes its largest value at $\eta = 0$, becoming singular if k approaches unity, it makes sense to space the evaluation points more closely in that region when the rings have very similar radii.

PURE DIFFERENTIAL PRECESSION

Differential precession occurs because the rings are not exactly polar and so do not lie in a symmetry plane of the inner galaxy. The galactic gravitational field has a quadrupole moment, which causes particle orbits to precess about the pole, at a rate that depends on the radius and orbital inclination. In the potentials given by (5) and (6), the rings regress, at a rate that decreases with radius. Hence an initially coplanar ring would develop a twist in the leading sense.

Differential precession of an inclined gas disk can explain much of the observed ring structure in NGC 3718.[44] This galaxy, classified SBa (peculiar), was mapped in neutral hydrogen by Schwarz;[27] he found a very complex gas distribution, which could be modeled as a warped and twisted disk. The gas orbits are obviously quite inclined to the optical disk, which appears near to face-on, while the HI disk passes from about 75° inclination, through edge-on, to $i=65°$ on the other side. At the same time, the major axis of the gas ring twists on the plane of the sky (see FIG. 1).

To model this, I assumed that the potential of the galaxy was given by a combination of a thin Kuzmin disk with a scale length taken as 1', a quarter of the quoted optical diameter, and a spherical pseudoisothermal halo. The parameters of the halo were chosen according to a rather crude "maximum disk"[7] model, which gave a nearly flat rotation curve with the measured amplitude of 250 km/s and the largest reasonable disk mass. The derived halo parameters were $V_H = 300$ km/s, and $r_H = 200''$, with a disk mass of $M_D = 10^{11} M_\odot$ for $H_0 = 75$ km/s/Mpc, corresponding to $M/L_B = 8$. In this potential, the precession of an orbit with any given tilt to the pole could be found. The calculation was started with all the gas orbits aligned at 10° to the pole of the galaxy (representing the plane of the orbit from which the disk

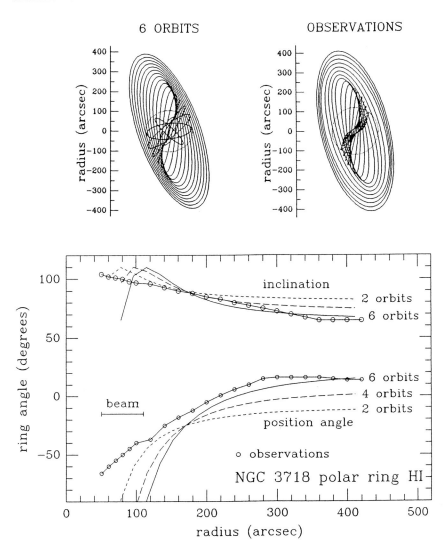

FIGURE 1. A precessing model for the polar ring in NGC 3718. **Top left:** The model, projected to look like the observed ring; the *dotted ellipse* shows the plane of the S0 disk. Time is measured in units of the orbital period at 250″ radius. **Top right:** The ring structure fitted by Schwarz[27] to his HI observations. **Bottom:** Inclination (*upper curves*) and position angle of the major axis (*lower*) of the ring as a function of radius. The observations (*circles*) are compared with the model at various times; the beam size of the HI observations is indicated on the left of the figure.

material was presumably captured), and precession was allowed to occur over several orbital times. The development of the gas ring is shown in FIGURE 1. At each step, the model is projected to look as much as possible like the observed galaxy, with the ring orbit at 160″ seen edge-on; this requires the S0 disk to be about 30° to face-on, with the major axis approximately East–West. This prediction may in principle be tested by determining the kinematic axes of the underlying disk, but so far the weather has not been cooperative.

The time has been measured in units of one orbit at 250″ radius, or about 6×10^8 years; after six orbits (3.5×10^9 years), the model (left) looks quite plausibly like the observed disk (right). The panel below shows how good the match is; starting from a nearly planar disk, differential precession seems adequate to explain the structure of this ring, at least outside 150″ radius. Schwarz found that, in a coordinate system defined by the plane of the *innermost gas orbits,* the gas disk has a shape that is warped by almost 90°, but is nearly untwisted (to within about 15°) about the pole of that system. According to the present model, this beautiful "restricted" warp results from the gas disk being nearly polar as seen from the *disk of the S0 galaxy—* coincidentally we observe it at a time when the twisting about the pole is close to 90°.

The self-gravity of the warped disk does not appear to be important. A model with the same galaxy potential, but assuming the gas disk to have a mass equal to the observed neutral hydrogen mass of $6 \times 10^9 \, M_\odot$, distributed between radii of 50″ and 420″, yields almost identical results. It is not particularly surprising to find that self-gravity does not have a strong effect, since the gas is distributed over such a large range in radius, so that the coupling torques are weak.

The model fits badly in the central regions; there are at least three possible reasons for this. The first possibility is that the disagreement may result from the large effective beam size of the HI observations (indicated in the figure), comparable to the range over which there is disagreement. Recent (March 1992) observations in the Very Large Array (VLA) C-array by van Moorsel, Sparke, and Schwarz have 13″ resolution, and may be able to eliminate this possibility by tracing the gas layer further into the central region. A second possibility is that inflow has occurred. If material is drifting slowly inward, then gas that is now at say 100″ from the center has not been there throughout the lifetime of the ring. The gas orbits at that radius are twisted by 62° relative to the outermost ring gas; it would take only about 1.2×10^9 years, or five local orbital periods, for so much differential precession to build up between this radius and the outer edge of the ring. The density in the HI disk decreases sharply inward of 200″; if the gas within that radius is falling toward the center, this argument suggests that it has taken a couple of billion years to move inward to 100″, implying an inward drift at 2–3 km/s. If the model is changed by reducing the mass of the galaxy disk while increasing the halo mass to keep the rotation speed the same, all these timescales become longer: for a disk with $M/L_B = 4$, the implied inflow speed is only about 1 km/s. This inflow rate is still ten times that expected if the dominant source of viscosity is cloud–cloud collisions,[28] but it is probably too small to be excluded on the basis of HI observations. Finally, it may be that the underlying dynamical model for the galaxy is incomplete, in lacking a bulge component. If the inner galaxy is substantially rounder than the disk, that will slow the rate of differential precession at small radii below what has been assumed in the present model. Near-infrared images showing the distribution of starlight, unobscured by the dust lane, are required to construct a more realistic model for the potential.

Steiman-Cameron, Kormendy, and Durisen[29] have recently made a study of the warped and twisted dust lane in the S0 galaxy NGC 4753. The dust lane is seen clearly in a *V*-band image taken in excellent seeing at the Canada–France–Hawaii Telescope (CFHT). The authors discuss a model in which an initially coplanar gas disk is allowed to twist under the influence of viscosity and the gravitational torques due to the central galaxy. They obtain a remarkable correspondence between the "folds" of their model gas sheet and the observed dust lanes. Viscosity apparently has had little effect; the gas layer retains a constant tilt with respect to the galaxy equator, while twisting by nearly 2π radians in a leading sense about the pole. Although inflow and settling must have occurred during the formation of this gas sheet, they do not seem to be happening now. The constant tilt suggests that self-gravity is probably unimportant as well.

In the scale-free potential of constant flattening that they use to represent the galaxy, the appearance of the twisted dust lane does not depend on the ellipticity, but the time required to arrive at a given degree of twistedness decreases as the potential becomes more flattened. Requiring that material at the outer edge of the gas disk (90″, or 4 kpc radius) has made at least six orbits restricts the potential so that it corresponds to a mass distribution flattened like E1.6. Since the isophotes of the galaxy appear to have a shape closer to E4, this would imply the existence of a massive halo substantially rounder than the luminous component. This result must be treated with a little caution, since the galaxy model was chosen for its computational convenience (no rotation curve was available for the gas component), but it points in the same direction as previous estimates of the flattening of the dark halo in polar ring galaxies.

EQUILIBRIUM SOLUTIONS

Equilibrium solutions for polar rings are discussed in detail by Sparke.[21] In a very simple model for the ring, consisting of two wires only, stable equilibria can be shown to exist with the wires nearly coplanar, but the outer wire slightly more inclined to the equatorial plane. In these configurations, the two wires precess together about the galaxy pole (*z* axis), at a steady rate determined by their average inclination. Coherent precession can occur because the inner wire exerts a torque on the outer, which reinforces that of the galaxy, speeding the regression of the outer wire; conversely, the regression of the inner wire is slowed. Stable solutions exist near the pole when the total ring mass exceeds some minimum value, increasing with the oblateness of the galaxy potential and the separation in radius between the two wires. If the ring mass is only slightly greater than this minimum, stable solutions exist only close to the pole; as the mass increases, equilibria at intermediate inclinations become stable as well. As the number of wires in the ring model is increased, the shape of these stable solutions converges to a smoothly curving limit.

The polar ring in the galaxy UGC 7576 is seen nearly edge-on; it appears extremely flat, and cannot be twisted about the pole by more than a few tenths of a radian. The ring does not lie exactly along the galaxy minor axis, and it must be at least 12° away from the pole.[4] Neutral hydrogen measurements[10] show that the ring contains $5 \times 10^9 \, M_\odot$ of gas, probably in a wide ring—the outer edge is around twice the radius of the inner edge. In the absence of stabilizing forces, differential precession should twist the ring quite rapidly. Nevertheless the ring appears smooth and relaxed; it is red, with little ionized gas,[30] suggesting that it is fairly old. Something appears to be acting to stabilize this ring.

A stable self-gravitating model for the ring in UGC 7576 is shown in FIGURE 2. Following Schechter *et al.*[10] the ring is taken to have constant density in the range $26'' < r < 49''$. The galaxy is modeled in the same way as for NGC 3718, with a Kuzmin disk of scale length $a = 3.8''$ (as indicated from I-band photometry[1]). The "maximum disk" model, chosen to make the rotation curve nearly flat at the largest measured value of 250 km/s at the edge of the ring, while putting as much mass in the disk as possible, yielded halo parameters $V_H = 265$ km/s, $r_H = 10''$. The disk mass was then $6 \times 10^{10} M_\odot$, corresponding to $M/L_B = 7.5$. The polar ring was given a mass equal to that measured in gas, $7 \times 10^9 M_\odot$ (corrected to $H_0 = 75$ km/s/Mpc, and multiplied by a factor of 1.4 to allow for the helium content). The model is displayed first with the galaxy disk tipped by 30° away from edge-on,[4] and then with the galaxy edge-on to show the structure more clearly. The model exhibits no twisting about the

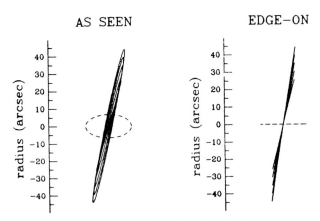

FIGURE 2. A self-gravitating equilibrium model for the polar ring in UGC 7576; the *dotted line* shows the plane of the S0 disk. The model is displayed first in the observed orientation, then with the disk edge-on to show the structure better.

galaxy pole, and a poleward warp is evident. This warping would be less if the ring mass were larger; if the adopted ring mass is too small, no stable solutions are found. For a given ring mass, the curvature is most critically dependent on the radial distribution of ring matter. Again, HI observations at high resolution would provide the best test of this model.

The polar ring round NGC 5122 is very similar in appearance to UGC 7576, with an apparently smooth, flat ring. Richter, Sackett, Sparke, and Cox have recently observed this ring in HI using the B-C configuration of the VLA, to map out the gas distribution and kinematics. We expect that it will be possible to describe this ring too by a stable equilibrium model. In the present volume, Arnaboldi *et al.*[31] discuss the polar ring around the elliptical galaxy AM2020-504, and present a stable self-gravitating model that reproduces the S-shaped twisted appearance of the ring as mapped in the $H\alpha$ line.

TIME-EVOLVING POLAR RINGS

Even if self-gravity does not lock a polar ring into a steady state, it can still cause the characteristic warp up toward the pole.[32] This may be seen by considering again the simplest two-wire model for the ring; let the inner wire have radius r, mass m, and be tilted by an angle θ away from the equatorial plane of the central galaxy, with the azimuth of the line of nodes at angle ϕ, while the outer wire has a radius r', mass m', and tilt angles θ', ϕ'. Any motion of the two wires must conserve both the total energy E and the angular momentum J_z about the symmetry axis of the galaxy. These quantities can easily be computed in a simple scale-free model, in which the rotation curve is taken to be completely flat, V = constant, and the oblateness η to be constant. Then the energy is given by

$$E = KE - 3V^2\eta[m \cos^2\theta + m' \cos^2\theta']/8 + V_m(\theta, \theta', \phi - \phi'), \qquad (14)$$

where the first term is the kinetic energy of the two wires, the middle term represents the potential energy of the wires in the galaxy potential, and V_m is the mutual potential energy; and the angular momentum about the z axis is

$$J_z = mrV \cos\theta + m'r'V \cos\theta'. \qquad (15)$$

If the ring is light, then the term in V_m is small compared to the others, since it is quadratic rather than linear in the ring mass. Then any motion of the wires must satisfy

$$\Delta E = 0 \approx \Delta(KE) - 0.75V^2\eta m\Delta(\cos\theta)[\cos\theta - (r/r')\cos\theta']. \qquad (16)$$

If the ring is initially static, and nearly coplanar ($\theta \approx \theta'$), then because $r' > r$, any motion requires $\Delta(\cos\theta) > 0$; the tilt of the inner wire must decrease. Thus the transfer of energy and angular momentum between the wires due to self-gravity causes the outer wire to be pushed up toward the pole, while the inner wire settles toward the equator.

This effect, of making the outer parts of the ring more nearly polar than the inner regions, is similar to what happens when dissipative processes cause an initially inclined ring to settle toward the equatorial plane of an oblate galaxy potential. Dissipation is fastest at small radii, where the orbital periods are short, so the inner part of the ring will be the first to reach the equatorial plane, while the outer disk is still highly inclined.[28] Dissipative settling requires that the ring be twisted under differential precession; this may or may not happen in a massive ring, depending on the strength of the self-gravity. The two mechanisms are physically quite different, however—self-gravity causes energy and angular momentum to be transported within the ring structure, while dissipative settling is essentially a local process that reduces the total energy of the system.

The ring in NGC 4650A is twisted, which shows that it is evolving in time, but it also bends toward the pole at the outer edge. Sparke *et al.*[33] showed that a time-dependent model that includes the self-gravity of the ring gas can reproduce the main features of the observations. The ring is not massive enough to hold itself together against differential precession, but self-gravity transfers angular momentum within the ring as it twists, so that the outer gas is thrown into a more nearly polar orbit. The model indicates that the ring is 3–5 orbits old, so that the material forming it may have been accreted a few billion years ago.

The small elliptical galaxy NGC 5077 has a twisted gas disk lying close to its minor axis. The gas kinematics have been mapped in $H\alpha$ by Bertola et al.;[34] they find that velocities along the major axis of the gas disk rise only very slowly with distance from the center of the galaxy. If the velocities are interpreted as circular motions in a coplanar gas disk, they indicate a severe decrease in the mass-to-luminosity ratio of the inner galaxy. Alternatively, it is possible to understand the velocity data in terms of elliptical or twisted orbits in the galaxy potential. The system is rich in HI; a measurement at Parkes yields 3×10^9 solar masses (for $H_0 = 50$ km/s/Mpc). In that paper, a model for the ring as a twisted self-gravitating polar disk is presented. Equilibrium solutions could not match the twisted appearance of the $H\alpha$ image or the velocity field of the gas disk, but a time-evolving model was able to reproduce the main features of both.

Eventually, an unstable ring will break up into a number of subrings that precess independently; the outer ring material is pushed into an orbit closer to the pole than the original ring plane, while inner gas sinks toward the equator of the S0 or elliptical galaxy. Thus a single accreted gas cloud might give rise to a multiple ring system, such as that seen in ESO 474-G26.[2] However, dissipative processes act more rapidly at smaller radii and lower inclinations to remove ring gas; if the inner material disappears completely, the remaining ring will be thinner and in a more nearly polar orbit than that on which the gas was originally accreted. This might resolve a puzzle pointed out by Schweizer et al.:[2] why so many polar rings are so nearly polar, when the initial orbits of the captured material must have been much more uniform in angle.

A MODEL FOR THE GAS DISK IN CENTAURUS A

Centaurus A is one of the closet bright ellipticals (distance estimates vary from 2 Mpc to 5 Mpc); it is also unusual in having a strong double-lobed radio source, and a prominent twisted dust lane lying approximately along the minor axis. The kinematics of the dusty gas have been mapped using the emission lines of ionized gas, most recently by a group using the Taurus imaging Fabry–Perot device.[19,35] The gas layer is found to have a warped and folded structure, but both the spatial distribution and the velocity field of the gas show approximate point-reflection symmetry about the galaxy center. Multiple peaks in the gas velocity profile are observed along certain directions, indicating that the line of sight passes more than once through the warped gas disk.

Nicholson et al.[19] present a kinematic model, in which material in the gas and dust disk follows a set of concentric but tilted circular orbits; the model is fit to the observed $H\alpha$ velocity field and multiple line profiles, and constrained by the morphology of the dust band. They find that at large distances, the SW part of the warped disk is in front; the gas disk warps through edge-on at about 350″ radius, and becomes more nearly face-on, with the NE side in front. There is then a second, abrupt warp through edge-on at about 100″, so that the SW side of the disk is again in front at small radii. The position angle of the major axis of the disk increases from close to 90° at large radii, crossing the minor axis of the galaxy (PA 125°) and reaching 130° at 100″ radius. Here the major axis twists sharply back, with the position angle dropping to 90° again close to the center. This information is summarized by the open symbols in FIGURE 3: the stars show the inclination of each tilted gas orbit, and the triangles mark the position angle of the major axis, as a function of radius.

Attempts have been made to model the warped dust lane under various assumptions about the potential of the underlying galaxy. Tubbs[36] assumed the galaxy to be a prolate spheroid; the gas disk is then in a transient phase, settling toward the symmetry plane at the equator. Steiman-Cameron and Durisen[37] suggested that the galaxy was a tumbling prolate system, with the gas following stable orbits tilted with respect to the symmetry planes of the potential. Van Albada, Kotanyi, and Schwarzschild[38] made a model in which the galaxy is triaxial and tumbling; the gas again followed stable tilted orbits in the potential. That model requires the galaxy to tumble about the short axis, in the opposite sense to the circulation of the gas orbits. However, the stars were subsequently found to stream about the minor axis of the galaxy in the same sense as the gas[39]—so the tumble sense of the potential would then have to be opposite to the sense of circulation of the stars. It has proved to be difficult, and may well be impossible,[40,41] to construct stable dynamical models in which the figure of a stellar distribution tumbles in a contrary sense to the rotation of the stars making it up.

Velocities of the planetary nebula system in Centaurus A[42] indicate that the outer regions of the galaxy are rotating rapidly about the photometric minor axis, with $V/\sigma \approx 1$, in the same sense as the stars. Such fast rotation is consistent with either a rotationally supported oblate system, or a prolate bar tumbling rapidly about its short axis. The rotation speed remains constant out to 20', implying that the galaxy must have an extended massive halo.

Because of the high rotation speeds, I have attempted to model the dust lane structure assuming that the central galaxy is an oblate system, seen almost edge-on. Photometry[43] shows that the flattening of the stellar distribution increases with radius; the galaxy is almost round in the central parts, but the ellipticity increases to E0.7 at 156″ radius, and reaches E2.6 at 540″. In the model it is assumed that the matter distribution at large radii is given by the flattened pseudoisothermal form, which ensures that the circular speed is asymptotically constant, and having a projected flattening of around E3. To take account of the round inner region, a fairly large core radius was chosen for the flattened distribution, and a more concentrated spherical component added at the center, to bring the rotation curve into approximate agreement with that used by Nicholson et al.[19] In practice, the torque on the ring was calculated from a density distribution of the form (7), with the parameters $V_H = 250$ km/s, ellipticity e between 0.3 and 0.4, depending on the assumed viewing angle (see below), and core radius r_H in the range 150″ to 200″. The rotation speed $\Omega(r)$, however, was calculated according to a spherical distribution with $r_H = 10″$. This split of the galaxy into two components is merely a computational convenience, not implying that these components correspond to physically distinct parts of the system.

The rate of free precession in this combined potential does not vary monotonically with radius, but is small in the center (because the galaxy is almost round) and at large radii (where all frequencies diminish to zero); the largest absolute value occurs close to the core radius r_H chosen for the flattened component. Thus if an initially coplanar disk is allowed to evolve under differential precession only, and is viewed from a position in the equatorial plane of the galaxy, it twists first away from the plane of the sky, and then back toward it. If viewed from the appropriate direction, the warped disk may pass twice through edge-on, exactly as Nicholson *et al.* observe.[19] The region of sharpest bending is determined mainly by the size of the core radius; the models fit best for $r_H = 180''$.

If the viewing angle is now shifted so that the SE side of the galaxy is in front, the position angle of the orbits shifts with radius, to produce an S-curve in the ring shape;

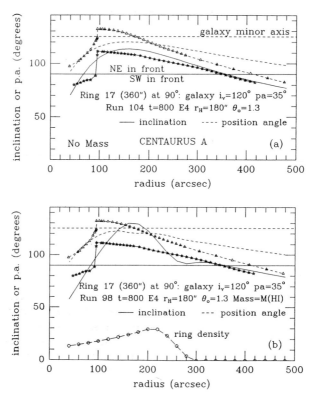

FIGURE 3. Inclination and position angle of gas orbits derived from a fit to kinematic data on Centaurus A, compared with (**a**) a model without mass, (**b**) a model including self-gravity.

although the gas orbits do not cross over the pole of the galaxy, they almost appear to do so in projection. FIGURE 3(a) shows the position angle and inclination for a massless ring, allowed to evolve from a planar initial state tipped by 15° from the pole of the galaxy, for a time corresponding to 1.1×10^9 years. The density distribution in the outer galaxy had a true flattening of E4, corresponding to a projected shape of E2.8 at the viewing angle of 30° from edge-on. The solid line shows the inclination of the wires making up the model disk; the double swing through edge-on ($i = 90°$) is evident, though the bend at $100''$ radius is not as sharp as that which Nicholson *et al.*

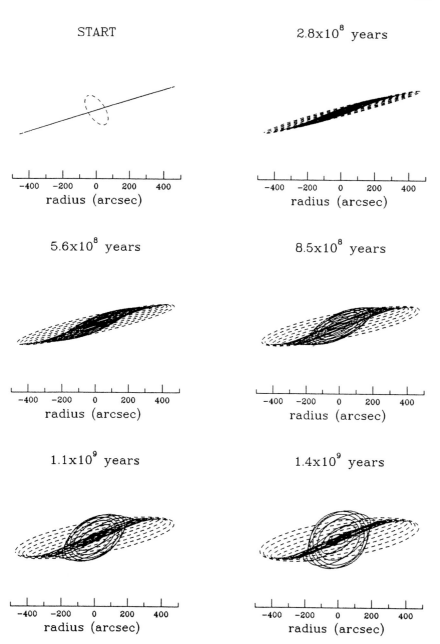

FIGURE 4. Time-evolution of a self-gravitating model for the gas disk in Centaurus A. In the **first frame,** the gas layer starts as a coplanar disk; the *dashed ellipse* shows the equatorial plane of the underlying galaxy. Subsequently, the viewing azimuth is chosen so that the ring at 306″ radius is edge-on. The *outer dashed rings* carry no mass, and represent the dust layer.

derive from the kinematic measurements. The dashed line shows the swing in position angle, up to the minor axis and away again. Tilting the view direction further to 45° would bring the shape of the gas disk closer to the kinematic fit, but it is unlikely that the galaxy is so inclined to the line of sight, since it would have to be a completely flat disk to appear with an E3 shape when viewed at that angle.

FIGURE 3(b) shows the results of a model in the same underlying potential, but including the self-gravity of the warped disk. Neutral hydrogen observations[16] show that a mass of around $2.6 \times 10^8 \, M_\odot$ of HI (rescaled to the Nicholson *et al.* distance of 3 Mpc) is associated with the dust lane; multiplied by 1.4 to take account of the primordial helium, this represents a lower limit to the mass of the ring. The HI observations did not have sufficient resolution to determine the radial distribution of the gas; the curve in the lower portion of FIGURE 3(b) shows the assumed surface density. A mass of $3.6 \times 10^9 \, M_\odot$ was distributed between the inner edge of the model disk at 50″ and the outer limit of the $H\alpha$ emission at 300″, with the density peaking around 200″ where the optical emission is brightest. Massless "test rings" out to 500″ were included to trace the outer dust lane. When self-gravity is included in the model, it forces the disk up toward the galaxy pole in regions where the precession rate is low (for the reasons explained in the fourth section), and away from the pole in the region around the transition radius r_H. This makes the swing in inclination around 100″ more violent, and forces the position angle to change more rapidly within that radius. It would have been reasonable to increase the ring mass still further, to allow for the presence of other material; but that did not change the appearance of the model very much.

The computed model curves are not an exact match to the kinematic fit of Nicholson *et al.;* that is to be expected, since the adopted mass distribution for the galaxy and the run of density in the ring are quite crude guesses, and it is unlikely that the coplanar initial state is exactly right either. Despite this, the model naturally reproduces a number of qualitative features of the kinematic data. First, the varying oblateness of the galaxy—spherical at small radii and more flattened further out—leads to the observed pattern of swings in inclination. In a galaxy of constant ellipticity, the ring inclination would have changed monotonically with radius, as in the model for NGC 3718 discussed in the third section. The swing in position angle develops if the galaxy is viewed not quite edge-on, but with the SE side in front. Including self-gravity in the model amplifies the twist in inclination around 100″, which becomes quite violent. The more face-on parts of the disk take on shapes similar to the secondary dust lanes discussed by Nicholson *et al.*

FIGURE 4 shows the time-evolution of the self-gravitating model. The initially coplanar gas disk develops a twist; orbits at large radii stay close to edge-on, providing an intense narrow dust lane. The best match to the observations is at about 10^9 years after the initial coplanar start; this is the stage illustrated in FIGURE 3(b).

SUMMARY

Because polar rings and gas disks contain material orbiting in different planes about the central galaxy, they offer a rare opportunity to probe the three-dimensional distribution of mass, including the dark material. Comparison of rotation speeds in the different planes suggests that the dark halo is somewhat oblate, but not as flattened as the stellar disk. Modeling the time evolution of the rings shows that many of their features—the near-polar orientation, warping, and twisting—can be understood in terms of a self-gravitating ring orbiting an oblate central galaxy. Such calculations set limits on the ring age if the flattening of the potential can be constrained in other ways; alternatively, requiring that the ring have a "reasonable" age limits the oblateness of the halo, which again appears to be flattened, but not as flat as the visible galaxy. The procedure requires detailed observations as input: photometry and kinematics of the stars to construct a mass model of the central galaxy, high-resolution HI mapping to find the distribution of matter in the rings, rotation speeds to constrain the dark halo, and velocity fields in the ring material to measure its twisting.

REFERENCES

1. WHITMORE, B. C., R. A. LUCAS, B. D. MCELROY, T. Y. STEIMAN-CAMERON, P. D. SACKETT & R. P. OLLING. 1990. Astron. J. **100:** 1489.
2. SCHWEIZER, F., B. C. WHITMORE & V. C. RUBIN. 1983. Astron. J. **88:** 909.
3. SCHNEIDER, S. E., *et al.* 1989. Astron. J. **97:** 666.
4. WHITMORE, B. C. 1984. Astron. J. **89:** 618.
5. BERTOLA, F. 1987. *In* IAU Symposium 127, "Elliptical Galaxies," P. T. de Zeeuw, Ed.: 135. Kluwer. Dordrecht, the Netherlands.
6. WHITMORE, B. C., B. D. MCELROY & F. SCHWEIZER. 1987. Astrophys. J. **314:** 439.
7. VAN ALBADA, T. S. & R. SANCISI. 1986. Phil. Trans. R. Soc. London A **320:** 447.
8. SACKETT, P. D. & L. S. SPARKE. 1990. Astrophys. J. **361:** 408.
9. JARVIS, B. & P. D. SACKETT. In preparation.
10. SCHECHTER, P. L., R. SANCISI, H. VAN WOERDEN & C. R. LYNDS. 1984. Mon. Not. R. Astron. Soc. **208:** 111.
11. VAN GORKOM, J. H., J. M. VAN DER HULST, A. D. HASCHICK & A. D. TUBBS. 1990. Astron. J. **99:** 1781.
12. KNAPP, G. R., W. VAN DRIEL & H. VAN WOERDEN. 1985. Astron. Astrophys. **142:** 1.
13. RICHTER, O.-G., P. D. SACKETT & L. S. SPARKE. In preparation.
14. GIOVANELLI, R. & M. P. HAYNES. 1988. *In* Galactic and Extragalactic Radio Astronomy, 2d ed., G. Verschuur and K. I. Kellermann, Eds.: 522. Springer-Verlag. New York/Berlin.
15. WHITMORE, B. C. & M. BELL. 1988. Astron. J. **89:** 618.
16. VAN GORKOM, J. H., P. L. SCHECHTER & J. KRISTIAN. 1987. Astrophys. J. **314:** 457.
17. RIX, H.-W. & N. KATZ. 1991. *In* Warped Disks and Inclined Rings in Galaxies, S. Casertano, P. Sackett, and F. Briggs, Eds.: 112. Cambridge Univ. Press. Cambridge, England.
18. QUINN, T. 1991. *In* Warped Disks and Inclined Rings in Galaxies, S. Casertano, P. Sackett, and F. Briggs, Eds.: 143. Cambridge Univ. Press. Cambridge, England.
19. NICHOLSON, R. A., J. BLAND-HAWTHORNE & K. TAYLOR. 1992. Astrophys. J. **387:** 503.
20. NICHOLSON, R. A. 1989. Ph.D. thesis, Univ. of Sussex, Falmer, Brighton, England.
21. SPARKE, L. S. 1986. Mon. Not. R. Astron. Soc. **219:** 657.
22. GOLDREICH, P. 1966. Rev. Geophys. **4:** 411.
23. GOLDSTEIN, H. 1980. Classical Mechanics, 2d ed. Addison-Wesley. Reading, Mass.
24. KUZMIN, G. 1956. Astron. Zh. **33:** 27.
25. TOOMRE, A. 1962. Astrophys. J. **138:** 385.
26. BINNEY, J. & S. TREMAINE. 1987. Galactic Dynamics. Princeton Univ. Press. Princeton, N.J.
27. SCHWARZ, U. J. 1985. Astron. Astrophys. **142:** 273.
28. STEIMAN-CAMERON, T. Y. & R. H. DURISEN. 1988. Astrophys. J. **325:** 26.
29. STEIMAN-CAMERON, T. Y., J. KORMENDY & R. H. DURISEN. 1992. Astron. J. In press.
30. MOULD, J., B. BALICK, G. BOTHUN & M. AARONSON. 1982. Astrophys. J., Lett. **260:** L37.

31. ARNABOLDI, M., M. CAPACCIOLI, E. CAPPELLARO, E. HELD, L. S. SPARKE & G. MACKIE. 1992. The polar ring galaxy AM 2020-504. This issue.
32. SPARKE, L. S. 1991. *In* Warped Disks and Inclined Rings in Galaxies, S. Casertano, P. Sackett, and F. Briggs, Eds.: 85. Cambridge Univ. Press. Cambridge, England.
33. SPARKE, L. S., R. A. NICHOLSON & K. TAYLOR. 1988. *In* The Few-Body Problem, M. J. Valtonen, Ed. Kluwer. Dordrecht, the Netherlands.
34. BERTOLA, F., D. BETTONI, J. DANZIGER, E. SADLER, L. SPARKE & T. DE ZEEUW. 1991. Astrophys. J. **369:** 390.
35. BLAND, J., K. TAYLOR & P. D. ATHERTON. 1987. Mon. Not. R. Astron. Soc. **228:** 595.
36. TUBBS, A. D. 1980. Astrophys. J. **241:** 969.
37. STEIMAN-CAMERON, T. Y. & R. H. DURISEN. 1982. Astrophys. J., Lett. **263:** L51.
38. VAN ALBADA, T. S., C. G. KOTANYI & M. SCHWARZSCHILD. 1982. Mon. Not. R. Astron. Soc. **198:** 303.
39. WILKINSON, A., R. M. SHARPLES, R. A. E. FOSBURY & P. T. WALLACE. 1986. Mon. Not. R. Astron. Soc. **218:** 297.
40. VIETRI, M. 1986. Astrophys. J. **306:** 48.
41. VAN ALBADA, T. S. 1987. *In* IAU Symposium 127, "Elliptical Galaxies," P. T. de Zeeuw, Ed.: 291. Kluwer. Dordrecht, the Netherlands.
42. FORD, H. C., R. CIARDULLO, G. H. JACOBY & X. HUI. 1989. *In* IAU Symposium 131, "Planetary Nebulae," S. Torres-Peimbert, Ed.: 335. Kluwer. Dordrecht, the Netherlands.
43. DUFOUR, R. J. *et al.* 1979. Astron. J. **84:** 281.
44. SPARKE, L. S. 1990. *In* Dynamics and Interactions of Galaxies, R. Wielen, Ed.: 338. Springer-Verlag. New York/Berlin.

The Polar Ring Galaxy AM 2020-504[a]

MAGDA ARNABOLDI,[b] MASSIMO CAPACCIOLI,[c]
ENRICO CAPPELLARO,[d] ENRICO HELD,[e]
LINDA S. SPARKE,[f] AND GLEN MACKIE[f]

[b]International School for Advanced Studies
34014 Trieste, Italy

[c]Department of Astronomy
University of Padova
35122 Padova, Italy

[d]Padova Astronomical Observatory
35122 Padova, Italy

[e]Bologna Astronomical Observatory
40126 Bologna, Italy

[f]Washburn Observatory
Department of Astronomy
University of Wisconsin-Madison
Madison, Wisconsin 53706-1582

1. INTRODUCTION

Gas rings in early-type galaxies tend to occur in two different morphologies: rings in S0 galaxies are normally wide annuli extending out to large radii, while those in ellipticals are narrow and internal to the optical radius of the galaxy.[1] The rings are not inclined at random angles, but appear either near to the equatorial plane of the galaxy or near to the orthogonal plane. Those systems where the ring is nearly orthogonal are classified as polar ring galaxies (PRGs), and the study of their dynamics gives the best opportunity to acquire information on the amount of matter they contain, both luminous and dark, and on their three-dimensional shape, since the velocity field is mapped on two different planes.[2-4] In particular, narrow polar rings in ellipticals may help us detect the presence of dark matter, if any, and give information on the intrinsic shape—triaxial, oblate, or prolate—of the total galaxy potential. The inclination of the ring, and the warps and ripples in it, together with analysis of the stability of orbits in the ring plane, give constraints on the "evolutionary scenario" for the PRGs, and may help to discriminate between recent merger or accretion of material from a companion or in a close encounter,[2] and old rings stabilized either by self-gravity or in a tumbling-triaxial potential.[3,5]

We have taken photometric and spectroscopic data for AM 2020-504, selected as the *best case* of the so-called narrow polar rings in the Polar Ring Catalog (PRC) of Whitmore *et al.*[6] This system has an E4 elliptical galaxy as its central component, with a luminous ring internal to the twenty-fifth B magnitude isophote; the ring plane is almost perpendicular to the projected major axis of the galaxy and is viewed close to

---

[a]Based on observations collected at the European Southern Observatory at La Silla, Chile.

207

edge-on. The system has a velocity redshift of $V_0 = 5046$ kms^{-1} and a total blue magnitude of $m_B = 14.5$.

We present our new data for AM 2020-504 in the next section; in the third section we present the analysis and the model for the geometry of the system and its dynamics; the results are discussed in the last section. In the discussion we will assume $H_0 = 75$ kms^{-1} Mpc^{-1}.

2. OBSERVATIONS AND REDUCTION

2.1 Photometry

We have taken broad-band images in Johnson B, V, and R filters, and two narrow-band images, $H\alpha$ and adjacent continuum, at the European Southern Observatory (ESO) 1.54-m Danish telescope, with seeing conditions $\sim 2''$. The two filters used for the narrow-band images were centered at 6672 Å, respectively, both with a full width at half maximum (FWHM) = 8 Å. The charge-coupled device (CCD) frames were bias subtracted and flat-fielded using the MIDAS data reduction package, and eight standard stars observed by Landolt[7] were used to calibrate the zero-magnitude point. We obtained values of the sky surface brightness in the B, V bands of $B_{sky} = 21.77 \pm 0.03$ mag arcsec^{-2} and $V_{sky} = 20.87 \pm 0.02$ mag arcsec^{-2}; the image of the system in the V-band is shown in FIGURE 1. The blue luminosity profiles are in good agreement with previously published ones;[8] no previous observations have been published for the R band and in the narrow-band filters.

The luminosity profile along the minor axis shows the presence of the ring as secondary peaks, NW and SE of the galaxy; the luminosity profile along the major axis shows perturbations on both sides of the center, but no absorption dips are immediately evident. The ring lies inside the twenty-fifth B isophote, and the intermediate isophotal map shows an S-shape feature superimposed on the elliptical isophotes of the host galaxy, as expected from a slightly twisted ring (see FIG. 2 and Section 3.3). To disentangle the emission structure we fitted ellipses to the isophotes in regions not perturbed by the ring. No isophote twisting was detected, but there is a rapid change in the ellipticity as a function of radius in the inner parts, $r \leq 6''$, while the isophotes in the outer regions, $r \geq 6''$, are well reproduced by concentric ellipses with constant ellipticity, $b^2/a^2 = 0.28 \pm 0.02$, and P.A. = $72.1° \pm 1.9°$.

The B–R image (FIG. 2) shows that the ring has bluer colors (B–$R \cong 0.2$) compared to the typical E and to the host galaxy (B–$R \cong 1.0$, and B–$R \cong 2.0$ in the core), and the color profile along the major axis shows the presence of excess reddening near the center. It is not immediately evident from the isophotal map and the B–R image which side of the ring is in front. Color profiles parallel to the major axis and offset from the center are generally bluer on the NE side of the galaxy, but the asymmetry is small: along the major axis the difference in color between the two sides, NE and SW of the core, is $\Delta(B$–$R) = 0.03$. From the B–R image we obtain approximate inner and outer radii for the ring:

$$R_{in} \cong 3.5'' \pm 0.5'' \qquad R_{out} \cong 19.0'' \pm 0.5''.$$

The *H*α image (FIG. 2) shows that the ionized gas is associated with the ring and is concentrated in clumpy structures following an S-shape, which is extended across the whole galaxy. Bright knots of *H*α are present at the NW and SE edges of the ring, and structures of similar and stronger intensity are present along the major axis of the elliptical, close to the center ($r \leq 5''$).

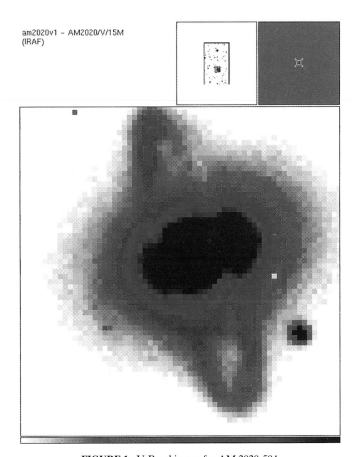

FIGURE 1. V-Band image for AM 2020-504.

2.2. Spectroscopy

The spectra were taken at the ESO 3.6-m + EFOSC (ESO Faint Objects Spectrograph and Camera), along the major axis (P.A. = 75°) and minor axis (P.A. = 165°) of the galaxy. They are long slit spectra covering the range 5100–7100 Å with a dispersion of 2.0 Å/pixel. The spectra have been bias subtracted and

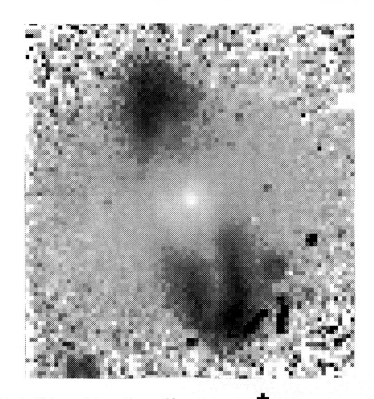

Ring 24 at   72.deg: gal inc −90. pa   90.

EQUILIBRIUM

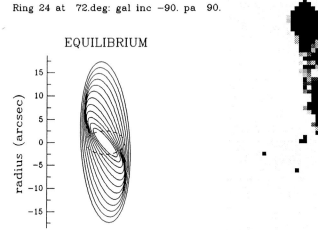

FIGURE 2. **Clockwise from top left:** *B–R* image: the difference in color between the material in the ring (*dark upper and lower arcs*) and that in the galaxy is immediately evident. The core appears much redder than the rest, with an excess of reddening on the SW side. *H*α image: the nice overall S-shape appears to be superimposed on substructures: the bright knots at the edges of the ring and the strong *H*α emission in the inner core of the elliptical. Equilibrium model for precessing rings in an oblate potential (see text); the *dashed line* shows an isophote of the galaxy.

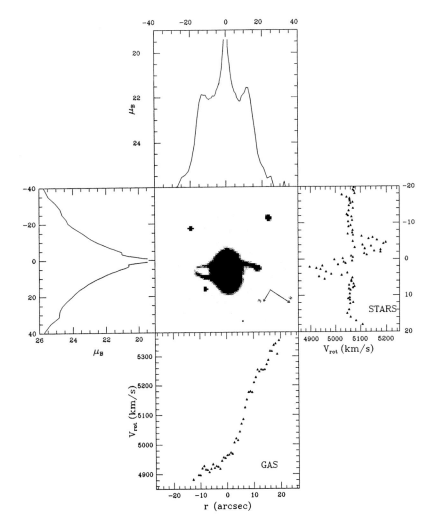

FIGURE 3. Photometric and kinematic data for AM 2020-504. The **upper and left panels** show the blue luminosity profiles along the minor and the major axes. The rotation curves for the stellar and the gaseous component are displayed in the right and lower panels. A small image of the system is displayed in the center.

flat-fielded, and row-by-row wavelength calibrated using a long-slit spectroscopy package especially tuned for EFOSC data.[9]

The rotational velocity of the stellar component along the major axis was measured from absorption lines (Mgb and NaD) in the range 5100–7100 Å; the kinematical measurements were extracted using the Fourier quotient package developed by G. Galletta. The cross-correlation package developed by Bender,[10] and a cross-correlation package developed by S. Levine in the Image Reduction and

Analysis Facility (IRAF) environment yield similar results. Data are summarized in FIGURE 3.

In agreement with the observations of Whitmore *et al.*,[6,8] the kinematical measurements reveal the presence of a fast rotating core inside $r = 7''$, reaching $|V_{rot}| = 150$ kms^{-1} at $r = 5''$ from the center, and nonrotating outer halo up to $r \sim 18''$. FIGURE 3 shows velocities on the major axis derived from two independent spectra. The spectra for the NE side of the core have a worse signal-to-noise ratio than those on the SW side, and this introduces more noise and larger errors in the rotation curve.

A comparison with published data for this system shows that the new data extend further, up to 18″ SW and 17″ NE from the nucleus (Whitmore's rotation curve reaches ~15″ SW and ~10″ NE). This is crucial for confirming the dynamical decoupling of the inner core and the outer halo. Moreover, thanks to the better spatial resolution of EFOSC, the inner rotation curve can be seen to peak at velocities around 150 kms^{-1}, higher than the 100 kms^{-1} measured by Whitmore *et al.*[6] The decoupled core is probably related to the excess of reddening revealed by the *B–R* image and to the *H*α regions along the major axis of the elliptical. The decoupled core may represent material acquired as the ring formed, or gas from the ring that has fallen into the center.

The emission-line rotation curve measured for the gas component along the minor axis of the galaxy is asymmetric with respect to the systemic velocity, $V_0 = 5046$ kms^{-1}: the NW side goes up to about 300 kms^{-1} at 15.5″, while the SE one reaches only 150 kms^{-1} at 13.5″. Whitmore *et al.*'s spectrum along the minor axis is taken at P.A. = 159°, 6° away from ours; velocities from that spectrum are symmetric in respect to the systemic velocity. The redshift velocities of the absorption lines present in our spectrum are always larger than the systemic V_0, and are comparable with the redshift value of the SW peak of the spinning core. This would suggest that our slit was offset from the nucleus toward the SW. We take this offset into account in deriving the galaxy mass in Section 3.2.

3. GEOMETRIC MODELS

3.1. Geometry of the System

Using the *B–R* and *H*α images we determined the three-dimensional orientation of the ring in respect to the galaxy. Following Whitmore,[11] the observed angle Φ between the major axis of the two components, and the angle θ_R of the ring from edge-on are

$$\Phi \cong 87.0° \pm 4.0° \qquad \theta_R = \pm\arcsin(B_{ring}/A_{ring}) \cong \pm 18.50° \pm 2.0°. \qquad (1)$$

If we assume that the observed flattening of the galaxy (E4) is the real one, then the intrinsic angle θ_I between the equatorial plane of the galaxy and the plane of the disk is equal to the observed angle Φ. If the galaxy is not viewed edge-on, but is intrinsically more flattened than E4, the intrinsic angle can be either closer to 90° or further away, depending on which side of the galaxy is in front. Calculating this angle using Whitmore's[11] prescription, we find that even if the galaxy is intrinsically as flat as E7, the ring can be no further than 20° from polar; depending on the galaxy tilt, the ring could also be exactly polar. In the absence of other indications, we assumed that the galaxy is seen edge-on. To determine the geometry, that is, the position of the ring with respect to the central bulge, we wrote a code that computes the surface brightness of an elliptical plus an outer ring.

1. The luminosity contribution from the host galaxy is fitted by an oblate Jaffe model[12] with constant ellipticity, seen edge-on. Its luminosity density is given in Cartesian (x, y, z) by:

$$\zeta(x, y, z) = \frac{\zeta_0}{(m^2/r_j^2)[1 + (m/r_j)]^2} \; ; \quad m^2 = \frac{x^2}{a^2} + \frac{y^2}{b^2} + \frac{z^2}{c^2}, \quad (2)$$

where ζ_0 is the luminous density in the center, r_j is the core radius, the x direction is along the line of sight, and a, b, c are the axis ratios. This model fits the observed luminosity profiles in the outer regions with a core radius $r_j = 16''$, $a = b = 1$ and $c/a = 0.6$. The fit along the major axis is shown in FIGURE 4(a).

2. The emission from the ring is determined from the luminosity profile along the minor axis, after subtracting the contribution coming from the Jaffe model. The ring is taken to be azimuthally symmetric, so that its emission is just a function of the radius; we adopted a Gaussian of the form:

$$\zeta_R(r) = B_R \exp\left\{-\left(\frac{|r - E_R|}{G_R}\right)^2\right\} \quad (3)$$

to reproduce the central peak in the residuals, and B_R, E_R, G_R are constants. We derived the parameters B_R, E_R, and G_R from fits to the luminosity profiles, taking average tilt of the ring into account. However, we do not include the twisting of the ring (see Section 3.3).

3. We assume that the ring absorbs light from that portion of the host galaxy that lies behind it:

$$I_{obs} = e^{-\tau/\sin\theta_R}I_{em}, \quad (4)$$

where I_{em} refers to the host galaxy emission behind the ring only, and I_{obs} is the flux measured by the observer. The optical depth τ was assumed constant.

4. The surface brightness obtained from the model is convolved with a Gaussian point spread function (PSF), and compared to the observed images. The PSF is obtained independently from stars in each frame to which the luminosity profiles were compared.

When the optical depth τ is zero, the computed luminosity contour is symmetric in respect to the center. When the ring is also absorbing, the emission from the two sides of the ring is asymmetric: a dip becomes evident where the ring passes in front of the galaxy. When we compare the isophotal map for AM 2020-504 with the contour plot of the model, we see that the ring must pass in front on the NE side; the data and the fits obtained are shown in FIGURE 4. In fitting the model to the observed photometric data we have taken the following constraints into account:

1. Our spectroscopic observations show that in the region inside $R = 7''$ the galaxy has an additional rapidly rotating component; our model does not include this component.

2. The projected inner radius of the ring on the major axis of the galaxy is $R_{\text{projected}} = 1.08''$, while the seeing during observations was at best $R_{\text{seeing}} = 1.4''$.

3. The S-shape of the asymmetric emission in the ring: the NW side passing SW of the core and the SE side passing NE are brighter than the NE, SW portions of the ring.

This implies that within $7''$ the model will not reproduce the profile along the major axis. Therefore the model surface brightness convolved with a PSF should be

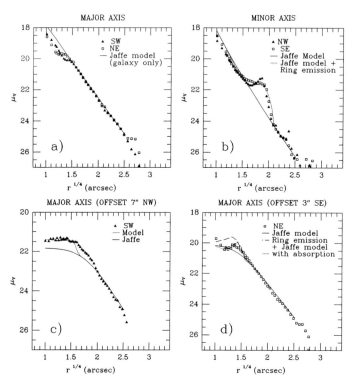

FIGURE 4. Luminosity profiles in the V-band and fits of the model to the surface brightness. The upper panels show the data and the fits along the major (**a**) and minor (**b**) axes; the lower panels show profiles taken parallel to and offset from the major axis. The SW side of the galaxy (**c**) is overluminous with respect to the model because the ring emission is not smooth; the NW side (**d**) shows the effect of adsorption by the ring.

compared with the obtained luminosity profiles, offset from the nucleus and parallel to the major axis. The NE side of our model (ring in front) fits the NE side of the luminosity profile, when they are compared at offset $3''$ SE, [see FIG. 4(d)] the SW side (ring beyond the galaxy) fits the SW side of the luminous profile, when both are offset $7''$ NW [see FIG 4(c)]. Comparing the fits in B and V, we estimate the reddening coefficient of the ring material to be $E(B-V)_{\text{tot}} \sim 0.14$; the intergalactic reddening is just $E(B-V) = 0.003.$[13] Assuming $N_{HI}/E(B-V) = 5.1 \cdot 10^{21}$ cm^{-2} mg^{-1},[14] the implied hydrogen mass would be $M_{HI} = 7.2 \cdot 10^8 M_\odot$: this is significantly less than the total HI mass measured with the 64-m Parkes telescope by O. Richter[15] of $9 \cdot 10^9 M_\odot$.

3.2. Total Mass of the System

Information on the dynamics of the system is given by the rotation curve for the ionized gas in the ring. Assuming (1) near-circular coplanar orbits and (2) centrifugal equilibrium in Newtonian dynamics, we can derive the total mass of the system. In this case, the rotation curve obtained for the ring is asymmetric, and this procedure cannot be applied straightforwardly. Since the projection of the ring on the sky is an ellipse, an offset of the slit from the center may generate asymmetry in the rotation curve. We checked this for a simple model with a disk embedded in a spherical pseudoisothermal halo. We assume that the center of the slit has been displaced to the SW of the nucleus, the tilt of the ring plane is given by the measured value (1), and the computed rotation curve is given by the velocity component along the line of sight for those points of the ring plane that fall along the slit. We obtain a good agreement using an offset of 1.7″ SW, a pseudoisothermal halo with core radius that equals 4″, and an asymptotic velocity of 320 kms^{-1}. This model gives a total mass inside $r = 17''$ of $M \sim 8 \cdot 10^{10} M_\odot$ and a mass-to-light ratio of $(M/L)_B \sim 7M/L_\odot$. We checked this model against the symmetric rotation curve for the gas in the ring obtained by Whitmore *et al.*[6] and the model fits this emission-line rotation curve quite well.

3.3. Dynamical Model for the Polar Ring

The large HI mass indicates that self-gravity may play an important role in the dynamics of the precessing rings.[5] We have checked whether the general shape of the polar ring in AM 2020-504 could be reproduced by a self-gravitating equilibrium, with a ring made up of a series of circular massive wires precessing in an oblate potential. We look for stable solutions with the outer rings at higher inclinations using the pseudoisothermal halo,[16] with core radius and asymptotic velocity as from Section 3.2, but flattened with axis ratio $c/a = 0.6$. In polar ring galaxies that have been mapped in HI with synthesis telescopes, the hydrogen is associated with the ring and not with the central galaxy.[17,18] Here we take the ring mass to be given by the measured HI mass, as a lower limit. Each of the wires, which are equally spaced in radius, has the same mass; the surface density thus varies like $1/r$. Stable solutions are possible with a range of inclinations: one such model is displayed in FIGURE 2.

DISCUSSION

We were particularly interested in determining the geometry of AM 2020-504 because of its crucial importance in any attempts to model the evolution of the polar ring. The absence of isophote twisting and the constant ellipticity of the isophotes in the host galaxy strongly indicate that the round component is an oblate galaxy. The intrinsic inclination of the ring plane derived using the $B-R$ and $H\alpha$ images is consistent with the ring being nearly or even exactly polar. With a detailed model of the surface brightness, assuming the real flattening of the central component to be equal to the observed one, we were able to determine the geometry of the system. The central galaxy in AM 2020-504 is well described by an oblate Jaffe model with axis ratio $c/a = 0.6$; the ring is inclined $10°$ from polar, and tilted $18°$ from edge-on, passing NE in front of the elliptical galaxy.

The better spatial resolution of the new spectroscopic data has confirmed previous indications of the dynamical decoupling of the inner core from the rest of the elliptical galaxy. This peculiar dynamical behavior, together with the excess of reddening in the inner region, and the bright $H\alpha$ structures present in the nucleus, suggest that the rapidly spinning core might be the result of part of the ring already settled in the equatorial plane of the galaxy. The evidence that the emission from the ring is bluer than the rest of the galaxy indicates that the material in the polar ring has a different origin, probably due to an accretion/merger event occurring at high inclination.

The large measured HI mass, almost $10^{10} M_\odot$, suggests that the gas in the ring is likely to be dynamically important. Taking the ring mass to be of the order of the measured HI mass, we find stable self-gravitating equilibria in a potential corresponding to the rotation curve of the galaxy, with its flattening given by the shape of the isophotes. The equilibrium states reproduce the "S" curve of the $H\alpha$ distribution. Further work on dynamical modeling is in progress.[19]

REFERENCES

1. WHITMORE, B. C. 1991. Preprint.
2. SCHWEIZER, F., B. C. WHITMORE & V. C. RUBIN. 1983. Astron. J. **88:** 909.
3. WHITMORE, B. C., D. MC ELROY & F. SCHWEIZER. 1987. Astrophys. J. **314:** 439.
4. SACKETT, P. D. & L. S. SPARKE. 1990. Astrophys. J. **361:** 408.
5. SPARKE, L. S. 1986. Mon. Not. R. Astron. Soc. **219:** 657.
6. WHITMORE, B. C., R. A. LUCAS, D. B. MC ELROY, T. Y. STEIMAN-CAMERON, P. D. SACKETT AND R. P. OLLING. 1990. Astron. J. **314:** 439.
7. LANDOLT, A. U. 1983. Astron. J. **88:** 439.
8. WHITMORE, B. C., D. MC ELROY & F. SCHWEIZER. 1987 IAU Symposium 127: Structure and Dynamics of Elliptical Galaxies: 413. Reidel. Dordrecht, the Netherlands.
9. CAPACCIOLI, M., E. CAPPELLARO, E. V. HELD & M. VIETRI. 1991. Preprint.
10. BENDER, R. 1988. Astron. Astrophys., Lett. **202:** L43.
11. WHITMORE, B. C. 1984. Astron. J. **89:** 618.
12. JAFFE, W. 1983. Mon. Not. R. Astron. Soc. **202:** 995.
13. BURSTEIN, D. & C. HEILES. 1982. Astron. J. **87:** 1165.
14. KNAPP, G. R. & F. J. KERR. 1974. Astron. Astrophys. **35:** 361.
15. RICHTER, R. Private communication, 10/6/1991.
16. DE ZEEUW, P. T. & D. PFENNIGER. 1988. Mon. Not. R. Astron. Soc. **235:** 949.
17. SCHECHTER, P. L., R. SANCISI, H. VAN WOERDEN & C. R. LYNDS. 1984. Mon. Not. R. Astron. Soc. **208:** 111.
18. VAN GORKOM, J. H., P. L. SCHECHTER & J. KRISTIAN. 1987. Astrophys. J. **314:** 457.
19. ARNABOLDI, M. & L. S. SPARKE. 1992. In preparation.

Testing the Stability of the Perfect Elliptic Disk Models in the Maximum Streaming Case[a]

STEPHEN E. LEVINE AND LINDA S. SPARKE

Washburn Observatory
Department of Astronomy
University of Wisconsin-Madison
Madison, Wisconsin 53706-1582

INTRODUCTION

The perfect ellipsoid (described in detail by de Zeeuw[1]) with a density given by

$$\rho(x, y, z) = \frac{\rho_0}{(1 + m^2)^2}, \quad m^2 = \frac{x^2}{a^2} + \frac{y^2}{b^2} + \frac{z^2}{c^2}, \tag{1}$$

has several useful properties as a model for elliptical galaxies. The mass is stratified on concentric, aligned ellipsoids and the potential satisfies Stäckel's criteria, so the integrals of motion are known analytically and the equations of motion are separable. A self-consistent equilibrium model of a galaxy would specify a distribution of stars among the set of possible orbits in the potential, for which the average density along the orbits generates the potential in which the stars move. Equilibrium models have been constructed,[2] but we do not know if the equilibria are stable or unstable. Due to the complexity of the problem, stability tests have to be carried out by gravitational N-body simulation methods and have only been tried on a restricted range of axisymmetric cases of the three-dimensional model.[3,4]

The perfect elliptic disks are the two-dimensional limiting case of the three-dimensional perfect ellipsoids; their surface density is given by

$$\Sigma(x, y) = \frac{\Sigma_0}{(1 + \tilde{m}^2)^{3/2}}, \quad \tilde{m}^2 = \frac{x^2}{a^2} + \frac{y^2}{b^2}. \tag{2}$$

Teuben[5] has constructed equilibrium models for the perfect elliptic disks. The question of whether the perfect elliptic disks are stable against large-scale instabilities has not yet been investigated. Testing the stability of the two-dimensional models is much easier than testing that of the three-dimensional models because we are working in only a four-dimensional phase space, and can cover that space with much higher resolution than we could the phase space of the three-dimensional models. The two-dimensional tests will also provide a guide to what to look for in later three-dimensional tests.

Elliptic disks can also be viewed as models for galactic bars, nonaxisymmetric structures that can have a large effect upon the gas and stellar dynamics of a disk

[a]This work was supported by NASA Theory Program Grant NAGW-2420.

galaxy. The rotational angular velocity of the bar, the *pattern speed,* substantially affects the types of orbits present and cannot be measured directly from observations. Tremaine and Weinberg[6] have proposed an indirect method to determine the pattern speed from the kinematics of a galaxy, but unfortunately, the method has been shown to be very sensitive to noise in the data.[7]

Equilibrium bar models have been generated with a wide range of pattern speeds. The only analytical bar models are Freeman's bars, which are based upon a two-dimensional harmonic oscillator potential, and the perfect elliptic disk models. All other models have been constructed as the evolutionary endpoint of *N*-body integrations of initially unstable disks. The *N*-body bars typically seen as the dominant unstable mode in galactic disk simulations rotate quickly (see, for example, Sellwood[8]). However, we do not know that actual bars are like this. We wish to test whether nonrotating models can be stable, and if so, whether any of them can fit the photometric and kinematic observations of real barred galaxies.

PERFECT ELLIPTIC DISKS

Because the elliptic disks are generated by a nonaxisymmetric potential, the orbit families divide into *box* and *loop* orbits. The box orbits resemble combinations of independent oscillations in the x and y directions (somewhat like Lissajous figures), and hence generally have no average circulation about the center of the potential. Loop orbits, on the other hand, are ellipses or rosettes with a definite sense of rotation about the center of the potential.

For two-dimensional Stäckel potentials, the equations of motions are separable in confocal elliptic coordinates, (λ, μ), which are the solutions to the quadratic equation

$$\frac{x^2}{\tau + \alpha} + \frac{y^2}{\tau + \beta} = 1, \tag{3}$$

where for the perfect elliptic disk $\alpha = -a^2$, $\beta = -b^2$. Curves of constant λ are confocal ellipses aligned along the minor axis, with $-\alpha \leq \lambda \leq \infty$, and curves of constant μ are hyperbolae, with $-\beta \leq \mu \leq -\alpha$ (see FIG. 1). All the curves share the foci $x = 0, y = \pm\sqrt{\beta - \alpha}$. We can find the momenta p_λ and p_μ conjugate to λ and μ explicitly[9,10] as

$$p_\tau^2(\tau) = \frac{(\tau + \alpha)[E + G(\tau; \alpha, \beta)] - i_2}{2(\tau + \alpha)(\tau + \beta)}, \tag{4}$$

where τ is either λ or μ; E (the energy) and i_2 are the two isolating integrals of the orbit upon which the point is placed; and $G(\tau; \alpha, \beta)$ is a known monotonically decreasing function.[1,5]

By solving the equations $p_\tau^2(\tau) = 0$, we can obtain an orbit's *turning points;* these extremal values of λ and μ uniquely specify the orbit. Alternatively, we can specify an orbit by its two isolating integrals, E and i_2. The transformation between turning points and integrals is unique and easy to compute. Loop orbits are bounded by ellipses of constant λ, the turning points λ_1 and λ_2. Box orbits are contained within an hyperbola of constant μ and an ellipse of constant λ, corresponding to the turning points μ_1 and λ_2. Outside of the foci, the minor axis is covered only by the loop orbits; the box orbits do not contribute any of the density there (see FIG. 1). The surface density at any point upon any orbit can be written as an explicit function of the position and of the isolating integrals.

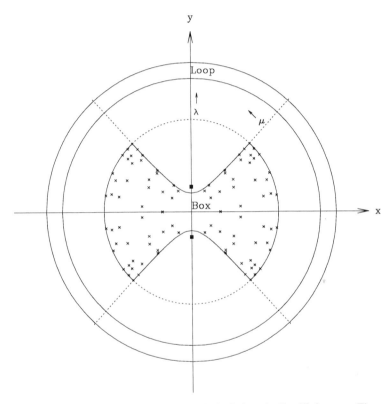

FIGURE 1. The confocal elliptic coordinates with the foci marked by *filled squares*. The *crosses* show the initial positions for the box orbit bounded by the *solid lines*.

SELECTING ORBITS

The task of setting up a perfect elliptic disk model for N-body integration breaks down naturally into two major steps: choosing the orbits that generate a self-consistent solution, and placing particles upon those orbits in a *quiet* manner (see the following section). For the perfect elliptic disks, de Zeeuw, Hunter, and Schwarzschild[11] (hereafter ZHS) have shown that the self-consistent solution is built up of both loop and box orbits, and in general is not unique. However, in the special case of the *maximum streaming* models, in which the largest possible amount of angular momentum is packed into the particles on loop orbits, the loop orbits are all closed and the set of these orbits that go into generating a self-consistent solution is unique. We look first at this case.

Loop Orbits

The closed loop orbits are nonoverlapping orbits characterized solely by the double turning point $\lambda = \lambda_1 = \lambda_2$, so that at any point on the minor axis, there is only one loop orbit contributing to the density. Thus, the density on the closed loop orbits is a function of λ. For the N-body calculations, to choose n_{loop} equally weighted orbits that approximate the continuous loop-orbit density, we begin at the inner elliptic coordinate boundary of the loop orbits, and integrate the closed-loop-orbit density outwards in λ until we have encompassed $1/n_{loop}$ of the total loop-orbit mass. A single loop orbit is then placed along the mass weighted center ellipse of the region. The process is then repeated.

Box Orbits

Since we can determine ahead of time the surface density that resides in the loop orbits, we know the remaining density that must be contributed by the box orbits. These orbits present a slightly more intricate problem, as they are specified by *two* turning points. The problem is how to distribute the turning points (i.e., choose the orbits) to match the remaining portion of the density.

To find a set of equally weighted box orbits that matches the remaining density requires using an iterative method, we use the technique of simulated annealing.[12] This process is patterned after the idea of annealing, the *slow* cooling of a substance, which allows the substance to find its state of minimum energy. The numerical process attempts to minimize some quantity analogous to *energy;* the mobility in the configuration space is like *temperature*. When the temperature is high, the system's energy can fluctuate wildly. As the temperature is slowly reduced, the likelihood of an energy change in any direction other than downwards decreases. Simulated annealing is not the fastest method available for performing minimizations, but it is less susceptible to getting stuck in local minima, since the function should bounce between local minima with a depth given roughly by the temperature. It is also very flexible, and easily adaptable to multiple minimization criteria. This will be important in the next stage of this project when we will include non-thin loop orbits in the orbit solution set.

Our configuration space is a set of box-orbit turning points. The turning points are selected from a continuous distribution that covers the whole area of the model, and each orbit will eventually be populated with the same number of particles, giving each equal weight. This is unlike the methods of Teuben,[5] ZHS,[11] and Statler,[2] all of whom use discrete libraries or orbits, and calculate weighting factors for them. But the occupation numbers thus found may be nonintegral, whereas we must place an integral number of particles upon each orbit.

We begin by dividing up the area covered by the elliptic disk into cells containing roughly equal fractions of the mass to be contributed by the box orbits. We define the *energy* E associated with a particular selection of box-orbit turning points to be the sum over the cells of the absolute value of the differences between the desired mass and the sum of the mass contributed by the box orbits composing the current configuration. The minimization was done using the mass, and not the density, because the density for any given orbit is singular along the orbit's bounding surface, while the total mass within any one cell is well-behaved. A rearrangement of the system consists of changing the turning points of one randomly selected box orbit. The turning points making up the configuration are stored in order of increasing λ; the new λ turning point is chosen randomly between the λ turning points of the adjoining orbits. The new μ turning point is permitted to vary between $-\beta$ and $-\alpha$. A rearrangement is accepted (the new configuration replaces the previous one) if the new configuration reduces E. It is also accepted with probability $\exp(-\Delta E/T)$ if it increases E by ΔE. The *temperature* T, initially large, is reduced by a constant multiplicative factor after either a fixed number of successful reconfigurations, or a fixed number of attempts.

The running time for simulated annealing goes up linearly as the number of evaluation cells, but roughly quadratically as the number of orbits in a configuration. For 40 orbits, with 400 cells, the process takes 24 hours on a DECstation 5000. We are working on modifications to the annealing process to reduce the required computer time. When the process is finished, we are left with a set of box-orbit turning points.

POPULATING ORBITS

Having chosen a set of orbits that generate the elliptic disk potential, we must now distribute particles on each of the orbits. We seek a *quiet*[13,14] particle distribution that will minimize the random noise in the initial conditions that might serve as the seed perturbation for instabilities, since we are looking for growth in a linear regime, not instabilities starting with some finite amplitude. A quiet start implies that particles are initially distributed as uniformly as possible in phase space, such that as we integrate forward in time in the initial potential, the phase space distribution should remain uniform.

For the closed loop orbits, we simply place the desired number of particles equal fractions of the period apart. The velocities for the loop-orbit particles are oriented so that the loops all circulate in the same direction. To avoid generating spokes, we cyclically offset the starting angle of successive orbits from the x axis by 0, ½, ¾, and ¼ of the interparticle spacing around the loop.

For box orbits, to solve the problem of finding the smoothest way to populate a space-filling orbit with a finite number of particles, we appeal to the action–angle formalism. Each orbit corresponds to a torus in action–angle space, the particular

torus being specified by the actions. The actions for a particular orbit defined by the
turning points (τ_1, τ_2) are defined by

$$J_\tau(\tau_1, \tau_2) \equiv \frac{1}{2\pi} \oint p_\tau(\tau; \tau_1, \tau_2)\, d\tau, \tag{5}$$

where τ is either λ or μ. The actions are constant for a given orbit, and can be
computed by quadrature from either the turning points or the two isolating inte-
grals.[9] The angles θ_τ are the coordinates conjugate to the actions J_τ, which are cyclic
because the Hamiltonian depends only upon the actions. Working in action–angle
coordinates, for a given orbit, the angles evolve linearly with time, each with its own
period. Because the dimensional frequencies are in general incommensurate, the
box orbits are multiply periodic in time.

To construct the angle coordinates on a torus defined by (J_λ, J_μ), we begin by
assigning a single arbitrary phase space point to the angle coordinate $(\theta_\lambda, \theta_\mu) =$
$(0, 0)$. Then, we mark out the θ_λ axis by integrating the coupled differential equations

$$\frac{dw_\alpha}{d\theta_\lambda} = [w_\alpha, J_\lambda], \tag{6}$$

where the w_α are the phase space coordinates $(\lambda, \mu, p_\lambda, p_\mu)$. The θ_μ axis is then
marked out in a similar manner. The coordinate axes defined in this manner remain
on the surface of the torus and close upon themselves: $w_\alpha(\theta_\lambda + 2\pi, \theta_\mu) = w_\alpha(\theta_\lambda, \theta_\mu)$
and $w_\alpha(\theta_\lambda, \theta_\mu + 2\pi) = w_\alpha(\theta_\lambda, \theta_\mu)$ for all starting points $(\theta_\lambda, \theta_\mu)$, forming a grid upon
the surface of the two-dimensional torus defined by the actions. [10, sec. 3.5] and [15,
sec. 49]. This construction of the angle coordinates gives us a map from the angle
torus onto an orbit in ordinary spatial coordinates. For a given orbit, if we lay down a
uniform grid of points upon the torus surface corresponding to (J_λ, J_μ), then because
forward evolution in time is area preserving, they will stay uniformly spaced. Hence,
mapping back to the $(\lambda, \mu, p_\lambda, p_\mu)$ coordinates, we have a quiet particle distribution.

Because our potentials have two isolating integrals, we know $p_\tau(J_\lambda, J_\mu; \lambda, \mu)$ and
so have to integrate only the equations for λ and μ

$$\left.\frac{d\lambda}{d\theta_\lambda}\right|_{(J_\lambda, J_\mu, \theta_\mu)} = \left.\frac{\partial J_{w_1}}{\partial w_3}\right|_{(w_1, w_2, w_4)} \qquad \left.\frac{d\mu}{d\theta_\lambda}\right|_{(J_\lambda, J_\mu, \theta_\mu)} = \left.\frac{\partial J_{w_1}}{\partial w_4}\right|_{(w_1, w_2, w_3)}$$

$$\left.\frac{d\lambda}{d\theta_\mu}\right|_{(J_\lambda, J_\mu, \theta_\lambda)} = \left.\frac{\partial J_{w_2}}{\partial w_3}\right|_{(w_1, w_2, w_4)} \qquad \left.\frac{d\mu}{d\theta_\mu}\right|_{(J_\lambda, J_\mu, \theta_\lambda)} = \left.\frac{\partial J_{w_2}}{\partial w_4}\right|_{(w_1, w_2, w_3)}, \tag{7}$$

which we get by carrying through the differentiations of (6).

Let us work out $\partial J_{w_j}/\partial w_3$, where $j = 1, 2$ as an example. The two isolating integrals
associated with the orbit passing through the phase space point (w_1, w_2, w_3, w_4) can
be written explicitly as functions of these coordinates, enabling us to write the
momenta p_{w_j} as

$$p_{w_j}(\tau; E, i_2) = \sqrt{\frac{G(\tau)}{2(\tau + \beta)} + \frac{E(w_1, w_2, w_3, w_4)}{2(\tau + \beta)} - \frac{i_2(w_1, w_2, w_3, w_4)}{2(\tau + \alpha)(\tau + \beta)}}. \tag{8}$$

Differentiating (5) and (8) gives

$$\frac{\partial J_{w_j}}{\partial w_3} = \frac{1}{2\pi} \oint \frac{\partial p_{w_j}}{\partial w_3} d\tau, \qquad \frac{\partial p_{w_j}}{\partial w_3} = \frac{(w_1 + \alpha)(w_1 + \beta)w_3}{w_1 - w_2} \left\{ \frac{\tau - w_2}{(\tau + \alpha)(\tau + \beta)p_{w_j}} \right\} \quad (9)$$

and finally

$$\frac{\partial J_{w_j}}{\partial w_3} = \frac{2\sqrt{2}}{\pi} \frac{(w_1 + \alpha)(w_1 + \beta)w_3}{w_1 - w_2} \int_{w_{j,min}}^{w_{j,max}} \frac{(\tau - w_2)\, d\tau}{\sqrt{(\tau + \alpha)(\tau + \beta)\{(\tau + \alpha)(E + G(\tau)) - i_2\}}}.$$

$$(10)$$

The procedure is identical for the two partial derivatives with respect to w_4. Thus the partial derivatives of (7) can all be computed by quadrature, and we need only integrate two coupled equations at any one time.

A single orbit will cover a rectangular region in elliptic coordinates given by the orbit's turning points and the coordinate boundaries, which we can write as $[w_{1,min}, w_{1,max}] \times [w_{2,min}, w_{2,max}]$. A box orbit with turning points μ_1 and λ_2 covers the rectangle given by $[-\alpha, \lambda_2] \times [-\beta, \mu_1]$, where $\lambda = -\alpha$ is the y axis, and $\mu = -\beta$ is the x axis. In fact, because of the fourfold symmetry in the coordinate transformation from Cartesian to elliptic coordinates, an orbit covers this region four times over. We define periodic extensions in both dimensions by reflections about the rectangle boundaries. A point in the above adjoining rectangle will map into our base rectangle by $w_i \rightarrow 2w_{i,max} - w_i$, and a point in the below adjoining rectangle will map into the base rectangle by $w_i \rightarrow 2w_{i,min} - w_i$. This reflection procedure can then be continued in both directions, folding the extended plane back into the base rectangle. We can now define a one-to-one map from this extended orbit rectangle to the (x, y) plane image of the orbit. The integration of (10) in the extended space is performed very quickly using the Bulirsh–Stoer integration scheme described by Press et al.[12]

That gives us the positions upon the orbit; the two isolating integrals give us values for p_τ^2. The signs for the velocities along the λ and μ directions, v_λ and v_μ, respectively, can be determined by choosing their values at the initial integration point and invoking continuity arguments. The velocities must be continuous, and are zero only upon the orbit boundaries. If we cross a coordinate boundary (i.e., the x or y axis), physical continuity requires that the velocity vector change continuously, since the θ_{w_j} change continuously. For a box orbit, as we cross the x axis, the direction of increasing μ reverses, and so the sign of v_μ will also reverse. Similarly, as we cross the y axis between the focal points, the sign of v_λ will change.

At the orbital bounding surfaces, the velocity component corresponding to the turning point goes to zero. By examining the derivatives of the velocities with respect to the angle coordinates, we can show that this velocity component changes sign at the orbit boundaries. Hence, we end up with a well-defined mapping from $(J_\lambda, J_\mu, \theta_\lambda, \theta_\mu)$ to $(\lambda, \mu, v_\lambda, v_\mu)$.

This method for constructing quiet initial conditions is generally applicable to any integrable system, including three-dimensional perfect ellipsoids and spherical systems.

MODELS AND INTEGRATIONS

The particle distributions and initial velocities are loaded into the N-body code, and permitted to evolve under the influence of their own self-gravity. We are using a two-dimensional polar-grid Fourier-transform N-body code developed by J. Sellwood (see Miller[16] and Sellwood[8,13] for a more complete description of the method used). The grid is defined by rings that are logarithmically spaced in radius with azimuthal grid points evenly spaced around each ring. We used a grid with 61 radial rings and 80 azimuthal lines. When lengths are expressed in terms of the length scale a of (2), the inner edge of the grid is bounded by a cirle of radius $r = 0.1$. The outer edge of the grid was at $r = 11.1$, and any particles going off the grid were discarded from the integration. The outermost populated cells had dimensions $\Delta r = 0.61$ by $r\Delta\theta = 0.64$.

The models were all constructed with total mass equal to unity, then truncated on a circle of radius $r = \sqrt{64 - (b/a)^2}$ (the radius of the point $\lambda = 64$ and $\mu = -\alpha$), leaving a mass M_{trunc} (see TABLE 1). Models were constructed with axial ratios b/a ranging from 0.13 to 0.92, chosen so that the mass M_{trunc} was most nearly an integral

TABLE 1. Model Specifications

b/a	M_{trunc}	M_{loop}	Number of Loop Orbits	Number of Particles per Loop Orbit	Number of Box Orbits	Number of Particles per Box Orbit
0.13	0.918	0.010	5	20	99	100
0.25	0.915	0.039	19	20	96	100
0.41	0.908	0.110	22	50	89	100
0.55	0.901	0.209	21	100	79	100
0.71	0.892	0.379	38	100	62	100
0.85	0.884	0.600	60	100	40	100
0.92	0.880	0.751	75	100	25	100

multiple of M_{loop}, the mass on the loop orbits. The models were typically constructed from 100 orbits, each containing 100 particles, placed as previously described.

The step size for integration was chosen to be small enough that there were at least twenty program steps per orbital period for at least 90 percent of the orbits in all the models. The model with axial ratio 0.41 was also run with the program step reduced by a factor of 10. No qualitative differences were seen in the results. In addition to the softening introduced by the grid, the N-body code can include explicit softening; to avoid the possibility that this would stabilize against instabilities, no additional softening was used here. The models were all run for 950 program steps, or roughly one orbital period at radius ~ 1.4.

All of the models appear to be unstable, even on this very short time scale. Looking at the results of the N-body runs, we find that the form of instability depends upon the axial ratio. For the nearly axisymmetric models, the dominant early instabilities are spiral. This is not unexpected because in the limiting case, cold axisymmetric disks are known to be violently unstable. We see a spiral grow from the inner regions outward among the loop orbits (see FIG. 2, left column).

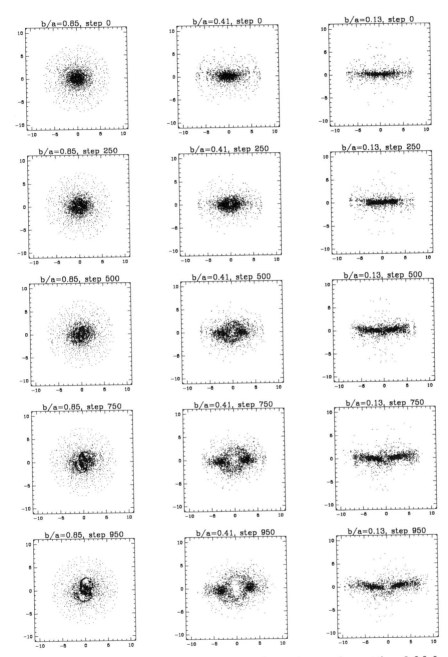

FIGURE 2. Positions for 2500 particles in the *N*-body integrations are shown at times 0, 2.5, 5, 7.5, and 9.5, for *b/a* = 0.85 (**left column**), *b/a* = 0.41 (**middle column**), and *b/a* = 0.13 (**right column**).

As the axial ratio decreases, the spiral decreases in strength. This is reasonable, as it is principally associated with the loop orbits, and as b/a decreases, so does the fraction of the mass contributed by the loops. For midrange axial ratios, the loop orbits are still unstable to spiral formation. The density enhancement of the spiral runs right through the center of two density peaks formed by the box orbit particles to either side of the center on the major axis of the model (FIG. 2, middle column). In the most elongated models (FIG. 2, right column), we see the beginnings of what appears to be a bending instability similar to that exhibited by the E9 model of Merritt and Hernquist.[4]

All of the perfect elliptic disk models with maximum streaming appear to be unstable. The very thin loop and box orbits seem to lead, respectively, to spiral and bending instabilities. For the nearly round elliptic disks, nonmaximum streaming models are perhaps more likely to be stable, as it may be possible to stabilize them by using thick loop orbits, which will increase the velocity dispersion and decrease the angular momentum in the model. But for the most elongated models, there is very little that can be done to try and stabilize them, as most of the orbits are already very thin boxes, and there is little room in the density distribution for any more loops, of any kind (thin or thick). Thus there may be a critical axis ratio below which the models are all unstable.

ACKNOWLEDGMENT

We are grateful to Jerry Sellwood for supplying us with his N-body code.

REFERENCES

1. DE ZEEUW, T. 1985. Mon. Not. R. Astron. Soc. **216:** 273.
2. STATLER, T. S. 1987. Astrophys. J. **321:** 113.
3. MERRITT, D. & M. STIAVELLI. 1990. Astrophys. J. **358:** 399.
4. MERRITT, D. & L. HERNQUIST. 1991. Astrophys. J. **376:** 439.
5. TEUBEN, P. 1987. Mon. Not. R. Astron. Soc. **227:** 815.
6. TREMAINE, S. & M. D. WEINBERG. 1984. Astrophys. J., Lett. **282:** L5.
7. KENT, S. M. 1987. Astron. J. **93:** 1062.
8. SELLWOOD, J. A. 1981. Astron. Astrophys. **99:** 362.
9. GOLDSTEIN, H. 1980. Classical Mechanics, 2nd ed. Addison-Wesley. Reading, Mass.
10. BINNEY, J. & S. TREMAINE. 1987. Galactic Dynamics. Princeton Univ. Press. Princeton, N.J.
11. DE ZEEUW, P. T., C. HUNTER & M. SCHWARZSCHILD. 1987. Astrophys. J. **317:** 607.
12. PRESS, W. H., B. P. FLANNERY, S. A. TEUKOLSKY & W. T. VETTERLING. 1986. Numerical Recipes. Cambridge Univ. Press. Cambridge, England.
13. SELLWOOD, J. A. 1983. J. Comput. Phys. **50:** 337.
14. ———. 1989. Mon. Not. R. Astron. Soc. **238:** 115.
15. ARNOLD, V. I. 1978. Mathematical Methods of Classical Mechanics. Springer-Verlag. New York/Berlin.
16. MILLER, R. H. 1976. J. Comput. Phys. **21:** 400.

Longevity of Disks in Galaxies[a]

R. H. MILLER[b] AND B. F. SMITH[c]

[b]Department of Astronomy and Astrophysics
University of Chicago
Chicago, Illinois 60637

[c]Theoretical Studies Branch
NASA-Ames Research Center
Moffett Field, California 94035

INTRODUCTION

Discussions of disks embedded in galaxies are usually based on the notion that the galaxy provides a nice smooth time-independent potential within which the disk material moves. Assumptions like this may seem plausible, but they are nothing more than hopes until they have been checked either observationally or through numerical experiments. We got into this question a few years back when Dr. Althea Wilkinson wanted to study dust-lane elliptical galaxies.[1,2] NGC 5128 (Cen A) is the prototype.[3-5] Many are radio sources.[4,6] A current picture has the dust lane made out of stuff that orbits within the gravitational potential of the elliptical galaxy, possibly having gotten there through capture and disruption of a (small) disk system whose debris settled into long-lived orbits within the galaxy's potential.[7-10]

The problem has two aspects: formation and lifetime. Formation is intrinsically the more difficult problem because there are so many possibilities and no assurance of a unique solution. Longevity is the best place to start. An experimental attack is to verify that debris, if once it managed to get into the form of a disk, would retain a sheetlike form (possibly twisted, stretched, folded, or warped) long enough to be of interest for dust-lane systems. It must survive as a recognizable feature long enough to satisfy observational statistics and it must retain reasonable shapes over that period. A dust lane that did not remain recognizable very long would exclude such a model right away, without need to ask how the disk might have been formed in the first place.

Many assumptions are implicit in the capture picture. Perhaps the most obvious is that the galaxy merely provides a smooth background potential within which disk material orbits, the question posed in this paper. But the galaxy is a dynamical object, and cooperative or collective many-body phenomena within the galaxy, for example, could produce time-dependent variations in the galaxy potential strong enough to tear the disk apart in a fairly short time.

Our approach is experimental. The key to disk survival lies in the dynamics of the underlying galaxy, and the study of that requires the kind of fully self-consistent

[a]This study was supported in part by the NASA-Ames Research Center under Cooperative Agreement NCC 2-265 with the University of Chicago. Computations for the 400,000-particle experiment 8 and for the million-particle 256^3 experiment 9 run on the Cray-2 were made possible by means of a grant of computing services from the NAS division at NASA-Ames.

227

treatment for which numerical experiments provide the only tool available today. All experiments start with a tracer disk embedded in an oblate galaxy. The experimental disk is a set of particles that represent the dust lane. It is a sensitive probe of dynamical effects within the galaxy. The numerical experiments reported here are not limited to the cooperative many-body effects mentioned earlier. They test for other dynamical processes that might affect a disk within a real galaxy as well. The tracer disk provides an accurate dynamical description of the disk whether it is made up of stars or of gas with little pressure.

We investigate the larger picture in this paper, to see whether the galaxy acts like a steady-state potential within which the disk can safely orbit. Disk properties are analyzed in conventional terms in which a smooth, steady potential is assumed.[11] If the analysis makes sense, we can safely infer that the assumption is justified. Fortunately, this turns out to be the case. However, smaller scale organized motions build up in the central regions in a manner that suggests overstability[12] and the galaxies ring like a bell, with normal modes excited to surprisingly large amplitudes.[13] These results relate to the level of disturbances, and they also affect the way we think about central regions of galaxies. They apply to galaxies in general, and they are likely to be very important for a fundamental understanding of galaxy dynamics. These motions chiefly affect the disk down near the center (within 5–10 core radii). They did not destroy its sheetlike character over the duration of these experiments.

The present study is quite different from that of Habe and Ikeuchi,[14] although disks within galaxies are addressed in both papers. They considered a gaseous disk in a given potential by means of smooth particle hydrodynamics, while we test the galaxy itself to see whether there is any dynamical process at work in a fully self-consistent galaxy that would damage or destroy a disk over a reasonably long time. Thus we test some of the assumptions on which their work is based, and we find them good enough for their purposes.

THE EXPERIMENTS

The experiments were run using n-body programs that have been described elsewhere.[15] Free boundary conditions make them appropriate for isolated galaxies. Our basic units are m, the mass represented by an individual particle; L, the physical distance to which the tabulation grid spacing scales; and T, the physical time interval that corresponds to an integration step. These are related to physical units through the dimensionless constant, $W = GmT^2/L^3$, which links m, L, and T through the requirement that G take its actual physical value, $G = 4.5 \times 10^{-6}$ kpc³/ ($M_\odot \times$ Gyrs²). The positions of 2048 particles are recorded in a plot file at each integration step. These files are saved for later analysis and to make motion pictures.

Starting Conditions

The initial galaxy in each experiment consists of a nearly equilibrium model based on an $n = 3$ polytrope. The initial galaxy model is somewhat flattened, and it is rotationally symmetrical about its short axis. Rotation encourages it to remain oblate and axially symmetrical. A disk, also made of particles, is embedded within the galaxy. Disk particles and galaxy particles are identical from a dynamical point of view. The disk is initially flat, and it is rotationally supported. Its normal lies at some prescribed angle to the galaxy's symmetry axis. That angle is one of the parameters used to define an experiment. There is so little mass in the disk that it has little effect on the overall dynamics, even though it and the galaxy are treated together as a self-consistent whole. It is a tracer that is sensitive to the dynamical effects in the galaxy. In particular, there is no risk of disk instability, a possibility that must be avoided in a study of dust-lane systems.

There are 100,352 particles in most experiments, of which 1024 are in the disk. The remainder are in the galaxy, making the disk represent a small fraction of the total mass. All 1024 disk particles are recorded in the plot file. Galaxy particles make up the remaining 1024. Only a small fraction of galaxy particles is sampled in the plot file: one in a hundred to one in a thousand.

Most experiments were run with 35 integration steps per initial crossing time $(T_{cr} = 35T)$ and typical runs extended 7 to 22 initial crossing times. With a reasonable scaling of 0.1 Gyr for a crossing time, this translates to 0.7 to 2.2 Gyrs for an experiment. The experiments are listed in TABLE 1. The third column of TABLE 1

TABLE 1. Experiments

Run Number	Disk Angle	Duration (T_{cr})	Particles	$10^5 W$	Steps Run
2	30	7.3	100,352	6.0160	256
3	60	7.3	100,352	6.0160	256
4	90	7.3	100,352	6.0160	256
5	30	21.9	100,352	6.0160	768
8	45	21.9	400,384	1.5078	768
9	90	7.3	1,048,576	2.3030	1,024
10	60	21.9	100,352	6.0160	768

gives the run duration in units of initial crossing times, and the last column gives it in the time unit of the integration. Most experiments were run on a 64^3 grid. Experiment 9 had a million particles on a 256^3 grid, and it ran at an initial crossing time $T_{cr} = 140T$. It was our first production run on the Numerical Aerodynamic Simulation (NAS) facility's Cray-2 at NASA-Ames. The finer resolution and larger particle number is a powerful addition to our tool kit for other experiments in the dynamics of galaxies.

Experiments 4 and 9 have polar disks. Their disks are inclined at 90°.

Response of the Galaxy

The galaxy quickly settled down into a steady state by means of a damped oscillation with a period of $(111 \pm 1)T$ and $Q = 6 \pm 1.3$, but a smaller amplitude oscillation continues undamped to the end of the experiment with the same frequency and with peak-to-peak kinetic energy variation at about 3–4 percent of the average. This is a radial pulsational mode of oscillation[13,16] whose frequency is given by the virial equations. The physics of damping is not understood; we have seen it in other experiments as well.[17] It is not a simple "phase mixing" of two or three identifiable modes; many modes would be needed to keep the amplitude from increasing again within the duration of the longer experiments. We are not aware of any simple theories that yield damped oscillations in self-consistent galaxies.

The galaxy is a stable self-consistent equilibrium configuration, and it is indeed oblate. It is assured of being stable because it developed through an experimental run. It rotates fairly rapidly, with $t_{OP} = 0.10$ (the ratio of kinetic energy in rotation to the total potential energy), or the other dimensionless quantity sometimes quoted, $\lambda = |J| |E|^{1/2}/(GM^{5/2}) \sim 0.10$.

Response of the Disk

A low-mass disk is an effective probe to test for dynamical effects in the underlying galaxy that might limit the lifetime of a dust lane. No physical process showed up in the experiments that would destroy the disk on a time scale of a few Gyr, other than the motions near the center. That conclusion becomes more forceful with additional experimental results to be presented later in the analysis of disk dynamics. This part of the experimental study, which was the part that motivated the experimental sequence, turned up no surprises.

The disk soon becomes warped as a result of differential precession. It develops a "hat-brim" warp, which becomes fairly extreme by the end of the longer runs. By the end of the longer experiments (5, 8, and 10) it is so warped that it no longer looks much like a dust lane in an elliptical galaxy. (But see the final section of this paper.) Nonetheless, it is still connected like a sheet, it is quite thin, and it has a generally symmetrical shape. We refer to it as a "disk," even though it hardly looks like one.

Warping is steady and relentless. The steady disk development is best seen in the movies. Dynamics from experiment 5 are shown in Ames Film AAV1165, "AW5 Dynamics" and from experiment 8 in Film AAV1127, "AW8 Dynamics." Fixed-time snapshots of the configuration, disk plus galaxy, are rotated to show the three-dimensional form at three times for experiment 5 and at the end of experiments 2, 3, and 4 in Ames Film AAV1166, "AWOBL Rotations," and at three times during experiment 8 in Ames Film AAV1127. Interesting patterns (spirals, rings, bars) come and go during the first half Gyr, and some of these patterns look quite different from different view directions. There are fascinating dynamical developments along the way as well. We return to them shortly.

A beautiful effect that shows up in the motion pictures is an apparent counter-streaming seen in proper motions. Once the central portions of the disk have precessed past edge-on, the outer regions still stream in the original direction while the center appears to stream in the opposite sense. This counterstreaming reminds one of the recently reported counterrotating cores in elliptical galaxies.[18 21] We return to this point in the final section.

DISK SHAPE AND VELOCITY FIELDS

Disk shapes and velocity fields afford the most direct comparisons between experiments and observation. Comparison of the experimental disk with disks in observed galaxies provides a powerful way to check for damage in dust lanes and disks in real galaxies.

We concentrate on the shape of the disk at the end of experiment 5. Its shape at earlier times is simply a less extreme example of its final form, and disk shapes in the other long experiments (except for the polar disk experiments) are so similar that there is no need to describe them in detail. Warps about half way through these longer experiments look like the "prodigious warp" Bottema, Shostak, and van der Kruit[22] reported for NGC 4013. We see even stronger warps by the end of an experiment.

Slices through the Disk

The disk shape does not admit simple analytic description. The best way we could find to illustrate its shape is to slice it in various directions. Plots of the disk particles within those slices are shown in Figures 1–3.

The coordinates used for these plots are appropriate to the disk itself. The innermost half of the particles (defined by the three-dimensional distance from the galaxy centroid) lie close to a plane; the z-axis is normal to that plane. It is 22° away from the symmetry axis of the galaxy. It is tipped 8° away from the initial disk inclination, an amount within the oscillation of the disk normals described in the next section.

The dominant shape of the sheet is like a stairstep, rather like a Z lying on its side. Many particles in the outermost half lie on the upturned edges of that Z. The sharp folds look very much like the 90° bends that have been suggested for polar disk S0 galaxies.[23] The x-direction lies along the fold of the Z, and the y-axis was chosen to form a right-handed system. Slices in the x-direction (cuts perpendicular to the x-axis; FIG. 1) have z vertical and y horizontal. There is a downward tail on the left side and an upward tail on the right side of a horizontal midsection. Panels are ordered in FIGURE 1 so slices at equal distances from the center in the ±x-direction are side-by-side to make it easier to look for symmetries. Slices at extreme distances look more like inclined lines, fanning out a bit. The thickness of the sheet can be appreciated from these plots. One gets the impression from the rotating scenes in the motion pictures that the sheet is still quite thin, but it is hard to be certain. These plots make it more certain.

The disk sliced in the y-direction shows a puff of stuff above or below the midplane at large distances from the center (FIG. 2), with the puff a little less high in panels closer to the center, until it degenerates into a kind of linear shape for slices through the center. Again, panels that display slices at equal distances from the center on opposite sides are placed side-by-side to make symmetries easier to appreciate.

The disk sliced in the z-direction (FIG. 3) also shows a puff of stuff in a line parallel to the x-axis at large distances from the center. Corrugations can be seen in the very thin slices near the center.

Boundaries for the slices are shown overlaid on projected views of the disk in FIGURE 4. The projected disk at the bottom of FIGURE 4 goes with FIGURE 1, while FIGURE 2 goes with the middle panel and FIGURE 3 with the top panel. Notice the extremely thin slices in the z-direction.

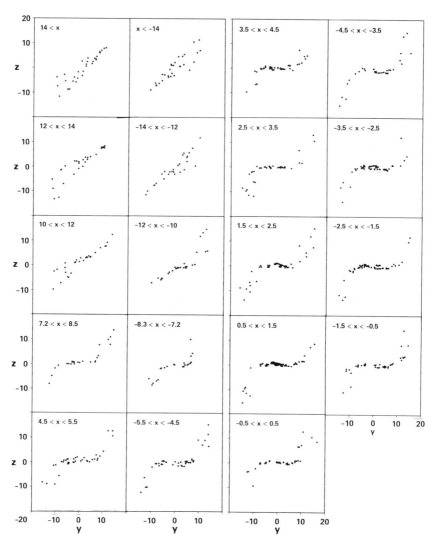

FIGURE 1. Slices through disk at end of experiment 5. This plot shows the locations of particles contained within a thin slice in the x-direction; z is plotted vertically, y horizontally. The axes, x, y, and z, are coordinates referred to the central parts of the disk; see text for details. The projection of the galaxy's symmetry axis is a line 11.7° clockwise from the vertical in these panels. Slices at equal distances from the center in the $\pm x$-directions are paired to facilitate comparison. The various frames are labeled according to the interval in x.

Tilted Rings

"Tilted rings" are often used to describe observational results; a particularly nice use is by Schwarz.[24] Particles left in a set of cuts that represent a tilted rings representation of our disk are shown in FIGURE 5. The top panel, marked 0°,

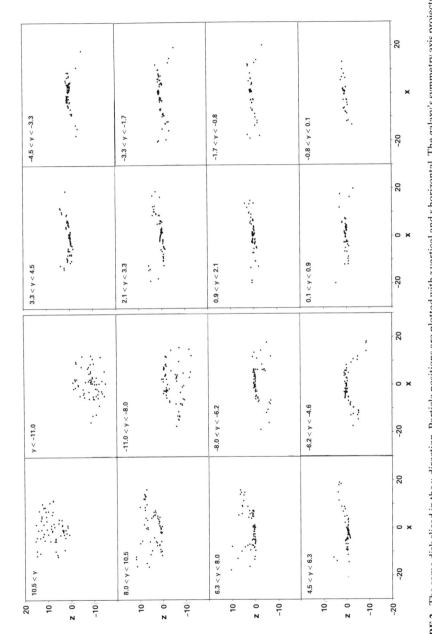

FIGURE 2. The same disk sliced in the *y*-direction. Particle positions are plotted with *z* vertical and *x* horizontal. The galaxy's symmetry axis projects to a line rotated 18.7° counterclockwise from the vertical. Slices at equal distances from the center are again paired.

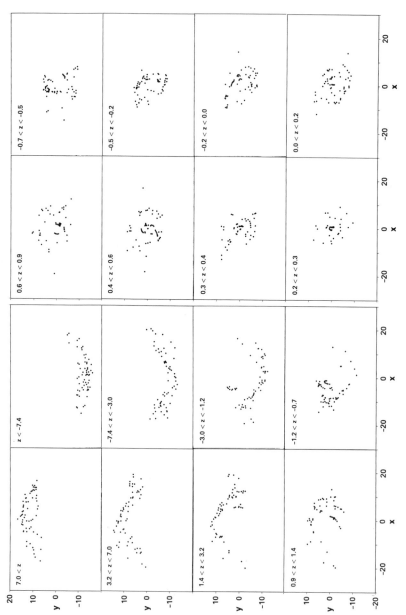

FIGURE 3. The same disk again, this time sliced in the z-direction. Particle positions are plotted with y vertical and x horizontal. The galaxy's symmetry axis is nearly out of the paper in this view. Its projection is a line rotated 31.5° clockwise from horizontal.

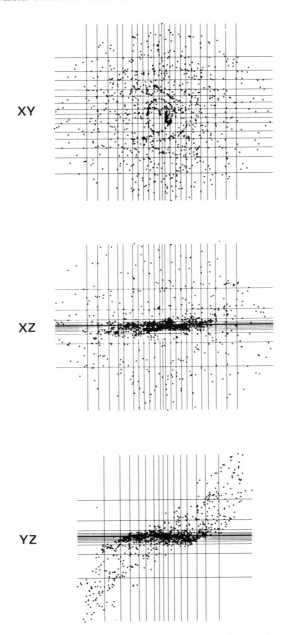

FIGURE 4. Three orthogonal projections of the disk image marked to show the cuts for the slices of FIGURES 2, 3, and 4.

contains all particles between a pair of planes that fan out at $\pm 5°$ to the x,y-plane and intersect along the x-axis. More precisely, the bin is bounded by a two-sheeted cylindrical hyperboloid with $\pm 5°$ asymptotes and separated by ± 1 in z above and below the x-axis. The left-hand panel of the second row contains particles within a similar set of hyperboloidal boundaries rotated to be asymptotic to $5°$–$15°$ planes that

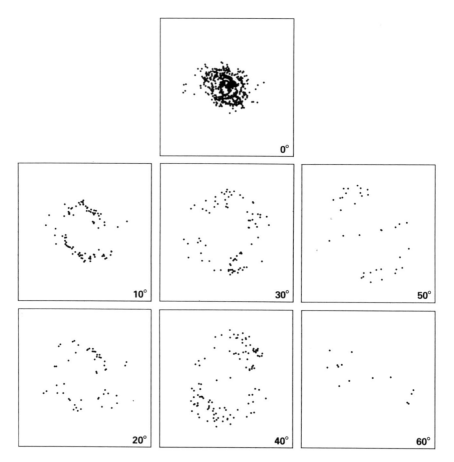

FIGURE 5. "Tilted Rings" sections of the disk at the end of experiment 5. Particles contained within various tipped planes are plotted in a projection perpendicular to that plane. The $30°$ ring already overlaps the $20°$ ring.

intersect in the x-axis. Any particle already plotted in the $0°$ panel was omitted from the $10°$ panel. The remaining panels were constructed the same way: particles that are plotted lie within the appropriate boundaries and did not appear in an earlier panel.

The tilted rings picture fits moderately well in the central region, but not as well in the outer regions. Particles should show up within nested annular regions of increasing diameter in these panels according to the tilted rings picture. However, at 30° there is considerable overlap with the particles in the 20° slice, and the same pattern persists at larger angles.

Schwarz[24] shows a nearly planar outer region for NGC 3718. The amount of warp is similar to our disk at early times, around $t = 256T$. Our disk remains nearly planar in the inner region. The differences may easily be explained in terms of the amount of residual quadrupole moment in the neighborhood where the disk is being studied and in terms of the length of time the disk system has been around. It takes some time for the outer regions to show appreciable warping.

Another way to check the tilted rings picture is to plot the y, z-projection of particles that lie between two spherical shells (in three dimensions). In an ideal twisted rings picture one should see a line segment in this kind of plot. It should be longer and inclined more and more toward the z-axis for particles farther from the center. A thick rectangular blob appears instead, with its long axis inclined in the expected manner. The rectangle is too fat (its ratio of edges is around 3:1). Again, tilted rings do not do very well. The plot we used for FIGURE 5 allows for noncircular rings; the plot described in this paragraph is not very good if the rings are not circular. Happily, FIGURE 5 shows that they are reasonably circular.

Velocity Fields

Full three-dimensional data on velocities and locations of particles that sample the disk within the experimental galaxies are available for all times throughout the experiments. Observers often have to infer three-dimensional shapes from velocity data because they lack the full spatial and velocity information available from experiments. By contrast, we have shape information we can use directly for the slices and the tilted rings picture.

Velocity data from these experiments have been studied fairly thoroughly. Velocity maps, as well as plots equivalent to single-dish radio observations, all as seen from several different view directions and at several different times, have been studied. Velocity maps for the experimental disk look like those from observed disks. They show that the experiments faithfully reproduce essential physical conditions in real galaxies. Velocity maps, coupled with full spatial information on both velocity and configuration data, contain many hints that might help observers interpret observed velocity maps.

DISK DYNAMICS

The disk was anything but quiescent during the experiment. Some fascinatingly complex phenomena are apparent in the motion pictures. Dynamical developments for experiments 5 and 8 are shown in the films mentioned earlier. There is so much going on that it is impossible to do justice to it in a few pictures or in a written description. Radial oscillations within the disk produce one of the most dramatic visual effects. Parts of the disk move inward and then outward. In the process, some parts overtake others, and ring-shaped density waves appear and move slowly outward, a bit like the rings that develop after a pebble has been dropped into a pool. They are fairly widely spaced. There are never more than two or three in the entire disk at any one time. These ring-shaped density waves are quite sharp at early times, a well-known effect for systems as "cold" as this disk. They blur by 400–500T as velocity dispersions grow through phase mixing.

But more is going on as well. Studies of some other dynamical effects follow. These dynamical effects, unlike the blurring of ring and bar patterns, continue undamped over the full duration of the experiments.

Analysis of disk dynamics was facilitated by dividing the disk particles into 16 ring-shaped bins, ordered according to distance from the center at the beginning of the experiment. We call these batches of particles "rings," even though they are not constrained to remain ringlike. The tip of a unit vector normal to a ring can explore the unit sphere. In FIGURE 6, we show the trajectories of the tips of the 16 unit vectors. The unit sphere itself projects to a circle with the galaxy's rotation axis at the center. The number beside each circle identifies the ring, numbered from the inside out: number 1 is a little disk at the center and number 16 is the outermost ring.

Each trajectory starts out to the right of the center, halfway from the center to the edge in experiment 5 (left frame) with 30° disk inclination. In experiment 8 (right frame, 45° disk inclination) each trajectory starts farther out, again in the horizontal position. Trajectories loop around a path that proceeds downward and to the left, in a clockwise sense, a general trend indicating precession. (Disk rotation is counter-clockwise in this view. Precession is retrograde to the mean disk flow, as expected for an oblate galaxy.) The inner rings precess farther than the outer rings, a differential precession that gives rise to the warp. Precession proceeds at nearly constant disk inclination. This is what one expects. However, the looping shows that each of these rings nutates as well. Nutation amplitudes are fairly steady in the outer rings, but they change appreciably during the experiment for the inner rings.

Our disks show no secular drift toward preferred orientations like the gaseous disks studied by Steiman-Cameron and Durisen[10] because there is no viscosity. Trajectories show no tendency to drift either toward the equator (outside of the circle, disk in polar orientation) or toward the pole (disk toward the equatorial plane). Over the 2-Gyr duration of these longer experiments, there is no detectable tendency for the bent flaps of the outer portions of our disks to drift toward a polar orientation. Sparke[11] argued that steady-state disks with some mass lie near a polar orientation, but ours are not in a steady state. Disks with appreciable mass open up the possibility of instability to nonaxisymmetric disturbances, however.

Longitudes of the tips of the unit vectors are shown as functions of the time in FIGURE 7. The 16 tracks have been spread out vertically to reduce confusion, and the sign has been reversed so precession looks positive. The bottom tracks represent the inner rings, and the outer rings are at the top. Again experiment 5 is shown in the left panel and experiment 8 in the right. A basic linear trend (204° by 800T) at the same slope is shown for the inner rings of both experiments. Nutation causes the wiggles in these tracks. The latitude component, so evident in FIGURE 6, is projected out in these plots.

Finally, in FIGURE 8, we show a "detrended" form of the data of FIGURE 7. The slope has been subtracted, rendering the innermost 9 or 10 rings (lower tracks)

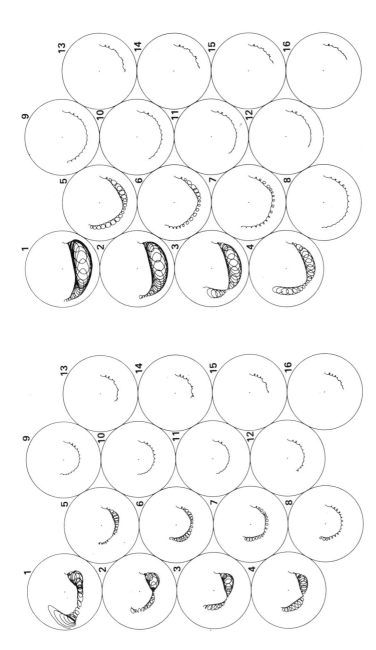

FIGURE 6. Trajectories of normals to each of 16 annular rings of material at different radii within the disk throughout the experiment. These show projections of the tip of the normal on the unit sphere, looking down along the rotation axis toward the pole of the sphere. The track numbered 1 represents the innermost 64 particles of the disk, increasing numbers indicate rings farther out until 16 is the outermost ring. The cluster on the left shows tracks from rings in experiment 5 and that on the right shows those from experiment 8. Each trajectory starts at the right and loops down and toward the left. The looping motion is nutation and the general trend shows precession.

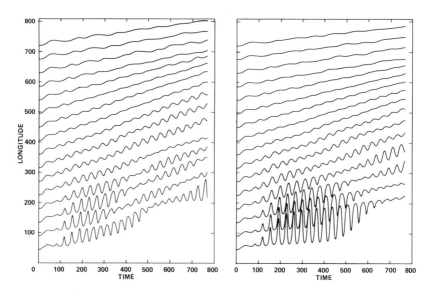

FIGURE 7. Longitude of the normals to annular rings as functions of time. The track at bottom represents the innermost ring and that at the top represents the outermost ring. The general trend represents precession and the wiggles are a consequence of nutation. Tracks have been separated vertically. Experiment 5 is on the left, 8 on the right.

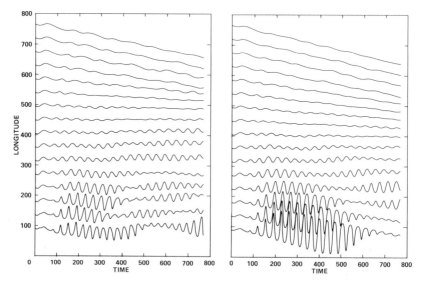

FIGURE 8. Detrended longitude of normals. Data of FIGURE 7 with the slope removed to make the pattern of variations in precession rate more apparent. The same slope (200° per 800T) has been subtracted from each track in each plot. Experiment 5 to the left, 8 to the right.

nearly horizontal, and showing clearly the reduced precession rates for the outer parts of the disk in the upper tracks. The nearly horizontal innermost tracks indicate that that portion of the disk generally precesses as a unit; it remains reasonably flat. Reduced precession rates for rings farther out means that they lag behind the inner disk in precession; a warp develops. The lines of nodes of all rings need not remain collinear.

Measured precession rates at different radii within the disk, as observed in the experiments, were checked against direct evaluations of the potentials. There is quantitative agreement between potentials evaluated from precession and those evaluated directly, which confirms the assumptions concerning smooth and nearly time-independent potentials.

The motions we have labeled "nutation" show many interesting features. Their amplitude grows, then diminishes, later to grow again. The phase of the oscillation has shifted by 180° from one side of a minimum to the other. That is a signature of two oscillations with nearly equal frequencies beating together. The times of the minima show interesting patterns in their own right. Beats between the two oscillations in nutation also show up clearly in FIGURE 6. The relation to total precession

TABLE 2. Measured Periodicities

Nutation	32
Epicyclic oscillations	36
Orbital period near center	65–67
Oscillation period of centermost particle	
x-, y-directions	72–74
z-direction (spheroid axis)	68
Fundamental radial pulsational mode	
Measured	111
Calculated	114
Precession	1,350

angle can be appreciated more clearly there, as can the way the longitudinal and latitudinal components couple.

It is natural to guess that the two interfering oscillations are something like epicyclic oscillations. The two frequencies identified here are analogous to radial and vertical epicyclic frequencies. They couple because the potential, though locally quadratic, is not diagonal as seen from the disk. Coupling gives risk to the observed beats.

A small variation of the nutation period with radius is apparent in FIGURES 7 and 8. That leads to a waving motion in the disk, undulating with the nutational period. It is quite distinct from the large-amplitude outer warp described earlier. It reaches larger amplitude in experiment 8 than in experiment 5. Even with frequencies near each other, that leads to appreciable wavelike motions of the disk surface. They are probably responsible for the corrugations noted near the center in FIGURE 3.

Several periodicities have been identified in these experiments. They are listed in TABLE 2. Periodicities in the other experiments are so close that there is no need to list them separately. We have identified the shorter of the two periods as nutation in TABLE 2, the longer as epicyclic. "Orbital Period near Center" in TABLE 2 measures the orbital period of a particle in circular orbit at some little distance from the center ($r \sim$ 3–5). It was determined from motion pictures showing the motions of particles near the center. Motions of the centermost particle have been studied in more detail.[12] Its periods were determined from plots of the x-, y-, and z-components of its position as a function of the time. Oscillations in the kinetic energy give the period of the fundamental radial pulsational mode. Finally, precession refers to the inner portions of the disk. That period was determined from the precession rates mentioned earlier. Epicyclic and nutation frequencies should reduce to twice the harmonic oscillation frequencies near the center. Measured values agree with that interpretation.

The method of analysis used in this section has some important differences from the usual "tilted rings" picture. Ours are not constrained to have a common line of nodes, to make a sheet, or to remain circular. Ring centers can move independently. The least eigenvalue of the inertia tensor for particles that make up a ring measures extension normal to the ring, whether that extension arises from fattening or from a wavy bent pattern. Checks show that each ring remains quite flat. The ratio of the two larger eigenvalues gives the extent to which the ring looks elliptical. There is some variation within the experiment, but seldom more than 1.5:1.

Polar disks were studied in experiments 4 and 9. They showed no signs of damage, deterioration, precession, or tipping. Oscillations similar to those noted in the inclined disks are apparent in motion pictures and in analyses. These are shown in Ames Film AAV1162, "Polar Disk Galaxies." There are fascinating patterns: a density wave arises in a diagonal line about 45° between the equatorial plane and the polar axis. It broadens to a trapezoidal shape and then it closes to a fairly narrow line with a period around 70–80T. Density wave rings propagate outward, generated by the opening and closing. Snapshots of this pattern, caught at fixed time and viewed from different directions, show a variety of forms often associated with spiral galaxies: rings, bars, lenses, and spiral patterns. The richness is amazing.

DISCUSSION

Among the large-scale properties examined in this paper, the experimental results show nothing that damages a disk fast enough to keep a low-mass disk model from being a good guess for dust-lane elliptical galaxies. The disk warps by differential precession, but it is not otherwise damaged if we leave aside the center motions.[12] Normal mode oscillations don't bother it.[13] The disk can be recognized as a disk for a Gyr or longer. This may be ascribed to the very round potential, which keeps the differential precession rate slow.[25] Nutation and radial motions are the most significant features that have not been emphasized in theoretical treatments, again apart from these small-scale (but important) center motions and normal mode oscillations.

The disk becomes strongly warped after a Gyr or so. It is more strongly warped than dust lanes in elliptical galaxies. That could mean any of several things: (1) The actual potential may be rounder than the potential of these experiments. Spherical potentials don't lead to any precession. (2) Whatever it is that makes up a dust lane may not extend all the way to the center. The dust lane might be a kind of belt around the luminous ellitical galaxy. If so, it is difficult to see why it should always be located fairly near the outside of the luminous galaxy. If dust lanes lie far outside the luminous galaxy, some should miss the center widely in the projected image. That does not seem to be observed. (3) It is not clear what a galaxy would look like if absorbing material extended all the way to the center. We rarely see contributions from the far side of the galaxy, so why should we see contributions from the center? It might be there, but simply not have been evident in the galaxy image. (4) Dust lanes may be fairly young objects that have not had enough time to warp appreciably. Bertola, Galletta, and Zeilinger[9] argue that observed dust lanes lose any warp with time, presumably through settling into a preferred orientation like those described by Steiman-Cameron and Durisen.[10] The collision-free objects studied here cannot settle this way. (5) A real dust-lane can hardly be expected to take the form of a flat sheet at the time of capture. Differential precession starts from whatever configuration was initially established at the time the dust lane was formed, whether by capture or by some other process.

The question how such a disk might have been formed in the first place and resolution of the possiblities enumerated in the previous paragraph (and other possibilities like them) are left as outstanding dynamical problems for the dust-lane systems. Collision-free systems have no incentive to settle into thin sheets, so formation may require the physics of gaseous systems.

While the disk in these experiments contributes to the total gravity, it has little mass. Thus the disk dynamics described here is quite different from that envisioned in most discussions of warps[11,25-32] where self-gravitation of the disk drives the dynamics of the warp. Similarly, since the disk has no viscosity, the damping discussed by Steiman-Cameron and Durisen[10] and by others does not apply either.

We remarked earlier about the beautiful effect of an apparent counterstreaming flow in the warped disk as seen from certain view directions. A similar effect can also appear in radial velocities from certain view directions. Imagine a sheet with a hat-brim warp and with a streaming flow in the same sense everywhere on the sheet. Imagine that you view this sheet from a direction nearly "face-on" such that the inner portion of the sheet is inclined in one direction and the outer portions in the other direction relative to your view. You will then see one sense of rotation indicated by radial velocities in the inner portion, the opposite sense in the outer portions. This reversal can be seen in our velocity maps. Apparent changes of radial velocity become much more pronounced if the central portion of the disk is viewed nearly edge-on. A fairly strong warp (such as that indicated by FIGS. 1–3) is required to make large velocity differences in projected counterrotations. A problem with this picture is that most of the signal comes from the central portions—there is very poor signal-to-noise in the outer portions. Nonetheless, one can easily imagine that the conditions of the counterrotating cores seen in some elliptical galaxies[18-21] could be met by a small disk of material near the center of the galaxy, precessing within the main potential field, showing apparent rotation in unexpected directions.

ACKNOWLEDGMENTS

Film or video transfer copies of the motion pictures mentioned throughout this paper are available at cost. Inquiries should be addressed to Imaging Technology Branch, Mail Stop 203-6, NASA-Ames Research Center, Moffett Field, CA 94035. Dr. Althea Wilkinson of the University of Manchester got us started on this line of investigation. She developed the starting condition used for these experiments. It is a pleasure to thank her for her many contributions to this effort. Judy Etheridge and Dan Dempsey of NASA-Ames helped considerably in handling the data on completion of the integration runs and in making motion pictures and other plots.

REFERENCES

1. BERTOLA, F. & G. GALLETTA. 1978. Astrophys. J., Lett. **226:** L115. [Fiche 128–B2]
2. BERTOLA, F. 1987. *In* IAU Symposium 127, Structure and Dynamics of Elliptical Galaxies, T. de Zeeuw, Ed.: 135–144. Reidel. Dordrecht, the Netherlands.
3. GRAHAM, J. A. 1979. Astrophys. J. **232:** 60. [Fiche 77–E8]
4. WILKINSON, A., R. M. SHARPLES, R. A. E. FOSBURY & P. T. WALLACE. 1986. Mon. Not. R. Astron. Soc. **218:** 297.
5. PHILLIPS, T. G., B. N. ELLISON, J. B. KEENE, R. B. LEIGHTON, R. J. HOWARD, C. R. MASSON, D. B. SANDERS, B. VEIDT & K. YOUNG. 1987. Astrophys. J., Lett. **322:** L73. [Fiche 152–B8]
6. KOTANYI, C. G. & R. D. EKERS. 1979. Astron. Astrophys. **73:** L1.
7. TUBBS, A. D. 1980. Astrophys. J. **241:** 969. [Fiche 110–C7]
8. VAN ALBADA, T. S., C. G. KOTANYI & M. SCHWARZSCHILD. 1982. Mon. Not. R. Astron. Soc. **198:** 303.
9. BERTOLA, F., G. GALLETTA & W. W. ZEILINGER. 1985. Astrophys. J., Lett. **292:** L51. [Fiche 57–B3]
10. STEIMAN-CAMERON, T. Y. & R. H. DURISEN. 1988. Astrophys. J. **325:** 26. [Fiche 19–C4]
11. SPARKE, L. 1986. Mon. Not. R. Astron. Soc. **219:** 657.
12. MILLER, R. H. & B. F. SMITH. 1988. *In* Applied Mathematics, Fluid Mechanics, Astrophysics, A Symposium to Honor C. C. Lin; D. J. Benney, F. H. Shu, and C. Yuan, Eds.: 366–372. World Scientific. Singapore.
13. MILLER, R. H. 1991. Ann. N.Y. Acad. Sci. **631:** 55–67.
14. HABE, A. & S. IKEUCHI. 1985. Astrophys. J. **289:** 540. [Fiche 18–C10]
15. MILLER, R. H. 1992. *In* Numerical Methods in Astrophysics, P. R. Woodward, Ed. Academic Press. Boston. To be published.
16. MILLER, R. H., P. O. VANDERVOORT, D. E. WELTY & B. F. SMITH. 1989. Astrophys. J. **342:** 105. [Fiche 102–C6]
17. MILLER, R. H. 1983. Numerical experiments on the self-consistent responses of galaxies (Unpublished). ESO Scientific Preprint No. 269.
18. FRANX, M. & G. ILLINGWORTH. 1988. Astrophys. J., Lett. **327:** L55. [Fiche 61–C2]
19. JEDRZEJEWSKI, R. & P. L. SCHECHTER. 1988. Astrophys. J., Lett. **330:** L87. [Fiche 104–F1]
20. BENDER, R. 1988. Astron. Astrophys. **202:** L5.
21. ILLINGWORTH, G. D. & M. FRANX. 1989. *In* Dynamics of Dense Stellar Systems, D. Merritt, Ed.: 13–23. Cambridge Univ. Press. Cambridge, England.
22. BOTTEMA, R., G. S. SHOSTAK & P. C. VAN DER KRUIT. 1987. Nature **328:** 401.
23. NICHOLSON, R. A., K. TAYLOR, W. B. SPARKS & J. BLAND. 1987. *In* IAU Symposium 127, Structure and Dynamics of Elliptical Galaxies, T. de Zeeuw, Ed.: 415–416. Reidel. Dordrecht, the Netherlands.
24. SCHWARZ, U. J. 1985. Astron. Astrophys. **142:** 273.
25. TUBBS, A. D. & R. H. SANDERS. 1979. Astrophys. J. **230:** 736. [Fiche 58–B8]
26. KAHN, F. D. & L. WOLTJER. 1959. Astrophys. J. **130:** 705.
27. LYNDEN-BELL, D. 1965. Mon. Not. R. Astron. Soc. **129:** 299.
28. HUNTER, C. & A. TOOMRE. 1969. Astrophys. J. **155:** 747.
29. BERTIN, G. & J. W.-K. MARK. 1980. Astron. Astrophys. **88:** 289.
30. BERTIN, G. & S. CASERTANO. 1982. Astron. Astrophys. **106:** 274.
31. TOOMRE, A. 1983. *In* IAU Symposium 100, Internal Kinematics and Dynamics of Galaxies, E. Athanassoula, Ed.: 177–185. Reidel. Dordrecht, the Netherlands.
32. MAY, A. & R. A. JAMES. 1984. Mon. Not. R. Astron. Soc. **206:** 691.

Combined Instabilities in Magnetic Galaxy Disks

BRUCE G. ELMEGREEN

IBM Research Division
T. J. Watson Research Center
P.O. Box 218
Yorktown Heights, New York 10598

The self-gravitational force of the gas in disk galaxies is so strong that it is likely to be involved with star formation from even the first step, when a giant cloud forms from the ambient interstellar medium. Gaseous dissipation is also very strong, so the pressure that resists gravity is quickly dissipated unless there is some local energetic event to restore it. The buoyancy of the magnetic field also drives gas condensation, as the Parker[1] instability develops. A recent calculation[2] of the general stability of the interstellar medium includes these three effects. We also find a torsional instability as part of the general solution, following suggestions by Tagger and Foglizzo.[3] The results are summarized here.

The calculation of the combined instabilities includes self-gravity, the Parker instability, and various degrees of thermal stability and instability, all in a shearing, rotating galaxy disk with an exponential density distribution perpendicular to the plane. The condensation mode has a true instability with an exponential growth at late times, unlike the situation for stars in which gravity gives only a transient growth followed by oscillations.[4] These oscillations are caused by restoring forces from pressure (i.e., the random motions of stars or gas) and the Coriolis force, which drives an epicyclic motion. Similar oscillations occur at late times for a magnetic self-gravitating gas with an adiabatic equation of state,[5] but cooling in the present calculation ensures that pressure is relatively weak then,[6] so pressure is not a strong restoring force, and the magnetic field removes enough angular momentum to prevent the coriolis oscillation.[5,7]

Self-gravity contributes to the instability by pulling together different parallel bundles of field lines, which would otherwise deform separately in the pure Parker instability, and by continuously driving the gas to a high density. As is well known, gravity alone gives a dispersion relation for instabilities in the radial direction (forming rings), that is

$$\omega^2 = 2\pi G\sigma k - k^2(c^2\gamma_{\text{eff}} + v_A^2) - \omega_{\text{ep}}^2 \tag{1}$$

for growth rate ω, mass column density σ, wavenumber k, rms velocity dispersion c, Alfvén speed v_A, and epicyclic frequency ω_{ep}. The thermal instability contributes to γ_{eff}, the effective ratio of specific heats; when $\gamma_{\text{eff}} < 0$, there is a thermal instability and no minimum wavelength (although there is a maximum wavelength from the ω_{ep} term). The gas is still unstable when perturbations exceed a minimum wavelength if $\gamma_{\text{eff}} > 0$, provided $Q = \omega_{\text{ep}}c\gamma_{\text{eff}}^{1/2}/(\pi G\sigma)$ is less than 1. Actually γ_{eff} depends on ω, so the instability criterion is slightly more complicated than this.

A new result from the recent calculation[2] is that self-gravity alone gives a dispersion relation for instabilities in the *azimuthal* direction, parallel to the mean magnetic field, that is approximately

$$\omega^2 = 2\pi G\sigma k - k^2 c^2 \gamma_{\text{eff}} - \frac{\omega^2 \omega_{ep}^2}{\omega^2 + k^2 v_A^2} . \tag{2}$$

Now the magnetic field enters into the term with the epicyclic frequency, not the pressure. This is because there is no pressure from the magnetic field that resists motions parallel to the field, but there is a magnetic tension that resists the twist from the Coriolis force. With this new dispersion relation, there is always an instability in the gas, regardless of Q, because at the threshold of instability, when $\omega = 0$, the epicyclic frequency drops out of the equation. FIGURE 1 shows solutions to this dispersion relation for various Q and for $\gamma_{\text{eff}} = 1$. As $Q \to \infty$ the growth rate goes to zero, but there is no threshold giving stability at large Q. This is an important result for shear instabilities in magnetic disks. It implies that the magnetic field makes perturbations in the gas always grow, regardless of rotation, and if the pressure is weakly dependent on density, then this growth persists even for late times (i.e., without pressure oscillations).

The role of the Parker instability[1] is to increase the growth rate because of the extra driving force parallel to the disk from field line curvature in the perpendicular direction, and from cosmic-ray pressure. The Parker instability contributes from the very beginning of the growth and is an inseparable part of the total process. Any positive density perturbation that is symmetric with respect to the midplane (or high off the plane) will weigh down the field lines and get pushed together by the resulting field line curvature. This occurs simultaneously with the gravitational and thermal (if present) instabilities.

One remnant of the Parker instability is that short wavelengths are stabilized by

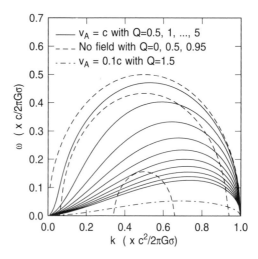

FIGURE 1.

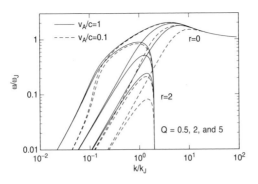

FIGURE 2.

field line curvature. At short wavelengths there is a competition between a strong thermal instability and the stabilizing influence of field line curvature, but the curvature always wins at short enough wavelengths unless the magnetic diffusion time becomes shorter than the instability time.

Another implication of the Parker instability is that the density dependence of the growth rate is negligible for this component of the total instability. As the contribution from the Parker instability becomes more important, the overall density dependence decreases from ρ^1 in the case of the pure gravitational instability, to ρ^0 in the pure Parker instability. For the combined instability with typical parameters, the density dependence is between $\rho^{0.3}$ and $\rho^{0.5}$. If the star formation rate scales with $\rho\omega$, which seems likely, then the combined instability gives a star formation rate that is proportional to something between $\rho^{1.3}$ and $\rho^{1.5}$, which is in the observed range.[8,9] This might explain the so-called Schmidt law of star formation.

The role of the thermal instability for macroscopic cloud motions has only recently been appreciated,[10–12] although applications to true thermal pressures have been discussed for a long time.[13] In the case of macroscopic cloud motions, an instability like the thermal instability operates because the heating or stirring of the gas has a weak density dependence and the cooling has a strong density dependence. If the heating rate is taken to scale as $\rho^r c^s$, for example, then cloud stirring by supernovae and expanding HII regions[14,15] give values of r less than zero.[16] This is a much smaller density dependence than for the cooling rate by cloud collisions, which is proportional to $\rho^2 c^3$. A linear perturbation analysis[17] suggests that thermal instability requires $r < (1 + s)/2$ for this cooling law, and such low values of r are plausible with supernova and HII region heating. Local fluctuations in the heating rate help the thermal instability, too, because if the heating rate at some time equals E times the equilibrium value, then $r < (1 + sE)/(2E)$ gives thermal instability,[17,18] which is easy to satisfy if $E < 1$. Such fluctuations are likely because of the patchy nature of the heating sources, which are strongly concentrated near OB-associations. Then macroscopic thermal instabilities should occur between OB-associations.

FIGURE 2 shows solutions to (2) in which

$$\gamma_{\text{eff}} = \gamma \left(\frac{\omega - \omega_c(1 - 2r + s)}{\omega + \gamma\omega_c(3 - s)} \right), \tag{3}$$

which is appropriate for cloud collisional cooling.[2,17] Here $\omega_c = (\gamma - 1)\Lambda_0/(2\gamma P)$ is the cooling rate for $\gamma = 5/3$, Λ_0 is equal to the equilibrium cooling or heating rate (to give the dispersion c), and P is the pressure. The growth rate and wavenumber in the figure are normalized to the standard Jeans threshold values, $\omega_J = \pi G\sigma/c$ and $k_j = \pi G\sigma/c^2$. We assume for FIGURE 2 that $s = 0$, and so various degrees of thermal instability are represented by the r values; $r = 0$ is for thermal instability and $r = 2$ is thermally stable. High values of r stabilize the gas at small wavelengths (large k in the figure).

This discussion has used (1) and (2) to illustrate the general nature of the instabilities,[2] but the full equations for a shearing thick disk require numerical solutions for the time dependence of the perturbed variables. The results are qualitatively similar to what these equations imply, that is, there is a true instability with no oscillations at late times, and there is no Q threshold for the shear instability, which involves mass motions primarily in the azimuthal direction, parallel to the field lines. This result seems to contradict the observation that Q is an important threshold for star formation in real galaxies,[8] but we have to remember that the shear instability produces only dense, infinitely long spiral wavelets, and not discrete clouds. That is why most of the motion is in the azimuthal direction and why (2) reproduces the full behavior of the equations so well. Cloud formation requires an instability in the third dimension, too, along the wavelet, so that separated, three-dimensional objects like giant cloud complexes can form. This third dimension is mostly in the radial direction, and so cloud formation effectively combines (1) and (2). As a result, the fragmentation of shearing wavelets has a sensitivity to Q unlike the pure shear instability.[2] We find a rapidly growing three-dimensional instability when Q is less than about 1 (depending on v_A/c, r, etc.) and a very slowly growing instability when Q exceeds about 1. There is also more stability from magnetic pressure in the radial direction in the case of the fragmentation of shearing wavelets, as in the pure radial instability.

These calculations illustrate one of several possible mechanisms for cloud and star formation in disk galaxies. A review of other mechanisms is in Elmegreen.[19] The new results suggest that there is a Q threshold for giant cloud and star formation, which should regulate the interstellar medium to keep Q close to 1, as long as most of the cloud velocity dispersion is related to the star formation process. They also suggest that the star formation rate scales as $\omega\rho \sim \rho^{1.3}$ to $\rho^{1.5}$ for growth rate ω, which is comparable to the density dependence observed by Kennicutt.[8]

According to this model, galactic star formation begins on a scale of 10^6 to $10^7 M_\odot$ as a result of gaseous gravity, magnetic forces, and energy dissipation via turbulence and cloud collisions. It then proceeds by dissipation, collapse, dispersal, and more collapse through various giant molecular cloud (GMC) stages, lasting for 10^8 years. At all of these stages there is a Q threshold, including the secondary stages that include propagating star formation.[20] Spiral density waves regulate where this process occurs by modulating the density, shear, and tidal forces, but these waves do not noticeably influence the overall star formation rate per unit gas mass, except perhaps at the 50 percent level.

The stability analysis in Elmegreen[2] also derives a dispersion relation for torsional waves, which are a noncompressive motion in the plane. Magnetic tension is a restoring force for this wave, and short wavelengths are stabilized by it, while long wavelengths are unstable because angular momentum is transferred from the inward-moving perturbations to the outward moving perturbations by magnetic tension. The dispersion relation for the wave is

$$\omega^2 = -v_A^2 \left(k^2 + \frac{4(A\Omega/c^2)(1 + L^2 k_z^2)}{2(1 + \alpha + \beta)(1 - 2Lk_z\rho G_z/\rho_T) - \gamma_{\text{eff}}(1 + L^2 k_z^2)} \right), \qquad (4)$$

where k_z is the wavenumber perpendicular to the plane, L is twice the disk scale height for an exponential disk, α and β are the ratios of the magnetic- and cosmic-ray pressures to the gas pressure, A and Ω are the Oort shear parameter and rotation rate, ρ and ρ_T are the midplane gas and total densities, and G_z is a number ~ 1 from an integral over the gravitational force with height.[2] Solutions $\omega(k)$ are shown in FIGURE 3 for $r = 1$ in γ_{eff}. Each different line represents a different value of k_z. The

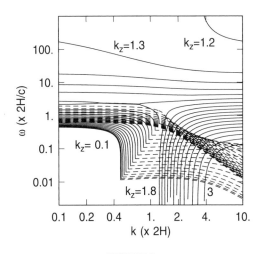

FIGURE 3.

solid lines are pure growing solutions and the dashed lines are growing oscillations (ω complex with a positive real part). There is a rich variety of solutions because of the ω dependence in γ_{eff}. The growth rate is small when k_z is small, and it increases as k_z increases until the denominator in (4) goes through 0, at $k_z \sim 1.2$. Then the growth rate has very large values for a range of k_z, and it decreases as k_z continues to increase. For large k_z, the growth rate is complex because of the large restoring force from magnetic tension at small perpendicular wavelengths.

The implications of this instability are not well understood. It may produce an interchange of gas between different radii in a galaxy, and it may drive turbulence. It is related to an instability found by Balbus and Hawley[21] and Tagger, Pellat, and Coroniti[22] for the case of a magnetic field perpendicular to the disk. It is currently under investigation.

REFERENCES

1. PARKER, E. N. 1966. Astrophs. J. **145:** 811.
2. ELMEGREEN, B. G. 1991. Astrophys. J. **378:** 139.
3. TAGGER, M. & T. FOGLIZZO. 1991. Preprint.
4. TOOMRE, A. 1981. *In* The Structure and Evolution of Normal Galaxies, S. M. Fall and D. Lynden-Bell, Eds.: 111. Cambridge Univ. Press. Cambridge, England.
5. ELMEGREEN, G. B. 1987. Astrophys. J. **312:** 626.
6. ———1989. Astrophys. J., Lett. **342:** L67.
7. LYNDEN-BELL, D. 1966. Observatory **86:** 57.
8. KENNICUTT, R. C. 1989. Astrophys. J. **344:** 685.
9. BUAT, V., J. M. DEHARVENG & J. DONAS. 1989. Astron. Astrophys. **223:** 42.
10. STRUCK-MARCELL, C. & J. M. SCALO. 1984. Astrophys. J. **277:** 132.
11. TOMISAKA, K. 1987. Publ. Astron. Soc. Japan **39:** 109.
12. ELMEGREEN, B. G. 1989. Astrophys. J. **344:** 306.
13. FIELD, G. B. 1965. Astrophys. J. **142:** 531.
14. McKEE, C. F., D. VAN BUREN & B. LAZAREFF. 1984. Astrophys. J., Lett. **278:** L115.
15. CIOFFI, D. F., C. F. McKEE & E. BERTSCHINGER. 1988. Astrophys. J. **334:** 252.
16. ELMEGREEN, B. G. 1992. Saas Fee Lectures "Large Scale Dynamics of the Interstellar Medium," D. Pfenniger and P. Bartholdi, Eds. Springer-Verlag. New York/Berlin. In press.
17. ———1991. *In* Physics of Star Formation and Early Stellar Evolution, C. J. Lada and N. Kylafis, Eds.: 35. Kluwer. Dordrecht, the Netherlands.
18. BALBUS, S. A. 1986. Astrophys. J., Lett. **303:** L79.
19. ELMEGREEN, B. G. 1992. *In* Protostars and Planets, III., E. H. Levy and M. S. Matthews, Eds. Univ. of Arizona Press. Tucson. In press.
20. ———*In* Evolution of Interstellar Matter and Dynamics of Galaxies, B. W. Burton, P. O. Lindblad, and J. Palous, Eds. Cambridge Univ. Press. Cambridge, England. In press.
21. BALBUS, S. A. & S. A. HAWLEY. 1991. Astrophys. J. **376:** 214.
22. TAGGER, M., R. PELLAT & F. C. CORONITI. 1991. Astrophys. J. In press.

The Development of Structure in Shearing Viscous Media. Flat Disks[a]

JAMES H. HUNTER, JR.

Department of Astronomy
University of Florida
Gainesville, Florida 32611

INTRODUCTION

In a generalization of earlier work by Goldreich and Lynden-Bell[1] (hereafter GB), Hunter and Schweiker[2] (Paper I) and Hunter and Horak[3] (Paper II) studied the growth of structures in a locally uniform, viscous, rotating fluid possessing macroscopic velocity shear, which is of infinite extent in the direction parallel to the rotation axis. The following points were established in these papers:

1. Density waves and vorticity may be excited, and grow spectacularly, in Chandrasekhar's singular modes, having wave vectors parallel to the axis of rotation.
2. In viscous media, such as protostellar disks, the familiar density waves may be strongly damped, or overdamped, with only the slowly propagating vorticity modes surviving.
3. Shear viscosity breaks Kelvin's circulation theorem by requiring that spin be exchanged between adjacent fluid elements. Consequently, shear viscous forces can effectively cancel the stabilizing Coriolis terms, thereby allowing gravitational instabilities to develop at roughly the Jeans length.
4. By assuming exponential solutions for the time dependences of the linear modes, the resulting approximate dispersion relation may be used to predict when self-gravitating structures can form. In the present communication, this approach is reformulated for the more realistic limiting case of an arbitrarily flat disk.

THE LINEAR PROBLEM

We formulate the problem in a local Cartesian coordinate system situated at radius r from the rotation axis. The coordinate origin is assumed to rotate at constant angular speed $\Omega(r) \equiv \Omega$. Following the convention of GB, we let the x coordinate increase radially ouward and the y coordinate increase in the direction opposite that of rotation. (This coordinate system is rotated by $\pi/2$ with respect to the system used in Papers I and II.) The undistributed flow is described by $x = b = y = a + 2Abt$, where A is one of the usual Oort constants describing the local shearing rate. The unperturbed pressure p and surface density v are assumed constant, and the shearing

[a]This research was supported in part by National Science Foundation Grant AST9022827.

speeds $v_x = 0$ and $v_y = 2Ab$. Comoving coordinates (a, b) are the (y, x) coordinates at $t = 0$. Denoting first-order quantities by prime $(')$, in comoving coordinates the linearized equation of continuity, the component equations of motion for a polytropic fluid and Poisson's equation read

$$\frac{\partial v'}{\partial t} + v\mathcal{D}v'_x + v\frac{\partial v'_y}{\partial a} = 0, \tag{1}$$

$$\frac{\partial v'_x}{\partial t} = 2\Omega v'_y - \frac{c^2}{v}\mathcal{D}v' - \mathcal{D}\phi' + \beta\left(\frac{\partial^2}{\partial a^2} + \mathcal{D}^2\right)v'_x - \frac{(\zeta + \beta/3)}{v}\mathcal{D}\frac{\partial v'}{\partial t}, \tag{2}$$

$$\frac{\partial v'_y}{\partial t} = -2Bv'_x - \frac{c^2}{v}\frac{\partial v'}{\partial a} - \frac{\partial\phi'}{\partial a} + \beta\left(\frac{\partial^2}{\partial a^2} + \mathcal{D}^2\right)v'_y - \frac{(\zeta + \beta/3)}{v}\frac{\partial^2 v'}{\partial a\partial t}, \tag{3}$$

and

$$\left(\frac{\partial^2}{\partial a^2} + \mathcal{D}^2 + \frac{\partial^2}{\partial z^2}\right)\phi' = 4\pi Gv'\delta(z). \tag{4}$$

In these equations, ϕ is the gravitational potential, δ the Dirac delta function, β the coefficient of kinematic shear viscosity, ζ the coefficient of bulk viscosity, c the unperturbed sound speed, and operators $\mathcal{D}$ and $\mathcal{D}^2$ are defined as

$$\mathcal{D} = \frac{\partial}{\partial b} - 2At\frac{\partial}{\partial a}, \tag{5a}$$

and

$$\mathcal{D}^2 = \frac{\partial^2}{\partial b^2} - 4At\frac{\partial^2}{\partial b\partial a} + 4A^2t^2\frac{\partial^2}{\partial a^2}. \tag{5b}$$

Oort's B constant is defined by $B = \Omega + A$, where $\Omega < 0$ in our right-handed coordinate system. We Fourier analyze the linear dependent variables, viz., $v' = v'(t)$ $\cos\chi$, $v'_{x,y} = v'_{x,y}(t)\sin\chi$ and $\phi' = \phi'(t, z)\cos\chi$, where $\chi \equiv k_a a + k_b b$; k_a and k_b are the wavenumbers characterizing a particular mode. To solve Poisson's equation, we integrate across the disk in the z direction, from z^- to z^+, to obtain the result

$$\frac{\partial\phi'}{\partial z}\bigg|_{z^+} = 2\pi Gv'. \tag{6a}$$

A solution of this equation is

$$\phi' = -\frac{2\pi Gv'}{\alpha}e^{-|\alpha z|}. \tag{6b}$$

The quantity α is determined by requiring that (4) be satisfied when $z \neq 0$. This yields the relation

$$\left(\frac{\partial^2}{\partial a^2} + \mathcal{D}^2 + \alpha^2\right)\phi' = 0. \tag{6c}$$

We define the time-dependent wavenumber $k_c \equiv k_b - 2Atk_a$; then (**6c**) has the solution

$$\alpha = \sqrt{k_a^2 + k_c^2} = k(t) \equiv k. \tag{6d}$$

Hence, in the disk plane,

$$\phi' = -\frac{2\pi G v'(t)}{k} \cos \chi. \tag{6e}$$

For the case of an infinite cylinder, devoid of structure in the z direction (the problem considered in Papers I and II),

$$\phi' = -\frac{4\pi G v'}{k^2} = -\frac{4\pi G v'(t)}{k^2} \cos \chi, \tag{6f}$$

where v' is the perturbed volume density. The differences between the two problems can be traced to the two distinct solutions of Poisson's equations given in (**6e**) and (**6f**). The time dependences of the Fourier components are described by the system of ordinary differential equations

$$\dot{v}'(t) = -v k_c(t) v'_x(t - v k_a v'_y(t), \tag{7}$$

$$\dot{v}'_x(t) = 2\Omega v'_y(t) + k_c(t)\eta(t) v'(t) - \beta k^2(t) v'_x(t) + \frac{a}{v} k_c(t) \dot{v}(t), \tag{8}$$

and

$$\dot{v}'_y(t) = -2B v'_x(t) + k_a \eta(t) v'(t) - \beta k^2(t) v'_y(t) + \frac{a}{v} k_a \dot{v}'(t), \tag{9}$$

where the dots denote time derivatives, $a \equiv \zeta + \beta/3$ and $\eta(t) = (c^2/v) - [2\pi G/k(t)]$ (flat disk), or $\eta(t) = (c^2/v) - [4\pi G/k^2(t)]$ (infinite cylinder). Hereafter, we will drop (t) in designating the time dependences. Upon differentiating (**7**) once with respect to time, we have

$$\ddot{v}' = -v k_c \dot{v}'_x - v k_a \dot{v}'_y - v \dot{k}_c v'_x = -v k_c \dot{v}'_x - v k_a \dot{v}'_y + 2Av k_a v'_x. \tag{10a}$$

We substitute for $\dot{v}'_x$ and $\dot{v}'_y$ from (**8**) and (**9**) and collect terms to obtain the result

$$\ddot{v}' + Ck^2 \dot{v}' + k^2 v \eta v' = -2\Omega v k_c v'_y + 2(B + A) v k_a v'_x, \tag{10b}$$

where $C \equiv (\zeta + \frac{4}{3}\beta)$. Equations (**7**) and (**10b**) may be solved for the perturbed velocity components in terms of v' and its time derivatives, viz.,

$$v'_x = \frac{(k_a \ddot{v}' + Ck^2 k_a \dot{v}' - 2\Omega k_c \dot{v}' + k_a k^2 v \eta v')}{2vD}, \tag{11a}$$

and

$$v'_y = \frac{(k_c \ddot{v}' + Ck^2 k_c \dot{v}' - 2k_a(B + A)\dot{v}' + k_c k^2 v \eta v')}{2vD}, \tag{11b}$$

where $D \equiv k_c^2 \Omega + k_a^2(B + A) = k^2 \Omega + 2k_a^2 A$.

Finally, either **(11a)** or **(11b)** may be differential once more with respect to time to yield a third-order equation for the time dependence of the perturbed surface density. After doing so, back substituting for the velocity components and their time derivatives and simplifying the result considerably, the resulting third-order equation reads

$$\dddot{v}' + \left[\frac{4\Omega A k_a k_c}{D} + (7/3\beta + \zeta)k^2 \right] \ddot{v}'$$

$$+ \left\{ k^2 \nu\eta + \kappa^2 + \frac{8\Omega A k_a^2}{D}(B + A) + 4A k_a k_c \left[(4/3\beta + \zeta)\frac{\Omega k^2}{D} - (5/3\beta + 2\zeta) \right] \right.$$

$$+ (4/3\beta + \zeta)\beta k^4 \right\} \dot{v}' + \left[k^2 \nu\dot\eta + \frac{K\Omega A k_a k_c}{D}k^2\nu\eta - 8A k_a k_c \nu\eta + \beta k^2(k^2\nu\eta) \right] v' = 0, \quad (12)$$

where the square of epicyclic frequency $\kappa^2 = 4\Omega B$. ($\kappa^2 > 0$ for stable disks.) If we substitute $\eta = (c^2/\nu) - (4\pi G/k^2)$, we recover [3, eq. (10)]. As discussed in that paper, several limiting cases of **(12)** have been considered by various authors. For the inviscid, rigidly rotating case, $k_c = k_b = $ constant and $A = \beta = \zeta = 0$, **(12)** reduces to the familiar result

$$\dddot{v}' + (k^2\nu\eta + \kappa^2)\dot{v}' = 0. \quad (13)$$

The coefficient of $\dot{v}'$ is constant in this limit; consequently, $v' \sim e^{\omega t}$, and instability is guaranteed in $k^2\nu\eta + \kappa^2 < 0$, or $k^2c^2 + \kappa^2 - 2\pi G\nu k < 0$, for a flat disk. If shear viscosity is included in the rigidly rotating problem, the coefficients of **(12)** remain constant. Therefore, exponential solutions are exact and the disk is unstable if the constant term of v' is <0—that is, if $k^2\nu\eta < 0$, or

$$k^2c^2 - 2\pi G\nu k < 0, \quad \text{(flat disk)} \quad (14a)$$

and

$$k^2c^2 - 4\pi G\nu < 0. \quad \text{(infinite cylinder)} \quad (14b)$$

Conditions **(14a)** and **(14b)** are exactly the Jeans criteria for the respective cases in nonrotating media—no stabilizing epicyclic terms appear. As a final limiting example, we consider ring modes in a flat shearing disk. For these axisymmetric disturbances, $k_a = 0$, $k = k_b$, and "wave fronts" are perpendicular to r. In this limit, $D = k_b^2\Omega$ and all coefficients of the differential equation are constant. For solutions of the form $v' \sim e^{\omega t}$, the dispersion relation is

$$\omega^3 + (7/3\beta + \zeta)k_b^2\omega^2 + [k_b^2\nu\eta + \kappa^2 + (4/3\beta + \zeta)\beta k_b^4]\omega + \beta k_b^2(k_b^2\nu\eta) = 0. \quad (15)$$

The sufficient condition for instability is that $\epsilon_J \equiv k_b^2\nu\eta < 0$, or $k_b c^2 - 2\pi G\nu < 0$ for a flat disk, exactly Jeans' criterion in the absence of rotation. While the medium is formally unstable if $\beta \neq 0$ and $\epsilon_J < 0$, the growth rate of this instability depends strongly upon the coefficient of shear viscosity.

In general, **(12)** has three linearly independent solutions. Under a wide range of conditions (e.g., β and ζ small and $\epsilon_J + k^2$ significantly > 0), these solutions will be two (density) waves and a third solution, which was designated a vorticity mode in Papers I and II. (The reason for this terminology will be explained in the next section.) The slowly propagating vorticity mode, corresponding to the real root due to the presence of the constant term in (15), has nonzero growth when $\beta \neq 0$. However, if the viscous coefficients are relatively large, as may be the case in gaseous circumstellar disks, the familiar density waves either will be strongly damped, or overdamped (no oscillatory solutions exist), and yet the vorticity mode may exhibit interesting growth. (If the viscous forces are too large, even that mode will be suppressed.) The best strategy for approaching a problem of this type is to develop, and carefully catalogue, the behavior of, the special functions representing each modal solution of (12). Once the character of these solutions is understood, the future (linear) evolution of an arbitrary disturbance can be predicted because the mode amplitudes are calculated from the initial conditions. We defer further discussion of these amplitudes until a later section.

THE VORTICITY CONNECTION

Vorticity is excited when torques stir a fluid. This can be done continuously through the action of shear viscosity and/or magnetic fields, periodically by a bar stirring a viscous fluid, impulsively by encounters, by the passage of shock fronts, when spin is exchanged between a collapsing protostar and its circumstellar disk, etc. In standard vector notation, the full equations of continuity and motion are

$$\frac{\partial \nu}{\partial t} + (\mathbf{v} \cdot \nabla)\nu \equiv \frac{d\nu}{dt} = -\nu \nabla \cdot \mathbf{v}, \tag{16}$$

and

$$\frac{\partial \mathbf{v}}{\partial t} + \frac{1}{2}\nabla v^2 - \mathbf{v} \times \mathbf{w} = \nu^{-1}\nabla p - \nabla \phi + \mathscr{F}, \tag{17}$$

where vorticity vector $\mathbf{w} \equiv \nabla \times \mathbf{v}$ and $\mathscr{F}$ represents all accelerations other than those exerted by pressure and gravity. (Note that symbol ω represents the growth rate, whereas $\mathbf{w}$ denotes vorticity.) Upon taking the curl of (17), combining the result with (16), and appealing to several vector identities we obtain the result

$$\frac{d\mathbf{w}}{dt} = \mathbf{w}\frac{d \ln \nu}{dt} - \nabla \times \nabla \left(\frac{v^2}{2} + \phi\right)$$

$$- \nu^{-1}(\nabla \times \nabla p) - \nu^{-2}(\nabla \nu \times \nabla p) + (\mathbf{w} \cdot \nabla)\mathbf{v} + \nabla \times \mathscr{F}. \tag{18}$$

The terms $\nabla \times \nabla(v^2/2 + \phi)$ and $\nabla \times \nabla p$ are identically zero and, if $p = p(\nu)$ (as was previously assumed with our equation of state), the term ν^{-2} $(\nabla \nu \times \nabla p)$ vanishes also. Moreover for a flat disk $(\mathbf{w} \cdot \nabla)\mathbf{v}$ is zero as well. If the nonconservative forces are due to viscosity, $\mathscr{F} = \beta \nabla^2 \mathbf{v} - (\zeta + \beta/3)\nabla(d \ln \nu/dt)$. Consequently, if β and ζ are constants, (18) becomes

$$\frac{d\mathbf{w}}{dt} = \mathbf{w}\frac{d \ln \nu}{dt} + \beta \nabla^2 \mathbf{w}. \tag{19}$$

In the absences of shear viscosity, this expression yields as an integral of motion the condition that the specific vorticity w/v is constant. If $\beta \neq 0$, the vorticity diffuses through the fluid in a fashion analogous to the conduction of heat, with the diffusion time being controlled by the shear viscous coefficient. Since the vorticity vector equals twice the angular velocity of a fluid element with respect to its instantaneous rotation axis,[4] it follows that the diffusion of vorticity describes the exchange of spins between fluid elements and their surroundings. The inviscid condition $w/v =$ constant is merely a statement of the conservation of angular momentum for each parcel of fluid. By applying Stokes' theorem to a small surface centered upon our rotating Cartesian system, it is easy to show that the unperturbed vorticity in the rotating frame $= 2A\hat{z}$, where $\hat{z}$ is a unit vector direct normal to the disk plane. (Exactly the same result follows from the definition $w = \hat{z}[(\partial v_y/\partial x) - (\partial v_x/\partial y)]$.) The inertial vorticity associated with the rotation of the coordinate frame $= 2\Omega\hat{z}$. Therefore, the inertial vorticity vector characterizing the unperturbed flow $= 2(\Omega + A)\hat{z} = 2B\hat{z}$.

In our linearized problem, the perturbed vorticity vector $= \hat{z}[(\partial v_y'/\partial x) - (\partial v_x'/\partial y)]$ $= \hat{z}[\mathscr{D} v_y' - (\partial v_x'/\partial a)]$, and the z component of vorticity of a particular Fourier term is

$$w' = k_c v_y' - k_a v_x'. \tag{20}$$

If (20) is differentiated once with respect to time and combined with (7) through (9), we arrive at the linearized version of (19), which must hold for each Fourier component

$$\frac{dw'}{dt} = \frac{2B}{v}\frac{dv'}{dt} - \beta k^2 w'. \tag{21}$$

If $\beta = 0$,

$$w' - \frac{2B}{v}v' = w_0', \tag{22a}$$

or

$$k_c v_y' - k_a v_x' = \frac{2B}{v}v' + w_0', \tag{22b}$$

where w_0' is the initial vorticity perturbation. Upon substituting the expressions for v_x' and v_y' from (11a) and (11b) into (22b), we deduce the following result for inviscid flow

$$\ddot{v}' + \frac{4k_a k_c}{k^2}A\dot{v}' + \left(k^2 v\eta + \frac{4BD}{k^2}\right)v' = -\frac{2vDw_0'}{k^2}. \tag{23}$$

If each term in this equation is multipled by $k^2/(2v D)$ and the resulting expression differentiated once with respect to time, we recover the inviscid version of (12).

The general solution of (23) consists of two linearly independent solutions of the homogeneous equation plus a particular integral, which depends upon w_0'. If the initial disturbance is contrived so that $w_0' = 0$, only the two homogeneous solutions remain, which often are waves. The behavior of such density waves has been studied extensively, especially in the context of galactic dynamics. However, in the general case in which both D and w'_0 are nonzero, the third solution exists, and it must be treated on an equal footing with the other two. In view of the fact $w'_0 \neq 0$ for the third solution to exist, it was christened a vorticity mode in Paper I. However, information about the vorticity perturbation is not restricted to that mode. For example, in the special case of a static medium ($\Omega = A = 0$), $w' = w'_0 = $ constant and the amplitudes of the two waves generally are functions of the perturbed vorticity. In the general solution of (12), all of the mode amplitudes are functions of w'_0; only with contrived initial conditions can the perturbed vorticity be isolated in the nonpropagating vorticity mode.

As originally argued by Lynden-Bell,[5] and later in detail of Elmegreen,[6] torques exerted by magnetic fields certainly play an important role in the redistribution of the angular momentum of the gas in disk galaxies. Since disk galaxies possess relatively strong magnetic fields, the analysis developed in this paper cannot be applied to them. In general, the inclusion of a magnetic field renders the viscous problem considered in the previous section much more difficult. However, if a uniform magnetic field having *constant* unperturbed components, B_x and B_y, is included, exact exponential solutions exist in a rigidly rotating medium, as well as for ring modes in a shearing medium. For the ring modes, $k_a = 0$ and the dispersion relation reads

$$\omega^4 + (7/3\beta + \zeta)k_b^2\omega^3 + [k_b^2\nu\eta + \kappa^2 + (4/3\beta + \zeta)\beta k_b^4 + v^2 k_b^2]\omega^2$$

$$+ k_b^2\left[\beta k_b^2\nu\eta + k_b^2\beta v_y^2 + k_b^2(4/3\beta + \zeta)v_x^2 + 2(B - \Omega)v_x^2\frac{B_y}{B_x}\right]\omega$$

$$+ k_b^2 v_x^2(k_b^2\nu\eta) = 0, \tag{24}$$

where $v^2 = v_x^2 + v_y^2$ is the square of the unperturbed Alfven speed. Jeans' criterion is the sufficient condition for instability if the magnetic field has a radial component ($v_x \neq 0$), which exerts a torque that allows angular momentum exchange to take place. A similar dispersion relation holds for the rigidly rotating medium, excepting that the $B - \Omega$ term is absent in the ω coefficient. Thus, the inclusion of magnetic fields increases the order of the dispersion relation, and, even in this highly simplified example, the straightforward classification of wave and vorticity modes no longer is possible.

SOLUTION OF THE EQUATIONS

Equation (12) may be solved by noting that, if its coefficients were time independent, each solution would be of the form $e^{\omega t}$. In the present case, let $v'(t) = v'_0 \exp$ [$\int \omega(t) \, dt$]. Hence, $\dot{v}' = \omega v'$, $\ddot{v}' = (\omega + \dot{\omega})v'$, and $\dddot{v}' = (\omega^3 + 3\omega\dot{\omega} + \ddot{\omega})v'$. If the coefficients of (12) are slowly varying, the terms in $\dot{\omega}$ and $\ddot{\omega}$ are relatively small and the instantaneous growth rates $\omega(t)$ may be calculated approximately by solving a cubic characteristic equation at each time. If both k_a and $k_b > 0$, self-gravitational resonance occurs at $t = k_b/(2Ak_a)$, when $k_c = 0$ and the Fourier wavelength has its maximum. Roughly speaking, when shear viscosity is present the vorticity mode will be unstable if the resonance wavelength $2\pi/k_1$ exceeds the Jeans length. Whether or not an instability would lead to significant growth depends upon the time interval near resonance over which the Jeans wavelength is exceeded, as well as the growth rate of the mode during that interval—large growth is guaranteed if $\int \omega(t)\,dt \geq 10$. For practical computation, the ratio k_b/k_a may be selected to be large enough that k_T varies sufficiently slowly with time that the roots of the characteristic equation are excellent gauges of the modal growth rates. (The value $k_b/k_a = 10$ is quite sufficient for this purpose.)

In order to establish the number of independent parameters characterizing the solutions, the problem will be recast in dimensionless variables closely similar to those used in Papers I and II. Letting l_0 be the extent if the local coordinate system in the x direction, the characteristic shearing speed $v_s = 2Al_0$. The dimensionless variable and parameters are defined as follows: $v' = vy$, $t = (2A)^{-1}\tau$, $k_{1,2} = l_0 k_{a,b}$, $k_3 = k_2 - k_1\tau$, $k_T^2 = k_1^2 + k_2^2$, $P_1 = c^2/v_s^2$, $P_2 = (\pi Gv)/(2A^2 l_0)$, $P_3 = \Omega/(2A) < 0$, $Q = v/(2Al_0^2)$, and $\mu = \zeta/\beta$. Defining t_s, t_c, t_r, t_f and t_v as the characteristic timescales associated with length l_0 for shear, sound travel, rotation, free fall, and shear viscous momentum transport, $P_1 = t_s^2/t_c^2$, $P_2 = t_s^2/t_f^2$, $|P_3| = t_s/t_r$, and $Q = t_s/t_v$. Finally, defining the dimensionless growth rate $\omega(\tau) \equiv \omega = \omega(t)/(2A)$, the characteristic equation reads

$$\omega^3 + \left[\frac{2P_3 k_1 k_3}{\mathscr{D}'} + Qk_T^2\left(\frac{7}{3} + \mu\right)\right]\omega^2$$

$$+ \left\{4P_3^2 + P_1 k_T^2 - P_2 k_T + \frac{2P_3}{\mathscr{D}'}[P_3(k_T^2 + 2k_1^2) + 3k_1^2]\right.$$

$$+ Q^2 k_T^4\left(\frac{4}{3} + \mu\right) + 2k_1 k_3\left[\frac{P_3(4/3 + \mu)}{\mathscr{D}'}k_T^2 - \frac{5}{3} - 2\mu\right]\right\}\omega$$

$$+ \left\{\frac{2k_1 k_3}{k_T}\left[\left(1 + \frac{k_1^2}{\mathscr{D}'}\right)\left(\frac{P_2}{2} - P_1 k_T\right) + \frac{P_2 k_1^2}{2\mathscr{D}'}\right] + Qk_T^2(P_1 k_T - P_2)\right\} = 0, \quad (25)$$

where $\mathscr{D}' \equiv P_3 k_T^2 + k_1^2$. From the preceding, it follows that $\omega(\tau)d\tau = \omega(t)\,dt$.

It is convenient to fit the local circular rotation law of a disk, $v(r)$, to the form $v(r) = v_0(r/r_0)^n$ where v_0, r_0, and n are constants; the corresponding local central force law $\sim r^{(2n-1)}$. With this choice for $v(r)$, $2A = (1 - n)|\Omega_0|$, $P_3 = (n - 1)^{-1}$, and epicyclic frequency $\kappa = \sqrt{2(n + 1)}|\Omega_0|$. The Keplerian shearing rate, for which $P_3 = P_{3K} = -\frac{2}{3}$, is a useful reference value. Accordingly, we defined $P_3 = -2q/3$, with $q > 1$ to characterize other reasonable rotation laws. With this convention, the law of force $\sim r^{(1-3/q)}$, $v(r) = v_0(r/r_0)^{[1-3/(2q)]}$, and the remaining dimensionless parameters scale as follows: $P_1 = P_{1K}q^2$, $P_2 = P_{2K}q^2$, and $Q = Q_K q$, where subscript K denotes the values the quantities would assume if Keplerian shear prevailed. (Keplerian motion is characterized by $n = -\frac{1}{2}$ and $q = 1$.) For flat rotation curves, $q = \frac{3}{2}$ and $P_3 = -1$, while rigid body rotation is approached as $q \to \infty$. A useful index of local disk stability is provided by the Toomre parameter, $Q_T = \kappa c/(\pi Gv)$. Inviscid disks should be locally stable if $Q_T > 1$. Expressed in terms of our dimensionless quantities,

$$Q_T = 2\sqrt{\frac{4q - 3}{q}}\,\frac{\sqrt{P_1}|P_3|}{P_2} = 2\sqrt{\frac{4q - 3}{q}}\,\frac{\sqrt{P_{1K}}|P_{3K}|}{P_{2K}}. \quad (26)$$

FIGURES 1 and 2 illustrate the instantaneous dimensionless growth rates of the three modes as functions of τ for a viscous disk having dimensionless parameters identical with those of the $q=3$ case shown in [3, fig. 8]: $P_1 = 1, P_2 = 8, P_3 = -2, Q = 2, \mu = 0, k_1 = 1$, and $k_2 = 10$. Since $Q_T = 0.866$, we might expect that density waves in an inviscid ($Q = 0$) version of this problem would be unstable. Surprisingly, however, this is not the case; when wave solutions exist, they are stabilized by Coriolis forces. At gravitational resonance ($k_3 = 0$, $k_T = k_1 = 1$, and $\tau = k_2/k_1 = 10$) density waves do not exist, and the corresponding real solutions are $\omega = \pm\sqrt{3}$. Inviscid density ring waves of the same wavelength, characterized by $k_1 = 0, k_2 = 1, P_1 = 1, P_2 = 8, P_3 = -2$, and $Q = 0$, are stable. The wave solutions of either (25) or (23) with the perturbed initial vorticity $w'_0 = 0$, are $\omega = \pm\sqrt{5}i$. Returning to FIGURE 1, it is apparent that the shear viscous coefficient is so large that density waves can exist only

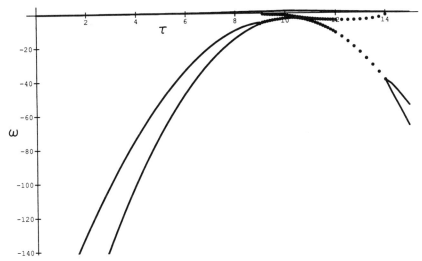

FIGURE 1. Instantaneous modal growth rates for a flat disk model, characterized by $k_1 = 1$, $k_2 = 10, P_1 = 1, P_2 = 8, P_3 = -Q = -2$, and $q = 3$ (one third Keplarian shear). The *solid curves* are real roots and the *dotted curves* are the real and imaginary (oscillatory) parts of damped waves. The imaginary parts are the *dotted curves* that start at zero where real roots either begin or vanish.

when $9 \lesssim \tau \lesssim 14$, and that they are strongly damped even in that regime. Moreover, the real growth rates, which replace the wave solutions elsewhere, decay very rapidly; for example, their growths < -100 for $\tau < 3$. Notwithstanding, an inspection of FIGURE 2 reveals that the vorticity mode grows quite respectably in the interval $2 \lesssim \tau \lesssim 18$, with $\int_2^{18} \omega(\tau)\, d\tau \approx 7.8$. Shown also as a dotted line in the figure is the growth of the vorticity mode for the infinite cylinder model of Paper II, having identical dimensionless parameters—for that model $\int_{7.3}^{12.4} \omega(\tau)\, d\tau \approx 3.0$. This comparison demonstrates in a fully time-dependent context that the flat disk is the more unstable of the two models; the disk self-gravity is stronger, thereby allowing the gas to be unstable for a longer time than in the cylindrical model. FIGURE 3

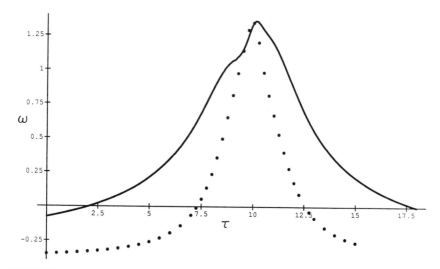

FIGURE 2. Instantaneous growth rates of the vorticity mode for the flat disk model shown in FIGURE 1 (*solid curve*). The *dotted curve* illustrates the growth rates of the vorticity mode in a cylindrical model having the same dimensionless characteristics as the flat disk model.

illustrates the growth rate of the vorticity mode in an identical flat disk model with less shear viscosity; $Q = 0.1$ and $\int_2^{18} \omega(\tau)\, d\tau \simeq 19.3$. The development of the vorticity mode in these examples demonstrates that shear viscosity can effectively cancel the Coriolis forces and yet allow structure to develop in viscous disks on scales not greatly exceeding the Jeans length.

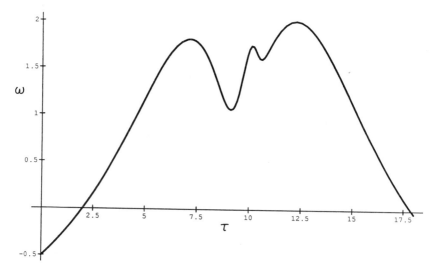

FIGURE 3. Instantaneous growth rates of the vorticity mode in a flat disk model identical with that of FIGURES 1 and 2, but with less shear viscosity, $Q_K = 0.1$.

If a shearing distrubance becomes gravitationally unstable near resonance (when $k_3 = 0$), that fact alone does not guarantee that significant growth will occur; it may swing so rapidly through resonance that gravity does not have sufficient time to act. As shown in [3, fig. 9], the maximum growth of a particular perturbation increases exponentially with q. The smaller the shearing rate, the larger the q and the greater the growth if the medium is unstable. Furthermore, if ring modes of significant amplitude are unstable, their growth is assured because they are unaffected by shear.

As a practical example of the theory, consider the development of structure in an idealized protoplanetary disk of mass $M_D = 2M_\odot$ and radius $R = 500$ AU. To simplify the calculation, the mean surface density was adopted, $\nu = M_D/(\pi R^2)$. Following Goldreich and Ward,[7] $c^2 = 5.78 \times 10^7 T$ and, recalling that the coordinate system is a local one, we let $l_0/R = 10^{-1}$. The Jeans ratio for the disk material,

$$\frac{P_2}{P_1} = \frac{2\pi G \nu l_0}{c^2} = \frac{2GM_D}{c^2 R}\left(\frac{l_0}{R}\right), \tag{27}$$

will be assumed to equal 2. Consequently, the product of the disk radius and absolute temperature, $RT = 4.591 \times 10^{17}$ cm K. The Keplerian shearing rate at radius $r \le R$, $2A = 1.5\sqrt{GM_D r^{-3}}$, and the corresponding characteristic shearing speed, $v_s = 2Al_0$. Hence,

$$P_{1K} = \frac{c^2}{(2Al_0)^2} = \frac{4c^2 R}{9GM_D}\left(\frac{R}{l_0}\right)^2\left(\frac{r}{R}\right)^3. \tag{28}$$

The ratio r/R was selected to be 0.866, yielding $P_{1K} = 2.887$, which implies $P_{2K} = 5.774$. Since the shearing rate of an extended disk of material would be less than the Keplerian value, it was assumed that $q = \sqrt{3}$. In this example, Toome's stability parameter, $Q_T = 0.680$, and the additional model characteristics were assumed to be $k_1 = 1$, $k_2 = 10$, and $Q_K = 0.1$. FIGURE 4 shows the growth rates of the modes in the neighborhood of resonance ($\tau = 10$). Not surprisingly, the density waves damp and are generally uninteresting, whereas the vorticity mode exhibits promising growth; $\int \omega(\tau)\, d\tau \simeq 11$ for that mode in the regime where $\omega > 0$. (Because of the abrupt change in the slope of $\omega(\tau)$ near $\tau = 11$, the algebraic method of developing a characteristic equation for the instantaneous growth rates breaks down. However, as demonstrated numerically in Paper II, the algebraic approach slightly underestimates the growth of the vorticity mode.) Consequently, if excited with significant amplitude, the vorticity mode in this model should lead to the development of interesting structure.

As outlined in Paper I, the mode amplitudes can be calculated if the initial distributions of density and velocity are known. If k_2/k_1 is large, the solutions of (25) provide accurate values for the growth rates. Assuming that density waves are present, the solutions have the forms $\omega_{1,2} = \omega_R \pm i\omega_I$ and ω_3. Then, letting the mode amplitudes be A, B, and C, write

$$y(\tau) = A \sin(\omega_I \tau)e^{\omega_R \tau} + B \cos(\omega_I \tau)e^{\omega_R \tau} + Ce^{\omega_3 \tau}, \tag{29}$$

whereupon $[dy(\tau)/d\tau]$ and $[d^2 y(\tau)/d\tau^2]$ may be calculated by differentiation.

Finally, $y(0) = B + C$, and the known functions of A, B, C, and the ω', $[dy(0)/d\tau]$ and $[d^2 y(0)/d\tau^2]$, can be related to $u_1(0)$, $u_2(0)$, and $y(0)$ through the dimensionless

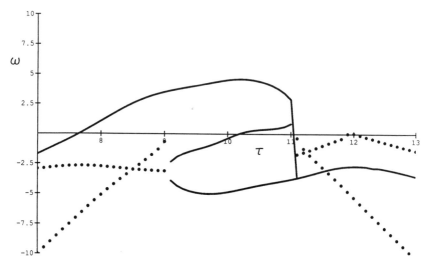

FIGURE 4. Instantaneous modal growth rates for a flat protoplanetary disk model, characterized by $M = 2M_\odot$, $R = 500$ AU, $r = 433$ AU, $T = 61$ K, $q = 3$, $P_1 = 8.661$, $P_2 = 17.322$, $Q = 0.3$, $k_1 = 1$, and $k_2 = 10$. The real roots are designated by *solid curves,* whereas the real and imaginary parts of the waves are shown as *dotted curves.* The imaginary parts are those that start at zero where real roots either begin or vanish.

versions of **(7)** and **(10b)**. Then, the mode amplitudes may be calculated as functions of $y(0)$, $u_1(0)$, $u_2(0)$, and other model characteristics $(k_1, k_2, P_1,$ etc.$)$.

CONCLUDING REMARKS

The behaviors of density waves and vortices in flat two-dimensional disks are qualitatively similar to their behaviors in cross sections of infinite cylinders, a three-dimensional problem discussed extensively in Papers I and II. However, the flat disks are more unstable then the cylinders because self-gravity is stronger in the disks. In particular, the roughly symmetric time interval, centered upon the time of gravitational resonance ($\tau = k_e/k'$) during which the Jeans criterion is satisfied, is longer for a flat disk than for its three-dimensional counterpart. A flat disk model should be roughly correct if the disk thickness (or, scale height) is significantly less than the perturbation wavelength. Hydrodynamic effects, including shear viscous actions, are essentially the same in both types of models. Shear viscous torques allow the transport of angular momentum out of a spinning, self-gravitating floccule, thereby allowing its growth to continue. (Radial magnetic fields can accomplish this same result.) Moreover, when significant shear viscosity is present ($Q \gtrsim 0.1$), the familiar density waves damp rapidly, and only the vorticity modes can persist. In viscous disks, therefore, it is the vortices that will develop and ultimately grow into structures rather than the waves. Thus, as envisioned qualitatively by von Weizsaker[8]

(1944) in the context of the solar nebula, it seems inevitable that vortices are interesting phenomena in protostellar disks.

ACKNOWLEDGMENT

I thank C. Davies for generating the figures and R. Drimmel for assisting in preparing the manuscript.

REFERENCES

1. GOLDREICH, P. & D. LYNDEN-BELL. 1965. Mon. Not. R. Astron. Soc. **130:** 125. (GB)
2. HUNTER, JR., J. H. & K. S. SCHWEIKER. 1981. Astrophys. J. **243:** 1030. (Paper I)
3. HUNTER, JR., J. H. & T. HORAK. 1983. Astrophys. J. **265:** 402. (Paper II)
4. LAMB, H. 1932. Hydrodynamics: 32. Dover. New York.
5. LYNDEN-BELL, D. 1966. Observatory **86** (571): 57.
6. ELMEGREEN, B. 1987. Astrophys. J. **312:** 626.
7. GOLDREICH, P. & W. R. WARD. 1973. Astrophys. J. **183:** 1051.
8. VON WEIZSACKER, C. F. 1944. Z. Astrophys. **22:** 319.

Unstable Interaction between a Self-gravitating Gaseous Disk and its Central Mass

G. J. SAVONIJE,[a] J. C. PAPALOIZOU,[b]
AND M. H. M. HEEMSKERK[a]

[a]Astronomical Institute "Anton Pannekoek"
University of Amsterdam
Kruislaan 403
NL 1098 SJ Amsterdam, The Netherlands
and
Center for High Energy Astrophysics
National Institute Voor Kern—En Hoge Energie Fysica-H
Kruislaan 409
NL 1098 SJ Amsterdam, The Netherlands

[b]School of Mathematics
Queen Mary & Westfield College
Mile End Road
London E14NS, United Kingdom

1. INTRODUCTION

Hydrodynamic calculations of collapsing protostars that take into account the rotation of the initial molecular cloud indicate that a substantial fraction of the protostellar material must be processed through a self-gravitating accretion disk.[1,2] Nonaxisymmetric instabilities may be important in driving mass accretion and angular momentum transport in such self-gravitating disks.[3,4] Papaloizou and Savonije[5] showed that global nonaxisymmetric modes can substantially alter the mass and angular momentum distribution of a self-gravitating disk on the dynamical timescale appropriate to its outer parts.

In the Wentzel–Kramer–Brillouin (WKB) approximation a nonaxisymmetric mode has negative energy and angular momentum in the region interior to corotation, where the pattern speed of the mode is less than the angular velocity of the gas, and positive energy and angular momentum in the region exterior to corotation. The generation of motions in one of these regions by disturbances in the other enables a mode to be self-amplifying, whereby the negative and positive energy disturbances can grow while still conserving total energy. This effect is limited because corotation lies in an evanescent region, the so-called Q-barrier, through which wave action must "tunnel" before amplification can occur. If the gradient of the vorticity per unit surface density ("vortensity") is nonzero at corotation, mode amplification can also occur by inverse Landau damping at the corotation resonance.[6–8]

In the WKB approximation[9] the well-known dispersion relation for nonaxisymmetric normal modes with amplitude $\propto \exp(i(\sigma t + m\varphi))$ is

$$(\sigma + m\Omega)^2 = \kappa^2 + k^2c^2 - 2\pi G\Sigma \,|k|, \tag{1}$$

where σ is the frequency of the normal mode, and m its azimuthal index assumed positive. Here Ω denotes the angular velocity, $\kappa^2 = (2\Omega/r)d(\Omega r^2)/dr$ is the square of the epicyclic frequency, k is the radial wavenumber, c is the speed of sound, G is the gravitational constant, and Σ is the local surface density. The corotation point (where $\sigma + m\Omega = 0$) lies between the inner Lindblad resonance [(ILR), where $\sigma + m\Omega = \kappa$] and the outer Lindblad resonance [(OLR), where $\sigma + m\Omega = -\kappa$]. For a fixed frequency σ the condition for evanescence is in general given by

$$(\sigma + m\Omega)^2 < \kappa^2(1 - 1/Q^2), \tag{2}$$

where Toomre's stability parameter $Q = \kappa c/(\pi G\Sigma)$ has to be greater than unity for stability to axisymmetric modes. When there is no disk self-gravity ($Q \to \infty$), the whole region between the two Lindblad resonances is evanescent, while with self-gravity this region shrinks to that between the points where $(\sigma + m\Omega)^2 = \kappa^2(1 - 1/Q^2)$. When $Q \to 1$ the evanescent zone around corotation collapses to zero width. When Lindblad resonances exist in the disk, waves propagate in the region outside them, taking on the character of short wavelength acoustic waves.

Adams *et al.*[11] stressed the possible importance of unstable nonaxisymmetric modes with azimuthal index $m = 1$. They have suggested that such modes may be responsible for global gravitational instabilities in disks around young stellar objects, which may ultimately lead to fragmentation and binary star formation. Modes with $m = 1$ have in general no ILR in the disk and the Q-barrier around corotation may be substantial, even occupying the whole disk, which is not a favorable situation for efficient wave amplification. However, perturbations with $m = 1$ symmetry force the central star to move away from the system's center of mass (COM). Shu *et al.*[12] interpreted the rapid growth of the *wavelike* $m = 1$ modes reported by Adams *et al.*[11] in terms of wave reflections at the OLR, the Q-barrier, and the outer edge of the disk, in resonance with the off-center motion of the central star.

We do not find evidence for this instability, but do find that the extra degrees of freedom possessed by the system through the possibility of motion of the central star are indeed enough to induce *nonwavelike* instabilities with a definite pattern speed. The interaction in the star/disk system is self-amplifying because the star's motion tends to be unstable due to the fact that in the equilibrium it is located at a maximum of the gravitational potential. When the stellar mass $M_S \to 0$, it induces a negligible perturbation to the density distribution in the disk, and the stability problem can be treated simply. This case corresponds to a test mass ($M_S \ll M_D$), which is slightly perturbed from its position in the center of the rigid disk or ring. It will fall immediately from its position at the maximum of the (now fixed gravitational potential Φ at $r = 0$) toward that part of the ring to which the perturbation directs it. In the opposite limit, $M_D \to 0$, the system becomes stable again because the massless disk cannot influence the position of the massive star. When neither the stellar nor the disk mass can be neglected, the central star moves in a spiral because the induced density disturbance in the disk is nonnegligible and it carries negative angular momentum, forcing the star to gain positive angular momentum. Since the disk's response shows a maximum on the opposite side to the star, it exerts a radial gravitational force that tends to drive the star back to its equilibrium position. Therefore the star can only be driven away from the COM (by the centrifugal force) if it is able to tap the disk's angular momentum efficiently. When the moving star has a corotation point in the disk, angular momentum exchange between the star and the induced disturbance appears efficient enough for the system to show effective dynamical instability. But when the mass of the star increases and becomes comparable to the disk mass, the motion of the star slows down and the corotation point appears to fall outside the disk. This causes the angular momentum exchange between the star and the disk to become inefficient, so that the instability weakens and eventually disappears.

2. BASIC EQUATIONS

We consider a flat differentially rotating disk orbiting a point mass M_S. We adopt a polytropic equation of state such that

$$P = K\Sigma^\gamma,$$

where P is the vertically integrated pressure, γ is the polytropic index, K is a constant, and Σ is the surface density. The local speed of sound, c, in the plane of the disk is given by $c^2 = dP/d\Sigma = \gamma K\Sigma^{\gamma-1}$. By choosing K sufficiently small we can ensure that the disk is geometrically thin. In the calculations described here, $\gamma = 2$. For a two-dimensional, self-gravitating disk the set of hydrodynamic equations can be written in cylindrical coordinates (r, φ) in the form:

$$\frac{\partial}{\partial t}\mathbf{U} + \frac{1}{r}\frac{\partial}{\partial r}r\mathbf{F}(\mathbf{U}) + \frac{1}{r}\frac{\partial}{\partial\varphi}\mathbf{G}(\mathbf{U}) = \mathbf{S}(\mathbf{U}), \tag{3}$$

where the state vector $\mathbf{U}$, the flux vectors $\mathbf{F}$, $\mathbf{G}$, and the source vector $\mathbf{S}$ are defined according to

$$\mathbf{U} = \begin{pmatrix} \Sigma \\ \Sigma v_r \\ \Sigma v_\varphi \end{pmatrix}, \qquad \mathbf{F}(\mathbf{U}) = \begin{pmatrix} \Sigma v_r \\ \Sigma v_r^2 + P \\ \Sigma v_r v_\varphi \end{pmatrix}, \qquad \mathbf{G}(\mathbf{U}) = \begin{pmatrix} \Sigma v_\varphi \\ \Sigma v_r v_\varphi \\ \Sigma v_\varphi^2 + P \end{pmatrix},$$

$$\mathbf{S}(\mathbf{U}) = \begin{vmatrix} 0 \\ \dfrac{P}{r} + \dfrac{\Sigma v_\varphi^2}{r} - \Sigma\left(\dfrac{\partial\Phi}{\partial r} + \dfrac{\partial\Psi_c}{\partial r}\right) \\ -\dfrac{\Sigma v_r v_\varphi}{r} - \Sigma\dfrac{1}{r}\left(\dfrac{\partial\Phi}{\partial\varphi} + \dfrac{\partial\Psi_c}{\partial\varphi}\right) \end{vmatrix}. \tag{4}$$

The velocity $\mathbf{v} = (v_r, v_\varphi)$ is the velocity in the plane of the disk. The gravitational potential Φ, arising from the mass distribution in the disk is given by the Poisson integral:

$$\Phi(r, \varphi) = -G\int_0^{2\pi}\int_{r_0}^{r_1} \frac{\Sigma(r', \varphi')r'\, dr'\, d\varphi'}{\sqrt{r^2 + r'^2 - 2rr'\cos(\varphi - \varphi')}}, \tag{5}$$

where r_1 is the outer radius of the disk, and Ψ_c is the gravitational potential due to the central star. Because we are studying $m = 1$ modes the central mass, M_S is displaced from the system's center of gravity during the disk's evolution, with the result that Ψ_c has a radial and azimuthal dependence. For a finite surface density at the boundaries, (3) needs to be supplemented by boundary conditions. For numerical convenience we assume simple boundary conditions, that is, v_r is adopted to be zero at both boundaries of the disk.

3. LINEAR ANALYSIS OF GLOBAL NORMAL MODES WITH $m = 1$ IN A SELF-GRAVITATING GASEOUS DISK

We consider an initially axisymmetric differentially rotating disk for which

$$\mathbf{v} = (0, r\Omega), \qquad (6)$$

where Ω is the angular velocity. In the unperturbed disk Ω, P, Σ, and Φ are functions of r alone. We now add a nonaxisymmetric disturbance and linearize the basic equations by writing:

$$v_r = v'_r(r)e^{(im\varphi + i\sigma t)} \qquad (7)$$

$$v_\varphi = r\Omega + v'_\varphi(r)e^{(im\varphi + i\sigma t)} \qquad (8)$$

$$\Sigma = \Sigma(r) + \Sigma'(r)e^{(im\varphi + i\sigma t)} \qquad (9)$$

$$P = P(r) + c^2\Sigma'(r)e^{(im\varphi + i\sigma t)} \qquad (10)$$

$$\Psi_c = \Psi_c(r) + \Psi'_c(r)e^{(im\varphi + i\sigma t)} \qquad (11)$$

$$\Phi = \Phi(r) + \Phi'(r)e^{(im\varphi + i\sigma t)}. \qquad (12)$$

Here Ψ_c is the gravitational potential of the displaced star, while m is the azimuthal mode number that is equal to 1 for the modes discussed in this paper, and σ the complex eigenfrequency. In linear theory, perturbations to the axisymmetric state are assumed small so that the basic equations may be linearized in them. For an unstable mode, the imaginary part of σ is negative. The linearized basic equations (3) then give

$$i\overline{\sigma}\Sigma' = -\frac{1}{r}\frac{d(r\Sigma v'_r)}{dr} - \frac{im\Sigma v'_\varphi}{r} \qquad (13)$$

$$i\overline{\sigma}v'_r - 2\Omega v'_\varphi = -\frac{\partial W}{\partial r} \qquad (14)$$

$$i\overline{\sigma}v'_\varphi + v'_r\frac{1}{r}\frac{dh}{dr} = -i\frac{m}{r}W, \qquad (15)$$

where $h = r^2\Omega$, $W = c^2\Sigma'/\Sigma + \Phi' + \Psi'_c$, and $\overline{\sigma} = \sigma + m\Omega$. The perturbed velocities may be eliminated from (13)–(15) in order to obtain a relation for Σ' in terms of W alone, which may be expressed in the operator form,[5]

$$\Sigma' = L(W), \qquad (16)$$

where

$$L(W) = -\frac{1}{r}\frac{d}{dr}\left(\frac{r\Sigma}{D}\left[\frac{dW}{dr} + \frac{2m\Omega\bar{\sigma}W}{\kappa^2 r}\right]\right) + \left[\frac{dW}{dr} + \frac{2m\Omega\bar{\sigma}W}{\kappa^2 r}\right]\frac{2m\Omega\bar{\sigma}\Sigma}{\kappa^2 rD}$$

$$+ \frac{mW}{\bar{\sigma}r}\frac{d}{dr}\left(\frac{\Sigma r}{h'}\right) - \frac{4m^2\Omega^2\Sigma W}{r^2\kappa^4}. \quad (17)$$

Here $h' = dh/dr$, and $D = \bar{\sigma}^2 - \kappa^2$. The perturbed gravitational potential arising from the disk may be found by linearizing the Poisson integral in the form

$$\Phi' = -G\int_{r_0}^{r_1} K_m(r, r')\Sigma'(r')r'\,dr', \quad (18)$$

where

$$K_m(r, r') = \int_0^{2\pi} \cos(m\varphi)\frac{d\varphi}{(r^2 + r'^2 - 2rr'\cos(\varphi))^{1/2}}. \quad (19)$$

For $m = 1$ modes, we must also take account of the fact that the central mass can move as a result of the perturbed disk potential. If $\mathbf{R} = (X, Y)$ denotes the location of the central mass, $\mathbf{R}$ obeys the equation of motion

$$\frac{d^2\mathbf{R}}{dt^2} = \mu^2\mathbf{R} + e^{i\sigma t}\mathbf{V}G\pi\int_{r_0}^{r_1}\frac{\Sigma'}{r'}\,dr',$$

where $\mathbf{V} = (1, i)$ and $\mu^2 = (-d^2\Phi/dr^2)$ evaluated at $r = 0$. From this we deduce that

$$\mathbf{R} = -e^{i\sigma t}\frac{\mathbf{V}G\pi}{(\mu^2 + \sigma^2)}\int_{r_0}^{r_1}\frac{\Sigma'}{r'}\,dr'.$$

The perturbation to the potential due to the central mass is then given by

$$\Psi'_c e^{im\varphi + i\sigma t} = -GM_S\frac{(\mathbf{r}\cdot\mathbf{R})}{r^3} = e^{i\sigma t}\frac{(\mathbf{r}\cdot\mathbf{V})G^2 M_S\pi}{r^3(\mu^2 + \sigma^2)}\int_{r_0}^{r_1}\frac{\Sigma'}{r'}\,dr'.$$

From the definition of W [see (13)–(15)] we deduce that

$$W = c^2\frac{\Sigma'}{\Sigma} - G\int_{r_0}^{r_1}K_m(r, r')\Sigma'(r')r'\,dr' + \frac{G^2 M_S\pi\delta_{m1}}{r^2(\mu^2 + \sigma^2)}\int_{r_0}^{r_1}\frac{\Sigma'}{r'}\,dr', \quad (20)$$

Equations (16) and (20) from a pair of simultaneous equations for Σ' and W. Assuming we can invert the operator L, we find $W = L^{-1}(\Sigma')$, and hence we obtain the single equation for Σ' in the form

$$O(\Sigma') = L^{-1}(\Sigma') - c^2\frac{\Sigma'}{\Sigma} + G\int_{r_0}^{r_1}K_m(r, r')\Sigma'(r')r'\,dr'$$

$$= \frac{G^2 M_S\pi\delta_{m1}}{r^2(\mu^2 + \sigma^2)}\int_{r_0}^{r_1}\frac{\Sigma'}{r'}\,dr', \quad (21)$$

which defines the operator O. In this section we adopt the convention that m and Ω are positive, so that σ must be real and negative for a corotation resonance to be possible. Note that this differs from the sections describing the numerical work where the mode frequency is taken to be positive. We first note that if σ is real, the only positive genuine singularity is at the corotation resonance for which $\bar{\sigma} = \sigma + m\Omega = 0$. For general complex σ, apart from very special circumstances for which L is noninvertible (which, it can be shown, may in fact be ignored by reformulation of the eigenvalue problem), L may be inverted by the standard Green's function technique,[5] such that

$$W = L^{-1}(\Sigma') = \int_{r_0}^{r_1} r'\Sigma'(r')H(r', r)\,dr', \tag{22}$$

where the kernel $H(r', r)$ is symmetric in r and r'. Then the operator O may be written in the form

$$O(\Sigma') = \int_{r_0}^{r_1} r'\Sigma'(r')S(r', r)\,dr' - c^2 \frac{\Sigma'}{\Sigma}, \tag{23}$$

where the kernel

$$S(r, r') = GK_m(r, r') + H(r, r').$$

We remark that when σ is real and such that there is no effective corotation singularity, the operator O is self-adjoint with weight r. If the central mass were to be artificially held fixed, the equation determining the normal modes would be

$$O(\Sigma') = 0.$$

The operator O is, of course, a function of σ, and the inverse operator $\mathfrak{R} = O^{-1}$ is singular when σ belongs to the spectrum of O, or in other words, it corresponds to a normal mode of the system, with the center artificially held fixed.

3.1. A Dispersion Relation for m = 1 Modes

For $m = 1$, (21) may be written in the equivalent form

$$\Sigma'(r) = \frac{\pi G^2 M_S}{(\mu^2 + \sigma^2)} \mathfrak{R}\left(\frac{1}{r^2}\right) \int_{r_0}^{r_1} \frac{\Sigma'}{r'}\,dr'.$$

Multiplying by r^{-1} and integrating over the disk, we obtain an equation that does not contain Σ' and that can be regarded as a dispersion relation in the form

$$\sigma^2 + \mu^2 = \pi G^2 M_S F(\sigma), \tag{24}$$

where

$$F(\sigma) = \int_{r_0}^{r_1} r \left(\frac{1}{r^2}\right) \mathfrak{R}\left(\frac{1}{r^2}\right) dr.$$

From (23) we see that the problem of determining $\mathfrak{R} \equiv O^{-1}$ is equivalent, after a simple transformation,[5] to solving a standard Fredholm integral equation. From the standard theory,[13] the integral $F(\sigma)$ is an analytic function of σ everywhere in the complex σ-plane, excluding a line on the real axis that contains the values of σ for which there is a corotation singularity, and for which the eigenvalue problem as described earlier has not been formulated. Outside this branch line, which defines a continuum, the spectrum of O must be discrete, and the only singularities in $F(\sigma)$ will be poles.

3.1.1. The Limiting Case $M_S/M_D \to 0$

In this case we use the dispersion relation in the form of (24). In the limit $M_S \to 0$, this gives $\sigma^2 = -\mu^2$, where μ^2 is given by $-(d^2\Phi/dr^2)$, evaluated at the center of the disk. Alternatively,

$$\mu^2 = \pi G \int_{r_0}^{r_1} r^{-2} \Sigma\,(r)\,dr, \tag{25}$$

where μ^2 is positive because the potential has a maximum at the disk center. Thus $\sigma = -i\mu$ gives a purely growing instability. This, of course, is just the instability that would be experienced by an infinitesimal mass at the center of a rigid ring or disk.

3.1.2. Stabilization for Large M_S/M_D

When M_S is small, but no longer negligible, the fact that $F(\sigma)$ is analytic, apart from possible poles, in the neighborhood of $\sigma = -i\mu$, guarantees that there will be a solution of (24) giving a normal mode with σ close to $-i\mu$. When the central mass is small compared to the disk mass, the induced response in the disk and its gravitational feedback on the central mass must be small, and so the growth rate is but slightly altered. But note that although the mode starts as purely growing, it is clear from the functional form of $F(\sigma)$ that this quantity will not be purely real for purely imaginary σ. Thus $\mathrm{Re}(\sigma)$ cannot be zero for finite M_S, and the mode must develop a pattern rotation. This, of course, must be in the direction of rotation of the system. Hence, for small M_S there exists an unstable mode with small pattern speed Ω_p. In the numerical calculations Ω_p is generally found to correspond to the rotation speed near the disk's outer edge. This implies that there is no outer (nor inner) Lindblad resonance and that the response in the disk is entirely evanescent.[14] Mathematically the eigenfrequency is far away from any singularities in $F(\sigma)$. Unfortunately, $F(\sigma)$ is difficult to analyze. However, if we ignore pressure and self-gravity in the disk when evaluating the linear response, the operator $\mathfrak{R}$ becomes identical to L in the dispersion equation (24), and $F(\sigma)$ can be evaluated explicitly. In order to do this, a fixed background potential is needed to maintain the initial equilibrium.

As confirmed by numerical experiments,[14] for small M_S, the previously mentioned instability persists, and its existence is independent of the form of $F(\sigma)$. In this case we can write

$$F(\sigma) = \int_{r_0}^{r_1} r\left(\frac{1}{r^2}\right) L\left(\frac{1}{r^2}\right) dr. \tag{26}$$

Using (17) we obtain, after an integration by parts, for $m = 1$

$$\int_{r_0}^{r_1} rWL(W)\,dr = \int_{r_0}^{r_1} \left(\frac{r\Sigma}{D}\left[\frac{dW}{dr} + \frac{2\Omega\bar{\sigma}W}{\kappa^2 r}\right]^2 + W^2\left(\frac{1}{\bar{\sigma}}\frac{d}{dr}\left(\frac{\Sigma r}{h'}\right) - \frac{4\Omega^2\Sigma}{r\kappa^4}\right)\right) dr. \tag{27}$$

By assuming $M_S/M_D \gg 1$, we may suppose that $(\Omega - \Omega_K)/\Omega = O(M_D/M_S)$ and $\Omega_K^2 =$

GM_S/r^3. Then we also expect $(\kappa - \Omega)/\Omega = O(M_D/M_S) > 0$ in the initial equilibrium. Bearing these conditions in mind we look for small eigenfrequencies such that $\sigma = O(\Omega M_D/M_S)$. By substituting $W = 1/r^2$ into (27) we find after some algebra[14] the following expression for $F(\sigma)$ correct to order $(M_D/M_S)^2$:

$$F(\sigma) = \int_{r_0}^{r_1} \frac{\Sigma}{r^5\Omega^2} dr - 2\sigma \int_{r_0}^{r_1} \frac{\Sigma (\kappa - \Omega)}{r^5\Omega^3 (\kappa - \Omega - \sigma)} dr. \tag{28}$$

After substituting this expression for $F(\sigma)$ and (25) for μ^2, together with Kepler's law where it may be used consistently, in the dispersion relation (24), we obtain an equation for σ, in the form

$$Z(\sigma, 1) = 0,$$

where

$$Z(\sigma, \epsilon) = \sigma^2 + \int_{r_0}^{r_1} \frac{\pi G\Sigma}{r^2} \left(1 - \frac{\Omega_K^2}{\Omega^2}\right) dr + 2\epsilon\sigma \int_{r_0}^{r_1} \frac{\pi G\Sigma}{r^2\Omega} \frac{(\kappa - \Omega)}{(\kappa - \Omega - \sigma)} dr,$$

and ϵ is a real parameter, introduced for convenience, such that $0 < \epsilon < 1$. We shall assume in what follows that the rotation in the disk is on average super-Keplerian, so that the integral

$$\int_{r_0}^{r_1} \frac{\pi G\Sigma}{r^2} \left(1 - \frac{\Omega_K^2}{\Omega^2}\right) dr > 0. \tag{29}$$

This is satisfied for the numerical models considered in this paper. By considering the behavior of $Z(\sigma, \epsilon)$ in the complex σ-plane, one can establish that there are two discrete roots of $Z(\sigma, \epsilon) = 0$ that must either be complex conjugates or on the negative real axis. This follows because when $\epsilon = 0$ and condition (29) is satisfied, there is a pair of purely imaginary roots. In addition, all unstable disturbances must rotate in a prograde sense, so that as ϵ is increased the only way the roots can become real is by moving onto the negative real axis. By inspection of the form of Z, the roots cannot move from there through the origin and onto the positive real axis although they might become complex conjugates again. Hence we conclude that there are either two negative real roots or a complex pair. To establish that there is a complex pair, it is sufficient to show that on the negative real axis

$$\sigma^2 > - \int_{r_0}^{r_1} \frac{\pi GE}{r^2} \left(1 - \frac{\Omega_K^2}{\Omega^2}\right) dr - 2\sigma \int_{r_0}^{r_1} \frac{\pi G\Sigma}{r^2\Omega} \frac{(\kappa - \Omega)}{(\kappa - \Omega - \sigma)} dr.$$

Because the second term on the right-hand side of the preceding inequality is increased in magnitude if σ is replaced by zero in the denominator, it is sufficient to demonstrate that the inequality holds if that replacement is made. This stronger inequality will be guaranteed if the roots of the quadratic are complex, or equivalently if

$$\left[\int_{r_0}^{r_1} \frac{\pi G\Sigma}{r^2\Omega} dr\right]^2 < \int_{r_0}^{r_1} \frac{\pi G\Sigma}{r^2} \left(1 - \frac{\Omega_K^2}{\Omega^2}\right) dr.$$

We can write this in terms of the stellar and disk mass as

$$M_S > \frac{1}{2} \left[\int_0^{M_D} \frac{1}{r^{3/2}} \, dM \right]^2 \left[\int_0^{M_D} \frac{1}{r^3} \left(1 - \frac{\Omega_K^2}{\Omega^2} \right) dM \right]^{-1}$$

If this condition is satisifed, there remains only a weak instability, the eigenfrequency approximately being given by one of the roots of the preceding quadratic. These roots tend to zero in modulus as the disk mass approaches zero, and we attain the strict Keplerian limit. In fact, for small M_D these roots owe their existence to the fact that because we neglected self-gravity and pressure when treating the perturbations, we must suppose there is a fixed background potential maintaining the equilibrium. Then the system is not invariant to a uniform translation and does not have zero-frequency modes corresponding to this. Instead there are the two low-frequency roots just given. These can make the disk more unstable when self-gravity is removed, as observed in our numerical calculations.[14] When we approach the strict Keplerian limit, however, self-consistency is regained and the two low-frequency roots coallesce at zero.

For the realistic case in which self-gravity is retained, the preceding low-frequency roots are zero and the system stabilizes to long wavelength perturbations for M_S/M_D larger than some critical value. Indeed, we would expect instability to persist to a finite value of M_S/M_D from general analytic considerations. In the next section we discuss some numerical calculations that indicate that the critical mass ratio M_S/M_D is in fact approximately unity.

4. NONLINEAR NUMERICAL SOLUTIONS

4.1. Numerical Method

The numerical method we use can be characterized as a two-dimensional, explicit finite difference scheme on an Eulerian nonequidistant grid, using the flux-vector splitting method[14,15] to calculate the fluxes in the advection terms, and the ADI-method[16] to advance the equations in time. For the results of test calculations see reference 17. We use a cylindrical grid with 100 zones in the radial and 64 zones in the azimuthal direction to integrate the set of (3). The computational grid was equally spaced in φ, while the zone centers of the radial grid were distributed to be equally spaced in $r^{1/2}$, so that the zones are more closely packed toward the center. The disk's gravitational potential was calculated using a fast Fourier transform in azimuth, coupled with a direct summation over radial annuli.

4.2. Equilibrium Model

We consider an axisymmetric stationary equilibrium disk centered on the star $(r = 0)$ with a surface density profile

$$\Sigma(r) = \Sigma_0 (r - r_0 + 0.05)^2 (r_1 - r + 0.05)^{5/2}, \tag{30}$$

where Σ_0 is a normalization constant, and r_0 and r_1 are the inner and outer disk boundary radii. We introduce units in which the gravitational constant G, the outer radius of the disk r_1, and the total mass of the system (disk plus central star) $M = M_D + M_S$ are all equal to unity. In these units the dynamical timescales at the disk's outer boundary is slightly less than 2π in all our models. For a given value of M_S we determine Σ_0 in (30) by requiring the total system mass to equal unity. In all our models we take the inner radius of the disk $r_0 = 0.10$. According to the local Toomre criterion,[18] the equilibrium disks are stable against small axisymmetric perturbations.

4.3. The Initial Perturbation

Before we started our numerical calculations we introduced a small $m = 1$ perturbation by changing the disk's surface density according to:

$$\Sigma\,(r, \varphi) = \Sigma\,(r)\left(1 + 10^{-3}\sin\left(\frac{\pi(r - r_0)}{r_1 - r_0}\right)\cos\varphi\right),\qquad(31)$$

where $\Sigma(r)$ is given by (30). The $m = 1$ perturbation shifts the disk's center of mass away from its geometrical center and, because no external forces are supposed to act on the system, the central star must be shifted correspondingly so as to keep the system's center of mass invariant. Conservation of momentum of the star/disk system therefore determines the position vector of the central star, relative to the COM as:

$$\mathbf{R} = -\frac{1}{M_S}\int_{r_1}^{r_0}\int_0^{2\pi}\Sigma\,(r, \varphi)\mathbf{r}\,dr\,d\varphi,\qquad(32)$$

which vanishes for an axisymmetric density distribution in the disk.

4.4. Numerical Results

We followed the evolution of the disk by solving (3) as an initial value problem with help of the method described in Section 4.1. The position of the star was determined by integrating its equation of motion in the form

$$\ddot{\mathbf{R}} = -\nabla\Phi,\qquad(33)$$

with the potential gradient due to the surrounding disk being evaluated at the star's location. This yields results consistent with (32) when self-gravity is included self-consistently in a coordinate system with origin at the fixed COM.

We also carried out test calculations in a frame of reference centered at the star. In this noninertial frame, the equation of motion of the gas has to be corrected for the acceleration of the star. These calculations also yielded similar results. Our numerical calculations show that for all masses $M_S < 0.5$ the disk's response exhibits large growth rates in spite of the fact that it is evanescent throughout the disk (see TABLE 1). Apparently, the amplification of the disk's response is not caused by the tunneling of wave action through the corotation region, but by the unstable interaction with the motion of the central star.

4.5. The Motion of the Star in the Potential Field of the Disk

For all stellar masses $M_S < M_D$ the system appears very unstable whereby the star moves exponentially away from the COM along a spiral-like trajectory until the inner disk boundary is approached and the calculations have to be stopped for numerical reasons. For negligible stellar mass the slightly perturbed mass immediately falls down from the maximum of the (fixed) potential of the disk. As expected from our linear analysis, the motion of the star away from the COM slows down with increasing stellar mass. For nonnegligible stellar mass the potential of the disk is no longer fixed, because the disk's density distribution responds to the displaced stellar mass. Note that a finite mass star can only be displaced if there is a corresponding density disturbance in the disk, since the star's position is restricted by the conservation of total momentum in the form of (32). For massive stars this precludes a free-fall to the disk's inner boundary. For stars with $M_S \geq 0.2$ a nonnegligible density disturbance develops in the disk, opposite to the star, that tends to pull the star back toward the COM. However, the disturbance in the disk also exerts a torque on the star by which the latter absorbs prograde angular momentum. For $M_S < M_D$ the centrifugal force associated with the absorbed angular momentum appears sufficient to drive the star away from the COM.

FIGURE 1 shows the motion of the star for $M_S = 0.3$. Initially the star falls back to the COM as the invoked density perturbation in the disk is smeared out by the differential rotation and the excited $m = 1$ response is still too weak to allow the star to move away from the COM. The lower right panel in FIGURE 1 shows the angular velocity of the star $\Omega_S = \dot{\varphi}_S$ about the COM as a function of time. Velocity Ω_S changes sign as the star approaches the COM and swings back to larger radii when the disk response gains strength.

4.6. Growth Rates of Unstable m = 1 Modes

TABLE 1 shows the growth rates γ and pattern speeds Ω_p of the unstable $m = 1$ modes found in our numerical calculations. It should be noted that the quoted pattern speeds are only approximate values, because the evolution is too fast to allow an accurate determination. For stellar masses $M_S = 0.1$–0.3, the angular velocity of the star about the COM settles at a value of about 1.3, which coincides with the

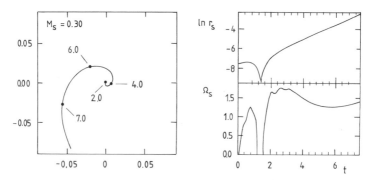

FIGURE 1. (left panel) The trajectory of the star with $M_S = 0.3$ about the COM; the elapsed time is indicated at the *marked positions* of the star. **(right panel)** The distance ($\ln r_S$) of the star from the COM and the star's angular velocity Ω_S about the COM, all as a function of time.

TABLE 1. Characteristics of the Unstable Modes[a]

M_S	m	γ	Ω_p	r_c	r_{ILR}	r_{OLR}	EV
0.1	1	1.9	1.3	0.9	—	—	All disk
0.2	1	1.3	1.4	0.9	—	—	All disk
0.3	1	0.8	1.3	0.9	—	—	All disk
0.4	1	0.4	1.1	1.0	—	—	All disk
0.5	1	0.1	1.0	≥ 1.0	—	—	All disk
0.1	2	3.2	1.3	0.9	0.23	—	$r > 0.46$
0.2	2	2.2	1.4	0.9	0.29	—	$r > 0.41$
0.3	2	1.2	1.3	0.9	0.35	—	$r > 0.44$
0.4	2	0.9	1.1	1.0	0.38	—	$r > 0.52$
0.5	2	0.5	1.0	≥ 1.0	0.44	—	$r > 0.60$

[a]The upper panel refers to the $m = 1$ modes, the lower panel to the nonlinearly induced $m = 2$ modes. Shown are the growth rates γ; pattern speeds Ω_p; the position of the corotation circle r_c, ILR, OLR; and the evanescent region, EV, around corotation (all in the WKB-approximation).

orbital angular velocity of disk gas near the disk's outer boundary. With increasing stellar mass the angular speed of the star about the COM and the pattern speed Ω_p of the disk's response slow down (TABLE 1), so that the corotation point in the disk moves toward the outer boundary. For $M_S = 0.5$ the corotation point hovers around the outer disk edge and amplification of the mode is weak and occurs only intermittently. For still larger stellar masses the corotation point shifts outside the disk ($\Omega_p < 1$), rendering the angular momentum exchange between the disk's response and the star inefficient, so that the instability vanishes.

Although we started the calculations with a pure $m = 1$ perturbation, nonlinear effects generate disturbances with azimuthal index $m = 2, 3, \ldots$. The nonlinearly generated $m = 2$ disturbances or modes have the same pattern speeds but grow

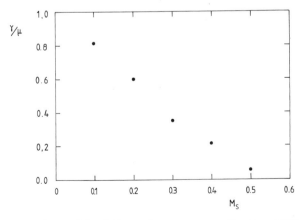

FIGURE 2. The growth rate of the disk's $m = 1$ response, normalized to μ [(25)], as a function of the stellar mass M_S. For $M_S \to 0$, the instability approaches that of an infinitesimal test mass at the center of a rigid ring.

faster than the original $m = 1$ modes (TABLE 1). Note that, once the central star is displaced from the COM, $m = 2$ disturbances with pattern speeds identical to the original $m = 1$ mode are produced naturally by nonlinear forcing. However, because these $m = 2$ modes start with much smaller amplitudes, they have no time to outgrow the $m = 1$ modes, and remain much weaker.

For the unstable cases ($M_S < 0.5$) the calculations had to be terminated once the orbital radius of the star approached the inner disk edge and the surface density became zero in some places near this edge. FIGURE 2 summarizes the growth rate of the nonwavelike $m = 1$ modes normalized to the limiting value μ [(25)], as a function of stellar mass M_S. It can be seen that for $M_S \to 0$ the normalized growth rate indeed tends to unity, while it becomes small when $M_S \to M_D$.

5. DISCUSSION

In this paper we have presented time evolution calculations of a disk orbiting a central star that is unstable to $m = 1$ modes. The instability occurs because the motion of the central star in the potential field of the disk is unstable. The motion of the star induces a response in the disk that, although it is evanescent, carries negative angular momentum. This in turn forces the star to pick up prograde angular momentum. When the central mass is small, this effect is insignificant and the central mass plummets almost radially toward the inner edge of the disk. As the mass of the central star increases, to become comparable to the disk mass, the angular momentum transfer increases in importance and the star moves in a spiral orbit. For large central masses ($M_S \geq M_D$) the star/disk system becomes stable. However, the *disk* remains unstable to wavelike global modes with $m > 1$, which show growth rates not much smaller than found earlier in this paper.[5]

We have found no evidence in any of our calculations for $m = 1$ modes of the type reported by Adams *et al.*[11] None of our $m = 1$ modes, calculated when the central star is allowed to move, have outer Lindblad resonances in the disk as exhibited by the modes of Adams *et al.* Curiously, we were able to obtain $m = 1$ modes with outer Lindblad resonances when the central star was fixed at the COM. However, these modes cannot be unstable through the mechanism proposed by Shu *et al.*[12] precisely because the central star has been fixed. Instead they can be destabilized by tunneling of wave action through the evanescent region around corotation and/or by the effect of the corotation resonance. The discrepancy between our results and those of Adams *et al.*[11] can be explained by the fact that the latter, working in the noninertial frame comoving with the star, did not fully incorporate the "indirect" potential, as they state in a note added in proof. They neglected the contribution from the distorted outer disk boundary (the "edge-effect"), which is important when the surface density does not tail off to zero there. In the later WKB analysis by Shu *et al.*,[12] it is stated in accordance with one's expectations from the analysis, that for the correct value (unity) of their parameter c, which is introduced as a multiplicative factor of previously mentioned correction, their reported $m = 1$ instabilities become at best weak.

REFERENCES

1. TEREBEY, S., F. H. SHU & P. CASSEN. 1984. Astrophys. J. **284**: 529.
2. BODENHEIMER, P., M. ROZYCZKA, H. W. YORKE & J. E. TOHLINE. 1988. *In* Formation and Evolution of Low Mass Stars, A. K. Dupree and M. T. V. Lago, Eds. Kluwer. Dordrecht, the Netherlands.
3. PACZYNSKI, B. 1977. Acta Astron. **28**: 91.
4. LIN, D. N. C. & J. E. PRINGLE. 1987. Mon. Not. R. Astron. Soc. **225**: 607.
5. PAPALOIZOU, J. C. & G. J. SAVONIJE. 1991. Mon. Not. R. Astron. Soc. **248**: 353.
6. PAPALOIZOU, J. C. & J. E. PRINGLE. 1987. Mon. Not. R. Astron. Soc. **225**: 267.
7. NARAYAN, R., P. GOLDREICH & J. GOODMAN. 1987. Mon. Not. R. Astron. Soc. **228**: 1.
8. SAVONIJE, G. J. & M. H. M. HEEMSKERK. 1990. Astron. Astrophys. **240**: 191.
9. BINNEY, J. & S. TREMAINE. 1987. Galactic Dynamics. Princeton Univ. Press. Princeton, N.J.
10. LIN, D. N. C., J. C. PAPALOIZOU & G. J. SAVONIJE. 1990. Astrophys. J. **364**: 326.
11. ADAMS, F. C., S. P. RUDEN & F. H. SHU. 1989. Astrophys. J. **347**: 959.
12. SHU, F. H., S. TREMAINE, F. C. ADAMS & S. P. RUDEN. 1990. Astrophys. J. **358**: 495.
13. COURANT, R. & D. HILBERT. 1953. Methods of Mathematical Physics. Wiley-Interscience. New York.
14. HEEMSKERK, M. H. M., J. C. B. PAPALOIZOU & G. J. SAVONIJE. 1992. Astron. Astrophys. **260**: 161.
15. VAN LEER, B. 1982. Lect. Notes Phys. **170**: 505.
16. BEAM, R. M. & R. F. WARMING. 1978. AIAA J. **16**(4): 393.
17. ARNOLD, C. N. 1985. Ph.D. thesis, Univ. Microfilms, Univ. of Michigan, Ann Arbor, Mich.
18. TOOMRE, A. 1977. Annu. Rev. Astron. Astrophys. **15**: 437.

Radial Oscillations in Viscous Accretion Disks in Low-mass X-ray Binary Systems[a]

RONALD E. TAAM AND XINGMING CHEN

Department of Physics and Astronomy
Northwestern University
Evanston, Illinois 60208

INTRODUCTION

The discovery[1] of quasi-periodic oscillations (QPOs) in the light curves of some low-mass X-ray binary systems has stimulated considerable theoretical activity directed toward understanding the nature and origin of these oscillations. Since the oscillations may provide a useful probe of the inner regions of the accretion disk in these systems, a detailed theory for these modulations may place important constraints on the physics of accretion in these objects.

The QPOs can be categorized into two classes.[2] In an X-ray color–color diagram, low-frequency oscillations (~ 5–8 Hz) are observed when the source is radiating near the Eddington limit on the so-called normal branch, whereas higher frequency oscillations (~ 20–50 Hz) are observed at lower luminosities on the horizontal branch. The mechanism responsible for the production of these oscillations has not been definitively identified. Most work to date has concentrated on the origin of the high-frequency oscillations in the context of the magnetospheric beat frequency modulated accretion model.[3,4] The theory for the origin of the normal branch oscillations is less well developed, and the proposed models attribute the oscillations to either a radiation instability in a spherical accretion flow[5] or to temporal variations in the structure of an accretion disk.[6] A common characteristic of both models for the low-frequency oscillations are the requirements that the oscillations reflect variations in the optical thickness of the accreting matter and that the source radiates near its Eddington luminosity.

With respect to models for the low-frequency oscillations, in which temporal variations in the accretion disk are invoked, QPOs may result from viscous or thermal instabilities in the inner region of the disk.[7] It has been recognized that the disk can be pulsationally unstable to axisymmetric perturbations in a variety of circumstances,[8,9] and there are some suggestions that phenomena similar to QPOs may have their origin in disks around white dwarfs[10] or around black holes.[11,12] In particular, Kato[8] demonstrated that an α disk model is pulsationally unstable in an optically thin state or in an optically thick state when electron scattering opacity and radiation pressure effects dominate. This result has been confirmed and generalized by Blumenthal *et al.*,[9] in which it was shown that the disk is pulsationally unstable in regions of the disk that are both thermally and viscously stable. The regions of the disk that participate in the oscillation are overstable, and the oscillations themselves

[a]This research was supported by NASA under Grant NAGW-2526.

are a consequence of the wavelike nature of the perturbations.[9] The results of these investigations, although interesting, are limited, however, since the dispersion relation for the waves were derived from a local linear stability analysis. Whether or not the disk exhibits global oscillations must be determined via a nonlinear time-dependent hydrodynamical calculation.

This global approach has been adopted by a number of groups;[10–13] however, the results, in aggregate, do not present a clear picture of the global evolution of disks surrounding compact objects. In this paper we briefly report on some new results[14] that suggest that the accretion disks surrounding weakly or nonmagnetic neutron stars in low-mass X-ray binary systems are likely to be stable with respect to axisymmetric perturbations.

RESULTS

We consider an accretion disk that can be described as geometrically thin, non-self-gravitating, axisymmetric, and optically thick. Gravity is assumed to be given by the Newtonian description (i.e., general relativistic effects are neglected). The local vertical scale height of the disk, H, is assumed small compared to the cylindrical coordinate, r, so that the equations describing the disk structure may be vertically averaged. We allow for departures from Keplerian motion and include a radial pressure gradient and a radial viscous force.[10,14] The latter term can be important, especially when departures from Keplerian motion are present or when the radial velocity and radial velocity gradients are large. The dominant sources of opacity are assumed to be free-free absorption and electron scattering. For the viscosity we assume a simple α model prescription introduced by Shakura and Sunyaev.[15] In this paper, we take the form of viscosity, ν, as

$$\nu = \tfrac{2}{3}\, \alpha C_s H, \tag{1}$$

where the dimensionless viscosity parameter, α, is less than unity and C_s is the local speed of sound. To avoid complications associated with instabilities resulting from the dominance of radiation pressure effects in the viscous stress,[16] we adopt the form of viscosity as proposed by Sakimoto and Coroniti[17] where the gas pressure is used for both the sound speed and scale height (the total pressure gradient is used in the radial equation of motion, however). The more general form for the viscosity is treated in Chen and Taam.[14] The viscous stresses in the azimuthal, ϕ, and radial direction, r, are given as[10,14]

$$F_\phi = \frac{1}{r^2} \frac{\partial}{\partial r}\left[\nu \Sigma r^3 \frac{\partial \Omega}{\partial r} \right] \tag{2}$$

and

$$F_r = \frac{\partial\{\tfrac{4}{3}(\nu_r \Sigma / r)[\partial(rV_r/\partial r)]\}}{\partial r} - \frac{2V_r}{r} \frac{\partial(\nu_r \Sigma)}{\partial r} \tag{3}$$

where Σ, Ω, and V_r are the column density, angular velocity, and radial drift velocity at a given radius, r, respectively. In (3) we have allowed for the possibility that the viscosity acting in the radial direction, v_r, can be different than in the azimuthal direction.

As an example of the time-dependent behavior of the disk, we have followed the nonlinear development of a locally unstable disk characterized by a mass accretion rate, $\dot{M}$, equal to the Eddington value, $\dot{M}_E$, a mass for the central object equal to $1.4M_\odot$, and the magnitude of the viscosity parameter, α, equal to 0.1. In the calculations to be presented, we use a total of 460 grid points and a grid resolution, $\Delta r/r$, equal to 0.01.

As a standard sequence we illustrate the temporal variation of the mass flow rate at a representative radius (2.72×10^7 cm) in the disk in FIGURE 1 for the case in which the radial viscous forces were neglected (i.e., $v_r = 0$ everywhere). It can be seen that matter in the disk is set into radial oscillation with a modulation timescale corresponding to its local Keplerian timescale (~ 0.07 s). The amplitude of the oscillation initially increases to over 80 times the steady-state rate. Such large variations in the mass flow rate reflect variations in the radial drift velocity since the relative variations in the column density are small ($\Delta\Sigma/\Sigma \sim 10^{-3}$). After about 4 s the amplitude of the oscillations declines to 10 percent of the Eddington value. A magnified view of the mass flow rate variations is shown in FIGURE 2, where it is seen that the long-term variability is not strictly periodic, with the form and amplitude of the oscillation changing from one period to the next.

The spatial dependence of the oscillatory behavior in the disk is exhibited in a

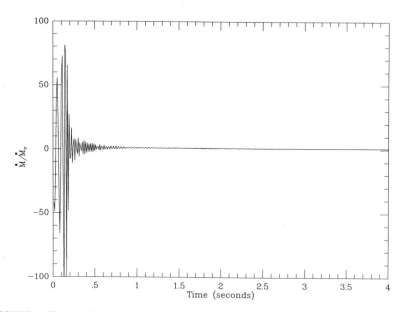

FIGURE 1. The mass flow rate as a function of time in the disk at a radius of 2.72×10^7 cm for the case in which viscous forces in the radial direction are neglected. The mass flow rate is normalized to the Eddington value. The amplitude of the oscillation initially rises to over 80 times the steady-state rate and then declines to a level at ~ 0.1 times the Eddington value. The temporal variations occur on the local Keplerian timescale of the disk.

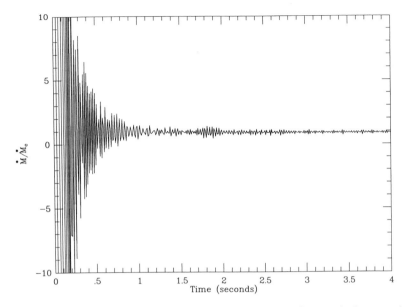

FIGURE 2. Same as for FIGURE 1 except that the scale of the mass flow rate is chosen so that the modulations at late times are evident. The small amplitude oscillations are not strictly periodic and are seen to vary from one period to the next.

series of illustrations in FIGURE 3 at different points in time. The time development clearly demonstrates that a larger part of the disk evolves to a steady state with increasing time. As the initial disturbances propagate outward, the length scale characterizing the variations of mass flow rate, initially given by the most unstable wavelength of the unstable mode, evolve to smaller scales and are eventually damped out. It is seen, on the other hand, that oscillations persist in the inner regions of the disk. Although this feature is present for a variety of boundary conditions at the inner edge of the disk, the existence and extent of this unstable region should be regarded as preliminary until a detailed investigation of the processes taking place near the inner disk edge is undertaken.

In the next sequence we examine the global stability of the disk when radial viscous stresses are included. In this calculation, we assume that the viscosity acting in the radial direction is the same as that in the azimuthal direction (i.e., $\nu_r = \nu$). The time-dependent results clearly show that the disk is stable. For example, in FIGURE 4 shows the variation of the mass flow rate in the disk at the same radius as in FIGURE 1. It is easily seen that the oscillation is significantly damped after about 0.3 s. Although the departure from Keplerian motion was small ($1 - \Omega/\Omega_k \sim 10^{-3}$, where Ω_k is the Keplerian angular velocity) and the disk remained geometrically thin ($H \sim 0.01\,r$) throughout, radial viscous effects were important in the evolution. The maximum radial velocities exceeded the steady-state values by factors of ~ 100 during the nonlinear development, and in these phases the radial viscous force term was sufficiently large ($\lesssim 10$ percent of other radial forces) to damp out the oscilla-

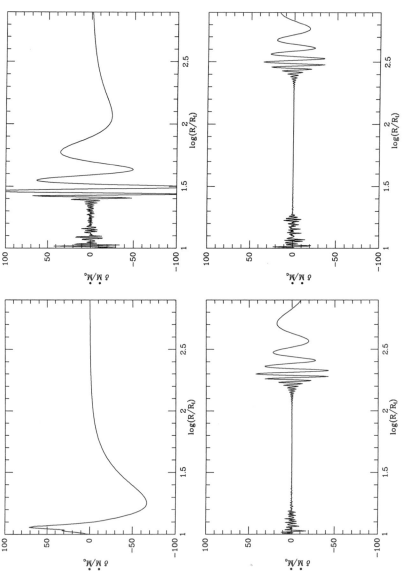

FIGURE 3. The radial variation of the deviation of the mass flow rate from the assumed steady-state value for four different times in the evolution of a disk in which the radial viscous force is neglected. The radius of the disk is scaled to the radius of the inner edge, R_I, and the deviations of the mass flow rate are given in terms of the Eddington value. The **top left panel** corresponds to an evolution time of 0.01 s, the **top right panel** to 0.16 s, the **lower left panel** to 4 s, and the **lower right panel** to 8 s. Note that the amplitude of the oscillations decreases over a greater fraction of the disk with time. The oscillations at large radii damp on the longest timescale, whereas the oscillations at small radii damp

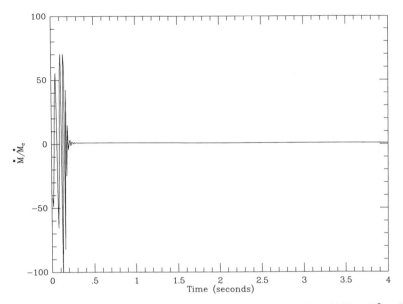

FIGURE 4. The mass flow rate as a function of time in the disk at a radius of 2.72×10^7 cm for the case in which viscous forces in the radial direction are included. The mass flow rate is normalized to the Eddington value. The amplitude of the mass flow rate rises to over 70 times the steady-state rate in response to an assumed steady-state Keplerian disk structure. After 0.4 s the mass flow rate has reached a steady state.

tions (provided that sufficient time had elapsed). This is seen in FIGURE 5 where the spatial variation of the mass flow rate is plotted as a function of time.

DISCUSSION

It has been demonstrated[14] that the linearly unstable oscillation modes in the disk are stabilized in the global approximation when radial viscous forces are included. Such effects are important even when departures from Keplerian motion are small. This result has been established for a viscosity prescription dependent upon gas pressure alone for a wide range of parameters ($\dot{M} \sim 0.01 \dot{M}_E - \dot{M}_E$ and $\alpha \sim 0.1$–1). It confirms and extends the validity of the results on global disk oscillations obtained for accretion disks surrounding white dwarf stars[10] to neutron stars.

The results of our study indicate that high spatial resolution is required to properly model the time-dependent behavior. Equally important is the requirement that the evolutionary time be sufficiently long so that one can distinguish between the response of the disk to an assumed initial state and its long-term global behavior.

Future work should be focused on the possibility of radial oscillations in the inner regions of accretion disks surrounding black holes. In contrast to disks around neutron stars, general relativistic effects are much more important, and the Newtonian approximation to gravity is inadequate. In this case, acoustic waves can be

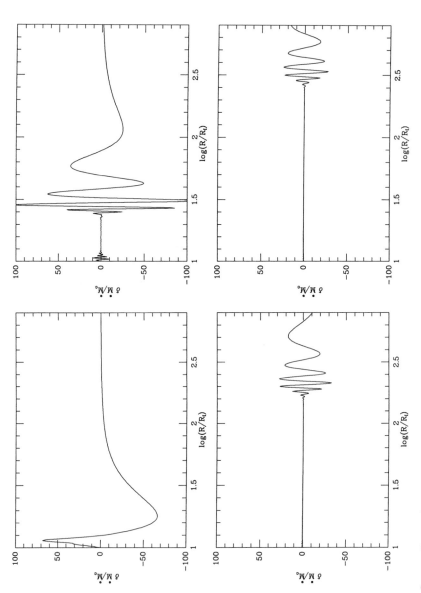

FIGURE 5. Same as FIGURE 3 except for the case in which viscous forces in the radial direction are included. Except for the oscillations in the outer disk (which have not had sufficient time to damp out) the disk is seen to evolve to a steady state.

confined to the inner region because the epicyclic frequency, κ, reaches a maximum,[11,12] and the low-frequency waves, whose frequencies are less than κ_{max}, are evanescent outside this trapped region.[11,12] Investigations of the inner regions of relativistic disks, including the effects of radial viscous forces, would be desirable to determine the viability of such waves to the QPO phenomenon.

REFERENCES

1. VAN DER KLIS, M., F. JANSEN, J. VAN PARADIJS, W. H. G. LEWIN, E. P. J. VAN DEN HEUVEL, J. E. TRÜMPER & M. SZTAJNO. 1985. Nature **316:** 225–230.
2. LEWIN, W. H. G., J. VAN PARADIJS & M. VAN DER KLIS. 1988. Space Sci. Rev. **46:** 273–378.
3. ALPAR, M. A. & J. SHAHAM. 1985. Nature **316:** 239–241.
4. LAMB, F. K., N. SHIBAZAKI, M. A. ALPAR & J. SHAHAM. 1985. Nature **317:** 681–687.
5. FORTNER, B., F. K. LAMB & G. S. MILLER. 1989. Nature **342:** 775–777.
6. ALPAR, M. A., G. HASINGER, J. SHAHAM & S. YANCOPOULOS. 1992. Astron. Astrophys. **257:** 627–631.
7. ABRAMOWICZ, M. A., E. SZUSZKIEWICZ & F. WALLINDER. 1989. *In* Theory of Accretion Disks, F. Meyer, W. J. Duschl, J. Frank, and E. Meyer-Hofmeister, Eds.: 141–166. Kluwer. Dordrecht, the Netherlands.
8. KATO, S. 1978. Mon. Not. R. Astron. Soc. **185:** 629–642.
9. BLUMENTHAL, G. R., L. T. YANG & D. N. C. LIN. 1984. Astrophys. J. **287:** 774–784.
10. PAPALOIZOU, J. C. B. & G. Q. G. STANLEY. 1986. Mon. Not. R. Astron. Soc. **220:** 593–610.
11. KATO, S., F. HONMA & R. MATSUMOTO. 1988. Mon. Not. R. Astron. Soc. **231:** 37–48.
12. MATSUMOTO, R., S. KATO & F. HONMA. 1989. *In* Theory of Accretion Disks, F. Meyer, W. J. Duschl, J. Frank, and E. Meyer-Hofmeister, Eds.: 167–172. Kluwer. Dordrecht, the Netherlands.
13. OKUDA, T. & S. MINESHIGE. 1991. Mon. Not. R. Astron. Soc. **249:** 684–692.
14. CHEN, X. & R. E. TAAM. 1992. Mon. Not. R. Astron. Soc. **255:** 51–60.
15. SHAKURA, N. I. & R. A. SUNYAEV. 1973. Astron. Astrophys. **24:** 337–355.
16. LIGHTMAN, A. P. & D. M. EARDLEY. 1974. Astrophys. J., Lett. **187:** L1–L3.
17. SAKIMOTO, P. J. & F. V. CORONITI. 1981. Astrophys. J. **247:** 19–31.

Relativistic Magnetically Driven Jets and Winds[a]

R. V. E. LOVELACE[b] AND J. CONTOPOULOS[c]

[b]Department of Applied and Engineering Physics
Cornell University
Ithaca, New York 14853

[c]Department of Astronomy
Cornell University
Ithaca, New York 14853

INTRODUCTION

High-velocity outflows or jets of matter are observed to emanate from the nuclei of active galaxies and quasars.[1] On a small scale, the apparently singular galactic object SS 433 exhibits oppositely directed high-velocity jets.[2] Both low-mass T-Tauri and high-mass pre-main-sequence stars exhibit bipolar mass outflows.[3] In active galaxies and quasars, the activity, including the jets, is thought to be powered by accretion onto a massive black hole with the accretion occurring through a disk of ionized gas. Highly ordered magnetic fields are deduced to exist in the nuclear regions of some of these sources due to the rapid time variations of the intensity and polarization of the synchrotron emission.[4,5]

The origin of the jets and outflows remains a fundamental open question. One idea for the origin of the jets is based on the occurrence of narrow, essentially empty vortex funnels in accretion flows of matter with angular momentum.[6-8] However, nonaxisymmetric instabilities of "fat" accretion disks are predicted to destroy the narrow funnels.[9,10]

An alternative idea for the origin of jets, which is discussed further here, is that the jets are magnetically driven.[11-14] We follow our earlier approach[15] where the interior of the disk is treated as viscous and resistive, with a stationary $\mathbf{B}$ field resulting from a balance of field diffusion against radial advection by the accretion flow. We assume even field symmetry so that the magnetic flux function $\Psi(r, z) = \Psi(r, -z)$, where, the poloidal field is given by $\mathbf{B}_p = \nabla \times (\Psi\hat{\phi}/r)$. The space exterior to the disk, where the jets accelerate and propagate, is treated using ideal magnetohydrodynamics. The approach we describe here involves averaging the different physical variables over the cross section of the jet at a given axial distance z from the equatorial plane.[13,16,17] The basic nature of a nonrelativistic solution close to the accretion disk is shown in FIGURE 1.

[a]This work was supported in part by NASA Grant NAGW 2293 from the Origins of the Solar System Program.

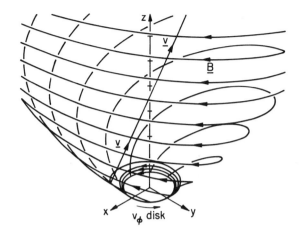

FIGURE 1. Perspective view of eight field lines and one streamline for a nonrelativistic jet solution. The z axis is tipped toward the viewer by 30°. Close to the disk the flow velocity of the jet is almost azimuthal with a magnitude close to that of the disk. The twist of the magnetic field corresponds to a magnetic torque acting to slow down the disk's rotation. (From Lovelace *et al.*[13] Reproduced by permission.)

THEORY

We use a cylindrical, inertial coordinate system (r, ϕ, z) with the origin at the central object, and the z axis perpendicular to the disk. The outflows or jets are considered to be axisymmetric $(\partial/\partial\phi = 0)$ and stationary $(\partial/\partial t = 0)$. The basic equations are those of ideal magnetohydrodynamics (MHD). Close to the central object, the flow is nonrelativistic and, for simplicity, we treat the gravitational field as being Newtonian. We are mainly interested in the axial (z) variations of the jet parameters, such as the jet velocity and radius, and the magnetic field components. Therefore, we consider a simple factorization of the radial and axial dependences,[13]

$$v_r(r, z) = \frac{r}{a(z)} \frac{da(z)}{dz} v_z(z), \qquad (1)$$

$$v_\phi(r, z) = r\omega(z), \qquad (2)$$

$$v_z(r, z) = v_z(z), \qquad (3)$$

$$\rho(r, z) = f_\rho(\alpha)\bar{\rho}(z). \qquad (4)$$

Here, $a(z)$ is the jet radius; $\omega(z)$ is the angular rotation rate of the jet at the axial distance z; $\bar{\rho}(z)$ is the average density of the jet; $\alpha \equiv (r/a(z))^2$ is a dimensionless measure of radial distance in the jet; and $f_\rho(\alpha) \geq 0$ is a dimensionless mass-density "profile function" normalized so that its integral over α is unity. The mass flow in the jet across any $z = $ const. surface is a constant so that

$$\dot{M} = \int_{z=\text{const.}} d^2x \, \rho v_z = \pi a^2(z)\bar{\rho}(z)v_z(z) = \text{const.} \qquad (5)$$

The magnetic field obeys the "frozen-in" field equation so that we may take[13]

$$\Psi(r, z) = \Psi_i(\alpha), \tag{6}$$

$$B_r(r, z) = \alpha^{1/2}\left(\frac{dR(Z)}{dZ}\right)B_z(r, z), \tag{7}$$

$$B_\phi(r, z) = \alpha^{1/2}\beta_i\left(\frac{\Omega(Z) - 1}{V_z(Z)R(Z)}\right)B_i(\alpha), \tag{8}$$

$$B_z(r, z) = \frac{1}{R^2(Z)}B_i(\alpha), \tag{9}$$

for $\alpha < \alpha_0$, within the jet, and $\mathbf{B} \approx 0$ for $\alpha > \alpha_0$, outside the jet, where $\alpha_0 = O(1)$. Here, $\Psi(r, z) \equiv rA_\phi(r, z)$ is the magnetic flux function that obeys $(\mathbf{B} \cdot \nabla)\Psi = 0$, or $(\mathbf{B}_p \cdot \nabla)\Psi = 0$, where $\mathbf{B}_p = (B_r, 0, B_z) = \nabla \times (\Psi\hat{\phi}/r)$ is the poloidal magnetic field. Thus, $\Psi(r, z) = $ const. labels the poloidal projection of a field line. Also, $Z \equiv z/a_i$ is a dimensionless axial distance; $R \equiv a(z)/a_i$ is the dimensionless jet radius; $a_i \equiv a(z = 0)$ is the "initial" jet radius; and $B_i(\alpha)$ is the axial field profile in the disk. Further, $V_z \equiv v_z(z)/c$ is the dimensionless jet velocity with c the speed of light; $\Omega \equiv \omega(z)/\omega(z = 0)$ is the dimensionless rotation rate of the jet; and $\beta_i \equiv \omega(z = 0)a_i/c$. Owing to the perfect conductivity and axisymmetry, we have $E_r = \alpha^{1/2}\beta_iB_i(\alpha)/R$, $E_\phi = 0$, and $E_z = -\alpha\beta_iB_i(\alpha)(dR/dZ)/R$.

An equation for the conservation of axial momentum flow of the jet can readily be obtained[13] by integrating the general momentum conservation equation over a volume of the jet between Z and $Z + dZ$. The result is

$$\frac{d}{dZ}\mathscr{F}_P = \frac{F_z}{V_z} + \pi P_{ex}\frac{dR^2}{dZ}, \tag{10}$$

where F_z is the axial gravitational force on the jet matter within Z to $Z + dZ$; P_{ex} is the pressure of the matter and weak magnetic field outside of the jet; and $\mathscr{F}_P$ is the dimensionless axial momentum flow of the jet. That is,

$$(a_iB_0)^2\mathscr{F}_P = \int_{z=\text{const.}} d^2x(T_p^{zz} + T_f^{zz})$$

$$= \dot{M}c\left(\gamma V_z + \frac{\tau}{V_z}\right) + \frac{1}{4}\int_0^{a(z)} r\,dr(B_r^2 + E_r^2 + B_\phi^2 - B_z^2 - E_z^2). \tag{11}$$

Here, T_p^{ij} is the stress tensor for the matter and T_f^{ij} is that for the electromagnetic field; $\tau \equiv kT(z)/(\mu c^2)$ is the dimensionless jet temperature (with μ the mean particle mass); and $B_0 \equiv \max|B_i(\alpha)|$ is a reference value for the poloidal magnetic field in the disk; and

$$\gamma = \{1 - V_z^2[1 + (R')^2] - \beta_i^2(\Omega R)^2\}^{-1/2} \tag{12}$$

is the Lorantz factor for the jet. Notice that the "initial" temperature of the jet, $\tau_i = \tau(z = 0)$, is expected to be the temperature of the coronal plasma of the disk, rather than the (lower) internal temperature of the disk. From **(7)–(9)** and **(11)** we obtain

$$\mathscr{F}_P = \mathscr{F}_M\left(\gamma V_z + \frac{\tau}{V_z}\right) + \tfrac{1}{2}\,\mathscr{F}_0\left[\left(\frac{R'}{R}\right)^2 + \beta_i^2\left(\frac{\Omega - 1}{V_z}\right)^2 - \frac{\eta_B}{R^2} + \beta_i^2 - \eta_E\beta_i^2(R')^2\right],$$

(13)

where, $R' \equiv dR/dZ$; $\mathscr{F}_M \equiv \dot{M}c/(a_iB_0)^2$ is the dimensionless mass-flow rate in one jet; $\mathscr{F}_0 \equiv \tfrac{1}{4}\int_0^\infty d\alpha\; \alpha B_i(\alpha)^2/B_0^2$ is a dimensionless constant; and $\eta_B \equiv (\int_0^\infty d\alpha\; B_i^2)/(\int_0^\infty d\alpha\; \alpha B_i^2)$, and $\eta_E \equiv (\int_0^\infty d\alpha\; \alpha^2 B_i^2)/(\int_0^\infty d\alpha\; \alpha B_i^2)$ are further dimensionless constants. Consider as an illustration the axial field profile $B_i = B_0 \exp(-\alpha/2)$. One then finds $\mathscr{F}_0 = 0.25$, $\eta_B = 1$, and $\eta_E = 2$. In general, $\eta_B \cdot \eta_E > 1$.

The gravitational force F_z in **(10)** depends of course on the distribution of density with r in the jet.[13] For example, if the density is peaked near $r = a(z)$,

$$F_z = -\frac{\beta_i^2 \mathscr{F}_M \delta_0 Z}{(R^2 + Z^2)^{3/2}},$$

(14)

where

$$\delta_0 \equiv \frac{GM g_R}{c^2 a_i \beta_i^2},$$

(15)

is a dimensionless measure of the strength of the gravitational force, and $g_R \leq 1$ accounts for the radiation pressure corresponding to a point source of radiation at $r = 0$. Notice that for a nonmagnetic, nonrelativistic Keplerian disk $GM/(c^2 a_i \beta_i^2) = 1$.

The force term $\pi P_{ex}\, dR^2/dZ$ in **(10)** represents the "tooth-paste tube" effect. The pressure of the external medium, which may include a contribution from a weak toroidal field of the jet, acts to increase (or decrease) the momentum flow in the jet if $dR/dZ > 0$ (or < 0). Notice that **(10)** simplifies, as it should, to Bernoulli's equation for an isotropic stellar wind[18] if the magnetic force terms are dropped ($\mathscr{F}_0 = 0$), the jet radius is proportional to Z, and P_{ex} is set equal to the internal pressure of the jet.

The conservation of angular momentum can be written as:[13]

$$(a_i^3 B_0^2)\mathscr{F}_L = \int_{z=\text{const.}} d^2x\; r(T_p^{z\phi} + T_f^{z\phi}) = 2\pi \int_0^\infty r\, dr\; r(\gamma\rho v_z v_\phi - B_z B_\phi/(4\pi))$$

(16)

$$= \text{const.},$$

(17)

where $\mathscr{F}_L$ is the dimensionless flux of angular momentum (about the z axis) carried by the jet. This can be simplified to give

$$\mathscr{F}_L = k_\rho\beta_i\mathscr{F}_M\gamma R^2\Omega + \beta_i\mathscr{F}_0\frac{1 - \Omega}{V_z} = \text{const.},$$

(18)

where $k_\rho \equiv (\int_0^\infty d\alpha\; \alpha\rho)/(\int_0^\infty d\alpha\; \rho)$ is a dimensionless constant characterizing the radial distribution of density in the jet. We assume a density distribution peaked near the jet's edge, so that $k_\rho = 1$, here, and subsequently.

Equation (18) can be rewritten as

$$\Omega = \frac{R_A^2(V_z - V_A)}{R^2\gamma V_z - R_A^2 V_A},$$ (19)

where $V_A \equiv \beta_i \mathscr{A}_0 / \mathscr{F}_L$ and $R_A^2 \equiv \mathscr{F}_L / (\beta_i \mathscr{F}_M)$ are dimensionless constants. For the physical jet solutions discussed subsequently, the numerator and denominator of (19) vanish simultaneously at an axial distance $Z = Z_A$, where $V_z(Z_A) = V_A$ and $R(Z_A) = R_A \gamma_A^{-1/2}$. This distance is termed the Alfvén point of the flow.[19] [Our relation $R_A^2 = \mathscr{F}_L / (\beta_i \mathscr{F}_M)$ is equivalent to the Weber–Davis relation $L = \Omega r_A^2$.] Notice that (19) implies

$$\frac{\Omega - 1}{V_z} = \frac{R_A^2 - R^2\gamma}{R^2\gamma V_z - R_A^2 V_A},$$ (20)

and because $V_z(Z \rightarrow 0) \approx 0$, $B_\phi(r, z \rightarrow 0) \rightarrow -\alpha^{1/2}(1 - 1/R_A^2)B_i(\alpha)/V_A$.

The conservation of energy can be written as:[13]

$$(a_i B_0)^2 \mathscr{F}_E = 2\pi \int_0^\infty r\, dr\, \rho v_z[(\gamma - 1)c^2 + w + \Phi_g] + 2\pi \int_0^\infty r\, dr\, q_z$$

$$+ \frac{c}{2} \int_0^\infty r\, dr\, E_r B_\phi = \text{const.},$$ (21)

where $\mathscr{F}_E$ is the dimensionless energy flux of the jet. The first integral represents the energy flux carried by the bulk motion of the matter, the second integral the flux carried by heat conduction, and the third integral the flux carried by the electromagnetic field (Poynting flux). In the first integral, $w \equiv \int dp/\rho$ is the enthalpy per unit mass.

Using the perfect conductivity relation $E_r = (v_z B_\phi - v_\phi B_z)/c$, and neglecting the heat conductivity, we obtain

$$\mathscr{F}_E = \mathscr{F}_M \left\{ \gamma - 1 + \frac{w}{c^2} + \frac{\langle \Phi_g \rangle}{c^2} \right\} + \beta_i^2 \mathscr{F}_0 \frac{1 - \Omega}{V_z} = \text{const.},$$ (22)

where $\langle \Phi_g \rangle$ is the average gravitational potential of a $z = \text{const.}$ slab of the jet. For example, for a density distribution peaked near the jet's edge,

$$\langle \Phi_g \rangle = \frac{GM g_R}{a_i(R^2 + Z^2)^{1/2}}.$$ (23)

In (22) notice that the Poynting flux, at any distance z, is outward if the angular rotation of the jet is less than its initial value, that is, if $\Omega(z) < 1$. Under the same condition, the magnetic field transport of angular momentum [the second term in (18)] is outward.

We can combine (18) and (22) to obtain the dimensionless energy per unit mass of the jet,

$$f_E \equiv \frac{\mathscr{F}_E}{\mathscr{F}_M} = \gamma - 1 + \frac{w}{c^2} + \frac{\langle \Phi_g \rangle}{c^2} + \beta_i^2 R_A^2 - \beta_i^2 \gamma R^2 \Omega.$$ (24)

If the heat conduction is negligible, then f_E is a constant for $Z > 0$, with the value equal to

$$f_E = \gamma_i - 1 + \frac{w_i}{c^2} - \beta_i^2 \delta_0 + \beta_i^2 (R_A^2 - \gamma_i), \tag{25}$$

where, $\gamma_i = (1 - \beta_i^2)^{-1/2} \approx 1 + \beta_i^2/2$.

A radial force-balance or virial equation for the jet can be obtained by multiplying the radial component of the Euler equation by $2\pi r^2 \, dr$ and integrating over the jet cross section.[13] Alternatively, the identical equation is found by considering $d\mathscr{F}_E/dZ - V_z(d\mathscr{F}_P/dZ) - \Omega(d\mathscr{F}_L/dZ)$.[14] The result is

$$\mathscr{F}_M R \frac{d}{dZ}\left(\gamma V_z \frac{dR}{dZ}\right) = \frac{2\mathscr{F}_M \tau}{V_z} + \mathscr{F}_0 \left[\frac{\eta_B}{R^2} - \eta_E \beta_i^2 R \frac{d^2R}{dZ^2} + \frac{d}{dZ}\left(\frac{1}{R}\frac{dR}{dZ}\right)\right]$$

$$+ \beta_i^2 \mathscr{F}_M \frac{\gamma(R\Omega)^2}{V_z} - \mathscr{F}_M \frac{\langle r\partial\Phi_g/\partial r\rangle}{c^2 V_z}, \quad - 2\pi R^2 P_{ex}. \tag{26}$$

The left-hand side of (26) represents the radial force due to the poloidal curvature of the jet. On the right-hand side of this equation, the different terms represent the outward thermal pressure force ($\propto \tau$); the magnetic ($\propto \mathscr{F}_0$) and electric ($\propto \mathscr{F}_0 \eta_E$) forces; the centrifugal force ($\propto \Omega^2$); the gravitational force; and finally the force due to the external medium ($\propto P_{ex}$). For a density profile peaked near the jet's edge,

$$\frac{1}{c^2}\left\langle r \frac{\partial\Phi_g}{\partial r}\right\rangle = \frac{GM g_R R^2}{c^2(R^2 + Z^2)^{3/2}}. \tag{27}$$

The correspondence of the parameters of the present relativistic equations with those of our earlier nonrelativistic treatment[13] is:

$$\mathscr{F}_M^{NR} = \beta_i \mathscr{F}_M = \text{const.},$$

$$\mathscr{F}_L^{NR} = \mathscr{F}_L = \text{const.},$$

$$\mathscr{F}_E^{NR} = \frac{1}{\beta_i}\mathscr{F}_E = \text{const.},$$

$$\mathscr{F}_P^{NR} = \mathscr{F}_P,$$

$$\tau_i^{NR} = \frac{1}{\beta_i^2}\tau_i = \text{const.},$$

$$V_A^{NR} = \frac{1}{\beta_i}V_A = \text{const.},$$

$$R_A^{NR} = R_A = \text{const.},$$

$$\delta_0^{NR} = \delta_0 = \text{const.} \tag{28}$$

The basic "input" parameters for a jet solution are δ_0, which measures the departure

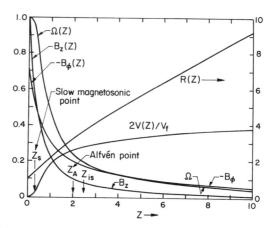

FIGURE 2. Axial dependences of the basic jet variables close to the central object for a nonrelativistic solution with $\mu^{NR} = 0.0735$, $R_A = 3.3$, $V_A^{NR} = 1.25$, and $\delta_0 = 3.0$. In the figure, the fields are normalized so that the axial field is $B_z = 1/R^2$ and the toroidal field is $B_\phi = -(1 - \Omega)/(V_z R)$. V_z is normalized to the fast magnetosonic speed, V_f. For $Z < Z_{is}$ the jet is treated as isothermal, while for $Z > Z_{is}$ it is treated as isentropic. That B_ϕ is negative corresponds to the magnetic torque of the jet-removing angular momentum from the disk. Also, that B_ϕ is negative corresponds to an outward Poynting energy flux. Notice, that the jet carries no net current, so that $rB_\phi(r, z) \to 0$ for $r \to \infty$. (From Lovelace et al.[13] Reproduced by permission.)

of the disk rotation from the Keplerian value; V_A, which is the axial jet velocity at the Alfvén point; R_A, which is the radius of the jet at the Alfvén point; and τ_i, which is a measure of the initial temperature of the jet. This large number of parameters complicates the task of surveying the space of all possible jet solutions.[14] For fixed δ_0, a clearly important parameter is $\mu \equiv \mathscr{F}_M / \mathscr{F}_0 = 1/(R_A^2 V_A)$, which is a measure of the "mass-loading" of the jet. For $\mu \ll 1$, the initial jet propagation is field dominated— the energy and angular momentum fluxes are carried by the electromagnetic field. In the opposite limit where μ is not small compared with unity, the matter and electromagnetic fields are important at all distances from the disk. In general, the maximum asymptotic ($Z \to \infty$) speed or Lorentz factor of the jet increases as μ decreases.

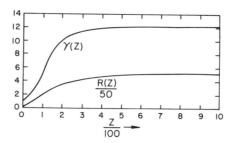

FIGURE 3. Axial dependencies of jet radius and Lorentz factor for a representative relativistic jet solution with $\mu \equiv \mathscr{F}_M / \mathscr{F}_0 = 10^{-2}$, $\delta_0 = 2.0$, $P_{ex} \propto (1 + Z^2/H^2)^{-3/2}$, and $H = 200$.

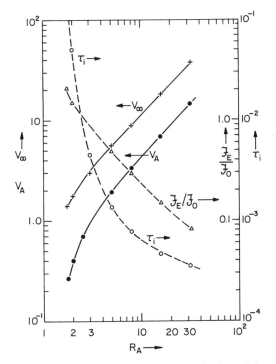

FIGURE 4. Summary of solutions for nonrelativistic jets for $\delta_0 = 1.1$, and with the fast magnetosonic point at a large distance from the disk.

FIGURE 2 shows a representative nonrelativistic jet solution from reference 13. FIGURE 3 shows a representative relativistic jet solution. FIGURE 4 gives a summary of the dependences for a class of nonrelativistic jet solutions with the fast magnetosonic point at a large distance from the disk.

CONCLUSION

Four equations for the origin and propagation of relativistic jets and winds have been derived from the basic conservation laws of ideal magnetohydrodynamics. These equations are obtained by averaging the exact equations over the radial cross section of the jet or wind at a given axial distance z. The equations allow the self-consistent determination of the jet's axial velocity, radius, angular rotation rate, and temperature for $0 \leq z \leq \infty$. At $z = 0$, we assume that the jet's velocity is close to zero, the radius is of the order of the inner radius of the disk, a_i, the rotation rate is that of the disk at a_i, and the temperature is that of the coronal plasma of the disk at a_i.

The nature of the jet solutions is determined by the main dimensionless parameters δ_0, R_A, V_A, and τ_i. FIGURE 4 summarizes the important properties of a class of nonrelativistic jet solutions. Some of the dependences are surprising: The asymptotic $(z \to \infty)$ jet speed, V_∞, increases as the initial jet temperature, τ_i, decreases. The total energy flux in the jet, $\mathscr{F}_E$, decreases as V_∞ increases, specifically, $\mathscr{F}_E \propto V_\infty^{-1}$. The total mass flux in the jet, $\mathscr{F}_M \propto V_\infty^{-3}$. Finally, notice that there is a minimum value of V_∞ that corresponds to a jet speed of the order of 1.4 times the disk rotational speed at a_i. It appears possible that the minimum speed for magnetically driven jets could explain the characteristic speed of the remarkable galactic object SS 433.

ACKNOWLEDGMENTS

The authors thank Drs. S. Dermott, J. Hunter, and R. Wilson for their hospitality at the Seventh Florida Workshop.

REFERENCES

1. HUGHES, P. A., Ed. 1990. Beams and Jets in Astrophysics. Cambridge Univ. Press. Cambridge, England.
2. MARGON, B. 1984. Annu. Rev. Astron. Astrophys. **22:** 507.
3. BALLY, J. & C. J. LADA. 1983. Astrophys. J. **265:** 824.
4. ANGEL, J. R. P. & H. S. STOCKMAN. 1980. Annu. Rev. Astron. Astrophys. **8:** 321.
5. WITZEL, A., *et al.* 1988. Astron. Astrophys. **206:** 245.
6. LYNDEN-BELL, D. 1978. Phys. Scr. **17:** 185.
7. PACZYŃSKI, B. & P. J. WIITA. 1980. Astron. Astrophys. **88:** 23.
8. ABRAMOWICZ, M. A., M. CALVANI & L. NOBILI. 1980. Astrophys. J. **242:** 772.
9. PAPALOIZOU, J. C. B. & J. E. PRINGLE. 1985. Mon. Not. R. Astron. Soc. **213:** 799.
10. ZUREK, W. H. & W. BENZ. 1986. Astrophys. J. **308:** 123.
11. UCHIDA, Y. & K. SHIBATA. 1985. Publ. Astron. Soc. Japan. **37:** 515.
12. SAKURAI, T. 1985. Astron. Astrophys. **152:** 121.
13. LOVELACE, R. V. E., H. L. BERK & J. CONTOPOULOS. 1991. Astrophys. J. **379:** 696.
14. CONTOPOULOS, J. 1992. Ph.D. Thesis, Cornell University, Ithaca, N.Y.
15. LOVELACE, R. V. E., J. C. L. WANG & M. E. SULKANEN. 1987. Astrophys. J. **315:** 504.
16. LOVELACE, R. V. E., C. M. MOBBARY & J. CONTOPOULOS. 1989. *In* Accretion Disks and Magnetic Fields in Astrophysics, G. Belvedere, Ed.: 79. Kluwer. Dordrecht, the Netherlands.
17. KOUPELIS, T. & H. M. vanHORN. 1989. Astrophys. J. **342:** 146.
18. PARKER, E. N. 1963. Interstellar Dynamical Processes. Interscience. New York.
19. WEBER, E. J. & L. DAVIS, JR. 1967. Astrophys. J. **148:** 217.

Self-similar Magnetically Driven Jets from Accretion Disks

J. CONTOPOULOS[a] AND R. V. E. LOVELACE[b]

[a]Department of Astronomy
Cornell University
Ithaca, New York 14853

[b]Department of Applied and Engineering Physics
Cornell University
Itaca, New York 14853

INTRODUCTION

Collimated outflows of matter—jets and winds—have been observed in association with galactic (for example, young stellar objects, SS 433), and extragalactic (for example, radio galaxies, quasars) objects.[1,2] Although their astrophysical environments differ enormously, we propose that their main characteristics can be described within the framework of magnetohydrodynamics (MHD).[3] The magnetic field is important in accelerating and collimating the flows. Previous studies of MHD jets and winds have obtained estimates of the parameters of the outflows (rates of mass, energy and angular momentum flow, average flow velocity, magnetic field configurations, etc.) without obtaining fully self-consistent solutions. This is because of the nonlinearity of the equations, and the complications associated with critical and singular points. Here, we present a method for obtaining quasi-analytic solutions to the full set of equations of *ideal, time-independent, axisymmetric* MHD that describe outflows from a thin disk accreting into a central compact object. We know of only two previous quasi-analytic solutions of the full set of equations, that of Blandford and Payne,[4] and that of Low and Tsinganos.[5] Our method turns out to be a generalization of Blandford and Payne's solution, although we have followed a different approach in that we use the formalism of the generalized Grad-Shafranov equation.[6]

EQUATIONS

We consider a thin ionized accretion disk around a central compact object. The disk is threaded by a poloidal magnetic field, and outflows of matter leave the top and bottom surfaces of the disk (see FIG. 1). The outflows are considered to be axisymmetric ($\partial/\partial\phi = 0$), stationary ($\partial/\partial t = 0$), nondissipative, and nonrelativistic (the relativistic treatment is given in reference 7). We use a cylindrical, inertial coordinate system (r, ϕ, z) with the origin fixed on the central object, and the z axis perpendicular to the disk. The full set of ideal MDH equations is equivalent to *one partial differential equation of second order* for the magnetic flux function $\Psi(r, z)$, the generalized Grad-Shafranov equation:[6]

$$\left(1 - \frac{F^2}{4\pi\rho}\right)\Delta^*\Psi - F\nabla\left(\frac{F}{4\pi\rho}\right) \cdot \nabla\Psi = -4\pi\rho r^2(J' + rv_\phi G')$$

$$- (H + rv_\phi F)(H' + rv_\phi F') + 4\pi r^2 p(S'/k_B), \quad (1)$$

where

$$\Delta^* \equiv r\frac{\partial}{\partial r}\left(\frac{1}{r}\frac{\partial}{\partial r}\right) + \frac{\partial^2}{\partial z^2},$$

and primes denote differentiation with respect to Ψ. The five arbitrary functions F, G, H, J, and S of Ψ enter through the following relations:

$$F(\Psi) = 4\pi\rho|\mathbf{v}_p|/|\mathbf{B}_p|, \quad (2)$$

$$G(\Psi) = \frac{1}{r}\left(v_\phi - \frac{F(\Psi)}{4\pi\rho}B_\phi\right), \quad (3)$$

$$H(\Psi) = rB_\phi - F(\Psi)rv_\phi, \quad (4)$$

$$S(\Psi) = S(p, \rho) = k_B(\gamma - 1)^{-1}\ln(p/\rho^\gamma), \quad (5)$$

$$J(\Psi) = \int (dp/\rho)|_{\Psi=\text{const.}} + |\mathbf{v}|^2/2 + \Phi_g - rv_\phi G(\Psi), \quad (6)$$

where k_B is the Boltzmann contant, γ the adiabatic index, and S the entropy per unit volume of the flow. The subscript p of a vector denotes the poloidal (r, z) component. This second-order partial differential equation is

- Elliptic for $v_p^2 < v_c^2$,
- Hyperbolic for $v_c^2 < v_p^2 < v_{sms}^2$,
- Elliptic for $v_{sms}^2 < v_p^2 < v_{fms}^2$,
- Hyperbolic for $v_{fms}^2 < v_p^2$,

and its numerical solution presents a computational challenge. Here, $v_p = (v_z^2 + v_r^{21/2})$ is the poloidal flow velocity, v_c the speed of the cusp of the slow mode wave front, and $v_{sms,fms}$ the slow and fast magnetosonic speeds, respectively. The Alfvén point $v_p = v_{Ap} \equiv |\mathbf{B}_p|/(4\pi\rho)^{1/2}$ is a singular, not a critical point.[8]

RENORMALIZATIONS

In the present work, we solve the Grad-Shafranov equation (1) by transforming it, from a *partial* to an *ordinary* differential equation. We then integrate this equation numerically. We first dedimensionalize r and z by redefining them as

$$\frac{r}{a_i} \text{ and } \frac{z}{a_i}, \quad (7)$$

where a_i is a "characteristic" initial jet radius. Next, we consider the equation for each poloidal field (and flow) line, $\Psi(r, z) = $ const., or equivalently,

$$r = r_\Psi(z). \tag{8}$$

The equation for the "characteristic" field line, labeled by $\Psi = \Psi_c$, is

$$r = r_{\Psi_c}(z) \equiv R(z), \tag{9}$$

where, clearly, $R(z = 0) = 1$. For a general field line,

$$r_\Psi(z = 0) \equiv r_{\Psi_0}, \tag{10}$$

which shows that there is a one-to-one correspondence between Ψ and the distance r_{Ψ_0}, where the Ψ-field line intersects the disk ($z = 0$).

In a previous paper (Lovelace et al.[9]), we made use of the approximation that $\Psi(r, z) = \Psi(r/R(z))$, or equivalently, $r_\Psi(z) = r_{\Psi_0} \cdot R(z)$. The following simple generalized form,

$$r = r_\Psi(z) = r_{\Psi_0}R(z/r_{\Psi_0}) \equiv r_{\Psi_0}R(Z), \tag{11}$$

where $Z \equiv z/r_{\Psi_0}$ is the "renormalized" z variable, makes it possible to take out the r-dependence from the equations, by considering how the different terms scale with r_{Ψ_0}. The rescaling (11) was assumed previously by Blandford and Payne.[4]

We can rescale the r_{Ψ_0} terms in the MHD equations by assuming the following power-law dependences, justifiable by dimensional analysis:[7]

$$\Psi = r_{\Psi_0}^x \Psi_0, \tag{12}$$

$$\mathbf{B}(r, z) = r_{\Psi_0}^{x-2}\mathbf{B}(Z), \tag{13}$$

$$\mathbf{v}(r, z) = r_{\Psi_0}^{-1/2}\mathbf{V}(Z)v_0, \tag{14}$$

$$\rho(r, z) = r_{\Psi_0}^{2x-3}\rho(Z)\frac{B_0^2}{v_0^2}, \tag{15}$$

$$p(r, z) = r_{\Psi_0}^{2x-4}p(Z)\,B_0^2, \tag{16}$$

$$F(\Psi) = r_{\Psi_0}^{x-3/2}F_0\frac{B_0}{v_0}, \tag{17}$$

$$G(\Psi) = r_{\Psi_0}^{-3/2}G_0\frac{v_0}{a_i}, \tag{18}$$

$$H(\Psi) = r_{\Psi_0}^{x-1}H_0a_iB_0, \tag{19}$$

$$J(\Psi) = r_{\Psi_0}^{-1}J_0v_0^2, \tag{20}$$

$$S(\Psi) = k_B(\gamma - 1)^{-1}(((2 - 2\gamma)x - (4 - 3\gamma))\ln r_{\Psi_0} + \ln \mathcal{K}), \tag{21}$$

where x is a free exponent that controls the initial field profile, $\Psi_0 = $ const., $B_0 = B_z$ $(Z = 0) \equiv x\Psi_0/a_i^2$, v_0 is the initial rotational velocity at the "characteristic" radius a_i (note that it can be different from the Keplerian value v_K), $\mathcal{K} = p(Z) \cdot \rho(Z)^{-\gamma}$, and $\mathbf{V}$,

ρ, p, F_0, G_0, H_0, J_0 are dimensionless. The Grad-Shafranov equation (1) is now reduced into *one ordinary differential equation of second order* for $R(Z)$ in terms of the renormalized variable $Z \equiv z/r_{\psi_0}$. As in our earlier work,[9] we reduce the MHD equations to the problem of obtaining the form of a characteristic field line, $r_{\psi_c} = R(z)$. However, we now obtain the full solution for the flow and the fields in the entire poloidal (r, z) plane. The different quantities are given by (11)–(21).

Care is needed in taking derivatives with respect to "unnormalized" variables, because they depend on the parameter r_{ψ_0}. As one moves away from a given point in their r–z plane, the nearby field lines have different values of r_{ψ_0}. Taking everything into account, the Grad-Shafranov equation (1) can be written as[7]

$$R'' = \frac{\mathcal{F}}{\mathcal{G}}(R, R', Z), \qquad (22)$$

where $(\ldots)' \equiv d(\ldots)/dZ$,

$$\mathcal{F}(R, R', Z) = F_0 \frac{R}{V(R - ZR')}(J_0 + RV_\phi \tfrac{1}{2} G_0) - (H_0 + RV_\phi F_0)$$

$$\cdot ((x - 1)H_0 + RV_\phi(x - \tfrac{1}{2})F_0) + 4\pi R^2 C_s^2 \left(\frac{F_0}{4\pi} \frac{1}{VR(R - ZR')}\right)$$

$$\cdot \frac{((2 - 2\gamma)x - (4 - 3\gamma))}{\gamma(\gamma - 1)} - [1 - F_0 VR(R - ZR')]$$

$$\cdot \left(-\frac{1}{R(R - ZR')} + (x - 1)\frac{1 + (R')^2}{(R - ZR')^2}\right)$$

$$+ F_0 \left(-\frac{Z + RR'}{(R - ZR')^2}(\mathscr{A} R(R - ZR') + VR'(R - ZR'))\right.$$

$$\left. + VR(R - ZR')(\tfrac{1}{2} - x)\frac{1 + (R')^2}{(R - ZR')^2}\right),$$

$$\mathcal{G}(R, R', Z) = [1 - F_0 VR(R - ZR')]\left(-\frac{R^2 + Z^2}{(R - ZR')^3}\right)$$

$$+ F_0 \frac{Z + RR'}{(R - ZR')^2}(\mathscr{B} R(R - ZR') - VRZ),$$

$$\mathscr{A}(R, R', Z) \equiv \left[-(R'G_0 + V_\phi F_0 VR'(R - ZR')) - \left(-C_s^2 \frac{R'}{R} + \frac{\overline{\Phi}_g'}{v_0^2} - R'V_\phi G_0\right)\right.$$

$$\left. \cdot \frac{(1 - F_0 VR(R - ZR'))^2}{V(R - ZR')(H_0 + G_0 F_0 R^2)}\right] \cdot$$

$$\cdot \left[\left(-C_s^2 \frac{1}{V} + V(1 + (R')^2)\right)\frac{(1 - F_0 VR(R - ZR'))^2}{V(R - ZR')(H_0 + G_0 F_0 R^2)}\right.$$

$$\left. + H_0(R - ZR') + V_\phi F_0 R(R - ZR')\right]^{-1},$$

$$\mathscr{B}(R, R', Z) \equiv \left[-\left(C_s^2 \frac{Z}{R - ZR'} + V^2 R' \right) \frac{(1 - F_0 VR(R - ZR'))^2}{V(R - ZR')(H_0 + G_0 F_0 R^2)} \right.$$

$$+ H_0 VZ + V_\phi F_0 VZR \Big]$$

$$\cdot \left[\left(-C_s^2 \frac{1}{V} + V(1 + (R')^2) \right) \cdot \frac{(1 - F_0 VR(R - ZR'))^2}{V(R - ZR')(H_0 + G_0 F_0 R^2)} \right.$$

$$+ H_0(R - ZR') + V_\phi F_0 R(R - ZR') \Big]^{-1},$$

$$V_\phi = \frac{RG_0 + H_0 V(R - ZR')}{1 - F_0 VR(R - ZR')}, \tag{23}$$

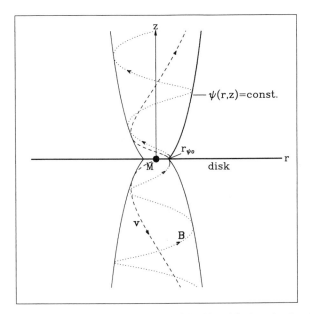

FIGURE 1. Three-dimensional view of a magnetic field (*dotted line*) and a flow (*dashed line*) line (the view is tilted by 10° toward the observer). Their projection on the poloidal $(r - z)$ plane is characterized by $\Psi(r, z)$ = const. The disk $(z = 0)$ rotates counterclockwise, and "drags" the field backwards.

and V as a function of R, R' and Z is given solving the Bernoulli equation

$$\frac{1}{\gamma - 1} (C_s^2 - C_{s0}^2) + \frac{V^2}{2} (1 + (R')^2) + \tfrac{1}{2} V_\phi^2 + \frac{\overline{\Phi}_g}{v_0^2} - RV_\phi G_0 = J_0, \tag{24}$$

where $C_s^2 \equiv \mathscr{K} \gamma (F_0/(4\pi VR(R - ZR')))^{\gamma - 1}$, and $C_{s0}^2 = C_s^2 (Z = 0)$.

We note again that **(1)** is *the* most general equation of axisymmetric ideal MHD flows. It includes matter flow and gravity, and hence our method can be applied to various regimes for special choices of parameters (for example, axisymmetric laboratory plasma configurations where flow and gravity are negligible, $F_0 = G_0 = \Phi_g = 0$;

configurations with no poloidal flow and no toroidal magnetic field,[6] $F_0 = H_0 = 0$, etc.). In the present work, we concentrate on collimated magnetized outflows of matter from thin accretion disks.

SOLUTION

The physical situation is the following: Within the disk, the flow velocity is mainly azimuthal, $\mathbf{v}(r = a_i, z = 0) \approx v_0\phi$, but there is also a small axial $V_0 v_0 \ll v_0$ and radial flow for $z > 0$. Therefore, we integrate (22) numerically from $Z = 0$, with the "initial" conditions $V(Z = 0) = V_0$, $R(Z = 0) = 1$, and $R'(Z = 0) \equiv R_0'$ a free parameter, determined by the condition that the flow goes smoothly through the

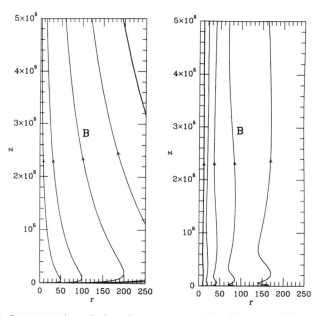

FIGURE 2. Representative solutions for two cases. Jets with zero axial electric current (**left-hand panel,** $x = 0.8 < 1$) recollimate at some very large distance. Jets with nonzero current (**right-hand panel,** $x = 1.02 > 1$) oscillate with a constant ratio of successive recollimation distances. As $x \to 1$, the distances go to infinity. For both cases shown, $H_0 = -1.9$, $\delta_0 = 1$.

Alfvén singular point. We start our integration at $Z = 0$ with $V_0 > V_{\text{sms}}$ in order to avoid the first two critical points (V_c and V_{sms}), which lie close to the disk and can be treated in an independent disk-structure calculation.[10] The magnetic field gradient is important in that it counteracts gravity.[9] Thus the jets are *magnetically driven*. At larger distances, the fast magnetosonic critical point is crossed without any numerical problems.

With increasing distance z, the jet's radius increases. The radius increases to a maximum value, and then begins to decrease, as suggested by earlier works.[9,11,12] The behavior of the solution after the initial recollimation is regulated by the value of the axial electric current. For essentially zero current ($x < 1$), the flow recollimates and the axial velocity approaches a constant asymptotic value, whereas for significant current ($x > 1$), the radius oscillates with z. The first few oscillations take place close to the origin of the jets, within the range of very long baseline interferometry (VLBI) resolution.

The three-dimensional nature of our solutions is shown in FIGURE 1. The magnetic field lines (dotted lines) are "frozen into" the conducting material of the disk. Consequently, the field lines are twisted backwards by the rotation of the disk given a toroidal (B_ϕ) field. The matter flow (dashed line) is initially azimuthal within the disk, but becomes more and more axial as it is accelerated at large distances. Two representative solutions are shown in FIGURE 2. More extended surveys of the parameter space are presented elsewhere.[7]

CONCLUSION

We have outlined a method for solving the equations of ideal, axisymmetric MDH, the Grad-Shafranov equation, exactly. This involves a self-similar rescaling of the variables to obtain a second-order *ordinary* differential equation. We integrate these equations to obtain the shape of the edge of the jet. A general outflow solution consists of an initial part close to the disk where the flow acceleration is mainly hydrodynamic, and an outer part where the magnetic field is important. An important new result of the present work is that the outflows are *recollimated* at a large axial distance. That is, the jet radius increases to a maximum and then decreases. If the total axial current is nonzero, the jet radius *oscillates* with axial distance. The recollimation of magnetized jets might be involved in the flaring of jets in FR I radio sources.[1] An extended survey of the parameter space of our solutions can give indirect information or constraints on the basic physical parameters of observed jets and outflows.[7] The important constants that characterize our solutions are the total mass efflux ($\propto F_0$), the total angular momentum efflux ($\propto H_0$), the value of the exponent in the initial magnetic field profile [$B(r, z = 0) \propto r^{x-2}$], and the ratio of the disk's azimuthal velocity to Keplerian velocity ($v_0/v_K \equiv \sqrt{\delta_0}$). Note that to obtain finite total mass, angular momentum, and energy effluxes, we need to truncate our self-similar solutions at inner and outer radii.

REFERENCES

1. MUXLOW, T. W. B. & S. T. GARRINGTON. 1991. *In* Beams and Jets in Astrophysics, P. A. Hughes, Ed.: 52. Cambridge Univ. Press. Cambridge, England.
2. PADMAN, R., A. N. LASENBY & D. A. GREEN. 1991. *In* Beams and Jets in Astrophysics, P. A. Hughes, Ed.: 484. Cambridge Univ. Press. Cambridge, England.
3. LOVELACE, R. V. E., C. M. MOBBARY & J. CONTOPOULOS. 1989. *In* Accretion Disks and Magnetic Fields in Astrophysics, G. Belvedere, Ed.: 79. Kluwer. Dordrecht, the Netherlands.
4. BLANDFORD, R. D. & D. G. PAYNE. 1982. Mon. Not. R. Astron. Soc. **199**: 883.
5. LOW, B. C. & K. TSINGANOS. 1986. Astrophys. J. **302**: 163.

6. LOVELACE, R. V. E., C. MEHANIAN, C. M. MOBBARY & M. E. SULKANEN. 1986. Astrophys. J., Sup. Ser. **62:** 1.
7. CONTOPOULOS, J. 1992. Ph.D. Thesis, Cornell University, Ithaca, N.Y.
8. HEINEMANN, M. & S. OLBERT. 1978. J. Geophys. Res. **83:** 2457.
9. LOVELACE, R. V. E., H. L. BERK & J. CONTOPOULOS. 1991. Astrophys. J. **379:** 696.
10. KÖNIGL, A. 1989. Astrophys. J. **342:** 208.
11. SAKURAI, T. 1985. Astron. Astrophys. **152:** 121.
12. CHAN, K. L. & R. N. HENRIKSON. 1980. Astrophys. J. **241:** 534.

Formation and Fragmentation of Protostellar and Protoplanetary Disks[a]

ALAN P. BOSS

Department of Terrestrial Magnetism
Carnegie Institution of Washington
5241 Broad Branch Road, NW
Washington, DC 20015

INTRODUCTION

Protostellar formation involves the dynamical collapse of dense ($n > 10^4$ H_2 cm^{-3}) molecular cloud cores toward stellar densities ($n \sim 10^{24}$ cm^{-3}). The collapse phase may begin following the loss of prior magnetic field support because of ambipolar diffusion, or following rapid compression produced by a strong shock wave. The collapse is halted temporarily at intermediate densities ($n \sim 10^{12}$ cm^{-3}) by the thermal pressure associated with compressional heating after the cloud becomes optically thick in the infrared. This first (or outer) quasi-equilibrium core has a size on the order of 10 AU, and after accreting sufficient mass to become hot enough to dissociate molecular hydrogen, the first core begins a second collapse phase, terminating in the formation of the final (or inner) protostellar core, several stellar radii in size. In the presence of even a small initial amount of rotation, these protostellar cores will be centrifugally flattened into disks. The residual cloud envelope continues to collapse, and may enter the protostellar disk through an accretion shock.

In this paper we describe the results of numerical calculations that seek to describe the two- and three-dimensional evolution of nonmagnetic protostellar disks during their formation phases. In general, the equations that must be solved are the equations of gas hydrodynamics in multiple spatial dimensions (yielding the density, velocity field, and internal energy), an equation describing the mean intensity of the radiation field in the (gray) Eddington approximation, and the Poisson equation for the gravitational potential. This set of equations is closed by specifying how the internal energy, pressure, and opacity depend on the density and temperature. Numerical solutions are often sought because of the complexity of this set of coupled, nonlinear, first- and second-order, partial differential equations. Two problems are examined in detail: (a) the prospects for fragmentation during the formation of protostellar disks, and (b) the structure of protoplanetary disks, that is, disks around single stars, from which planets could later form.

[a]This work was supported in part by the National Science Foundation and in part by the National Aeronautics and Space Administration.

FRAGMENTATION OF PROTOSTELLAR DISKS

Fragmentation is commonly defined as break-up into multiple objects during the dynamical collapse phase of protostellar formation. Fragmentation may be the mechanism that is responsible for the formation of the majority of binary stars (Bodenheimer, Ruzmaikina, and Mathieu[1]).

Initial Uniform Density Clouds

For over a decade, three-dimensional numerical calculations have been performed[2] in search of initial conditions for cloud cores that might lead to fragmentation. Nearly all of these calculations started from uniform density and rotation clouds. Recently, a new generation of hydrodynamics codes has been developed and applied to the fragmentation problem, including both improved smoothed particle hydrodynamics (SPH) codes (Monaghan;[3] Bonnell *et al.*[4]) and the more traditional finite-difference codes (Sigalotti;[5] Myhill and Kaula;[6] Boss[7]).

Sigalotti[5] developed two- and three-dimensional donor cell codes that relax the assumption of symmetry above and below the equatorial plane. Sigalotti[5] found that equatorial asymmetry could grow in axisymmetric, isothermal clouds with a range of initial thermal and rotational energies, with growth being strongest for high $\alpha_i = E_{thermal}/|E_{gravity}| \sim 0.4–0.6$ and low $\beta_i = E_{rotational}/|E_{gravity}| < 0.1$ models. The axisymmetric clouds collapsed to produce moderately flattened rings. Sigalotti then demonstrated that in three dimensions, this equatorial asymmetry could lead to the growth of asymmetry around the rotation axis (nonaxisymmetry), thereby fragmenting a cloud that might otherwise be stable. Felice and Sigalotti[8] used the same code to study the ability of tidal forces to induce fragmentation, finding that such forces can lead to enhanced fragmentation, provided that the tidally perturbing bodies are comparable in mass to the collapsing cloud, and are at distances similar to the cloud radius.

Bastien *et al.*[9] used both finite-difference and SPH codes to model the fragmentation of isothermal, elongated, nonrotating cylinders. As the initial thermal energy was lowered, the cylinders fragmented into more objects. However, Bastien *et al.*[9] found that the number of fragments produced saturated at a value of $\sim 2L/D$, where L is the length and D is the diameter of the initial cylinder ($10 \geq L/D \geq 2$), even for low values of α_i (> 0.08). This result shows that simple Jeans mass arguments, which would predict steadily increasing numbers of fragments with decreasing α_i, need not apply to geometries more realistic than an infinite medium. Observational evidence for prolate molecular cloud cores has been assembled by Myers *et al.*,[10] suggesting that collapse calculations starting from such strongly nonaxisymmetric initial conditions as cylinders could very well be representative of the star formation process.

Bonnell *et al.*[4] used an SPH code to model the fragmentation of rotating, isothermal cylinders, with $L/D = 2$ or 3, $\alpha_i = 0.25$ to 0.5, and $\beta_i = 0.01$ to 0.1. In each case, Bonnell *et al.*[4] found that the cylinder collapsed and fragmented directly into at least a binary protostellar system; some models produced three fragments directly from the cylinder, while several models produced fragments that subfragmented into hierarchical multiple systems. The binary mass ratios ranged from ~ 0.2 to 0.8. The fragments were followed long enough to estimate their orbital eccentricities, which were large ($e \sim 0.4$ to 0.8), because fragmentation in these models occurs prior to the formation of a centrifugally supported disk. Finite-difference models by Boss[11] similarly found that binaries formed by fragmentation generally have large eccentricities and mass ratios that may range from ~ 0.1 to 1.

Monaghan and Lattanzio[12] used their SPH code to study the fragmentation of both initially uniform density clouds and Maclaurin disks, which have surface densities $\propto (1 - r^2/R^2)^{1/2}$, where r is the spherical radius and R is the disk radius. The clouds and disks were assumed to be either isothermal, or were cooled as a result of radiative losses in molecular lines. They found that the cooling disk models rapidly underwent fragmentation into many more clumps than the isothermal models,

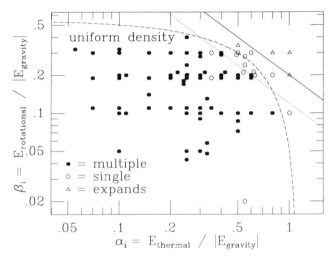

FIGURE 1. Results of all three-dimensional calculations of isothermal protostellar collapse starting from uniform density initial clouds. A fair degree of agreement is obvious: (a) clouds with large α_i and β_i do not collapse, but expand instead; (b) clouds with small α_i collapse and undergo fragmentation into binary and higher order systems; and (c) clouds with intermediate values of α_i collapse but do not appear to fragment, and so may form single protostars, particularly if $\beta_i < 0.02$. The curve and lines give criteria for (a) collapse, Boss and Haber[13] (*dashed curve*); (b) fragmentation, Miyama *et al.*[14] (*dotted line*), and (c) expansion, Miyama *et al.*[14] (*solid line*).

though even in the latter case many clumps (~ 12) could be formed. Initially smooth clouds showed a tendency to collapse and form rings, whereas clouds with initial density perturbations either formed disks (for isothermal thermodynamics) or fragmented into multiple clumps (for cooling thermodynamics). These models show that initially uniform density clouds that collapse with initial temperatures on the order of 70 K may encounter greatly enhanced fragmentation during their subsequent cooling to $T \approx 10$ K.

The results for all published three-dimensional calculations of protostellar collapse starting from uniform density are shown in FIGURE 1. FIGURE 1 includes the results of the new models described earlier, as well as all the older models referenced in Boss.[2] With the exception of two dubious models with $\alpha_i = 0.35$ and $\beta_i = 0.30$ and 0.19, both calculated with a "sticky particle" code, there is a quite satisfactory degree of agreement about the three possible end states for collapse: uniform density clouds can expand, collapse to form a single protostar, or collapse and undergo fragmentation. Fragments can grow[2] directly from the initial density perturbations in the case of low α_i, or indirectly through a rotationally driven instability in the case of high β_i.

Initially Nonuniform Density Clouds

The use of initially uniform density clouds is a theoretical simplification dating back to the pioneering spherically symmetric, numerical models of Larson.[15] A second theoretically attractive initial state is the singular isothermal sphere, with $\rho \propto r^{-2}$, whose collapse was shown to be semianalytically calculable through a similarity solution found by Shu.[16] These two choices appear to bracket the extremes possible for realistic molecular cloud cores, which must be centrally condensed to some extent if thermal pressure is to help support a nearly isothermal, precollapse cloud. Observations of the envelopes of dense, star-forming cloud cores (e.g., Zhou et al.[17]) are consistent with the power-law density profiles ($\rho \propto r^{-n}$, with $n \approx 1.5$ to 2), though there is always the problem that the envelope density profile of an evolved cloud may not be indicative of the precollapse cloud.

Power-law initial density profiles with $n = 1$ were originally found[18] to have a strongly inhibiting effect on fragmentation; the presence of a single, initial central concentration of mass prevented the cloud from undergoing fragmentation. However, Myhill and Kaula[6] found that fragmentation could still occur in clouds with initial power-law density profiles ($n = 1$ or 2), provided that the cloud was also initially in differential rotation such that the central regions were rotating much more rapidly than the outer regions. Their finite-difference models all started from initial clouds with $\alpha_i \approx 0.16$ and $\beta_i \approx 0.17$; the differentially rotating models had $\Omega_i \propto \rho^{2/3}$, consistent with prior contraction with conserved angular momentum. Evidently the differentially rotating models undergo fragmentation in spite of their initial central concentration because the strong initial rotation quickly produces a flattened disk that undergoes a rotational instability.

Models of the onset of dynamic collapse in magnetically supported clouds undergoing loss of field support through ambipolar diffusion (Tomisaka et al.;[19] Mouschovias[20]) show that the power-law profiles of such clouds flatten out near the cloud center. This behavior suggests that a Gaussian ($\rho_i \propto \exp[-(r/R)^2]$) initial

---

FIGURE 2. Time evolution of a collapsing dense cloud core that undergoes fragmentation into a binary protostellar system. Density contours and velocity vectors in the equatorial plane are shown at four times (**a**)–(**b**) 0.0 t_{ff}; (**c**)–(**d**) 1.427 t_{ff}; (**e**)–(**f**) 1.432 t_{ff}; and (**g**)–(**h**) 1.437 t_{ff}. Density contours represent changes in density by a factor of 2. The logarithms of the maximum density (in g cm^{-3}) and maximum velocities (in cm s^{-1}) and the radius of the region plotted are noted. The initial cloud had a Gaussian radial density profile with a central density (2×10^{-18} g cm^{-3}), which was 20 times that at the boundary, distorted into a spheroidal configuration with a 2:1 axis ratio, and with random noise added as well. The initial cloud had a mass of $1.5 M_\odot$, with $\alpha_i = 0.39$, $\beta_i = 0.012$, and $T_i = 10$ K. The central regions heat up to ~ 100 K during this early formation phase.

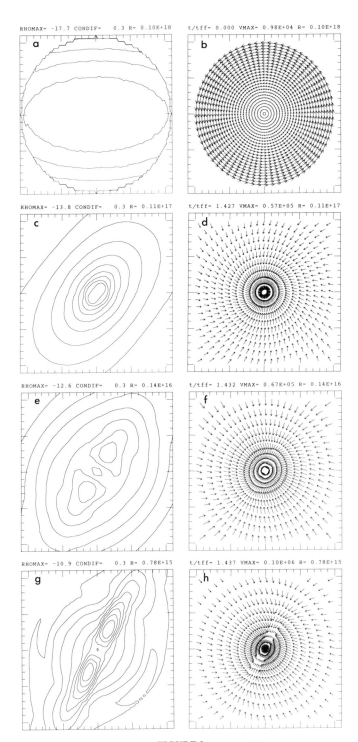

FIGURE 2.

radial density profile might be a reasonable approximation for clouds starting collapse from previously magnetically supported configurations. A new sequence of isothermal models[21] with Gaussian profiles such that the central density was 20 times that at the boundary, $\beta_i = 0.16$, and varied $\alpha_i = 0.06$ to 0.4, all collapsed and underwent binary fragmentation. The binary fragments in the model with $\alpha_i = 0.26$ each underwent subfragmentation, forming a hierarchical system of four protostellar cores.

Lower initial rotation rates ($\beta_i \sim 0.01, 0.0001$) have also been examined with a new finite-difference code;[7] such models quickly reach central densities in excess of $\sim 10^{-13}$ g cm^{-3} and so require the solution of the equation of radiative transfer. The new set of models also starts from Gaussian initial density profiles, though now with the prolate spheroidal configuration suggested by observations of dense cloud cores.[10] As in the case of initially uniform density (FIG. 1), the models show that the result of the collapse depends on α_i. For a sequence of models with $\beta_i = 0.01$ and a 2:1 ratio between the axes of the prolate spheroidal initial cloud, a cloud with $M = 1.5M_\odot$ and $\alpha_i = 0.39$ collapses to form a bar that fragments into a binary (FIG. 2), a cloud with $M = 1.25M_\odot$ and $\alpha_i = 0.46$ collapses but does not appear to undergo fragmentation, while a cloud with $M = 1.0M_\odot$ and $\alpha_i = 0.56$ expands. This work is still in progress, with the intent being to map out the parameter space for initially nonuniform density clouds in a manner similar to that of FIGURE 1.

All of the three-dimensional collapse calculations discussed so far depict the initial collapse phase, starting from dense molecular cloud cores. One set of models[22] evaluated the possibility of fragmentation during the second collapse phase, starting from the first protostellar core at the point of dissociation. Those calculations suggested that fragmentation generally would not occur during the second collapse phase, because any final protostellar core fragments that form cannot contract to much smaller sizes, and so are much more susceptible to orbital decay and merging caused by the loss of orbital angular momentum to trailing, nonaxisymmetric nebula structures.

FORMATION OF THE SOLAR NEBULA

The calculations of the previous section imply that single stars may form from the collapse of centrally condensed, molecular cloud cores that have intermediate values of thermal energy and relatively small amounts of rotational energy. After such a cloud collapses and forms a central protostellar core, several of the main questions of interest have to do with the centrifugally supported disk that builds up around the protostar. The great majority of the disk material (with high specific angular momentum compared to even a rapidly rotating pre-main-sequence star[23]) must lower its specific angular momentum so that it can accrete onto the protostar. What is the physical mechanism primarily responsible for this large-scale processing? What is the physical structure of the disk during these early phases when matter is accreting onto the disk from the envelope of the cloud core, at the same time disk matter is accreting onto the central protostar? Can one find plausible initial cloud cores that would collapse to form a disk (the solar nebula) likely to be able to produce a planetary system resembling our own? The third question is perhaps the ultimate unknown driving theoretical studies of the solar nebula, and its solution is intimately tied to the answers to the first two questions.

Nonaxisymmetry

Several physical mechanisms have been proposed for driving solar nebula evolution: viscous stresses due to turbulent viscosity, magnetic fields, acoustic waves, and gravitational torques from nonaxisymmetric mass distributions. Here we discuss briefly the few studies related to the question of the degree of nonaxisymmetry in the solar nebula. This topic has received much less attention than many other solar nebula problems, no doubt largely because of the difficulty: a rigorous solution would require a fully three-dimensional calculation of the evolution of a rotating disk over the timescale of many orbital revolutions. While some progress has been made, we are still far from being able to solve this problem in its entirety.

Cassen et al.[24] performed the first major study of the nonaxisymmetric structure of possible preplanetary disks. Using an N-body code to simulate the fluid dynamics of a thin, isothermal disk confined to a plane, Cassen et al.[24] found that the stability of the disk was a strong function of two parameters, the ratio of the mass of the disk to that of the central protostar, and the disk temperature. For a cool disk at 100 K, the disk rapidly broke up into ~ 5 clumps when the disk mass was ten times that of the star. This self-gravitational instability occurred within two-thirds of the rotation period at the outer edge of the disk. Such a massive disk, however, presumably would have undergone dynamic evolution prior to reaching this strongly unstable initial state. Cassen et al.[24] also showed what would happen in the more realistic situation of a disk with a mass comparable to that of the central star: rather than undergoing break-up, such a disk quickly develops a strong pattern of trailing spiral arms, resembling the appearance of some spiral and barred galaxies.

Adams, Ruden, and Shu[25] have performed a linearized analysis of the growth of spiral density waves in a thin, nearly Keplerian disk with specified radial surface density and thermal profiles. They found that the dominant unstable mode was the $m = 1$ mode, which would shift the center of mass of the system were it not balanced by a shift in the position of the central protostar. The resulting wobble of the protostar excites these density waves, which propagate outward, reflect off the outer boundary of the disk, and propagate back into the disk, resulting in growth on the timescale of the rotation period at the disk edge. This mechanism requires that the disk have a relatively sharp edge (see also the paper by G. Savonije et al.[26] in this volume for another investigation of this instability). The evolution of these eccentric disk modes in the nonlinear regime is just beginning to be uncovered, but Adams, Ruden, and Shu[25] suggest that the instability could either lead to significant mass accretion by the central protostar or even to formation of a binary companion.

The only three-dimensional study of the nonaxisymmetric structure of solar nebula models[27] attempted to model the structure of disks as they formed by collapse from an extraordinarily dense cloud core into the equatorial plane of a preexisting protostar capable of accreting disk mass. A sequence of models involving the collapse of a $1M_\odot$ cloud onto a protostar with its initial mass varied from 0 to $0.1M_\odot$ to $1M_\odot$ showed again[24] the importance of the disk to central star mass ratio (M_d/M_s). The first model formed a disk with $M_d/M_s \sim 100$, and fragmented into a binary system.

The second model formed a disk with $M_d/M_s \sim 5$, and became mildly nonaxisymmetric, while the third model formed a disk with $M_d/M_s \sim 2$, and remained fairly axisymmetric. The second model is perhaps the most realistic, considering that final protostellar cores start out with masses on the order of $0.01 M_\odot$. This model developed a trailing spiral arm pattern that produced gravitational torques strong enough (if sustained over many rotation periods) to transport all of the disk's angular momentum over a time period of less than 10^5 years, which is a relatively short time on the scale set by pre-main-sequence stellar evolution.

Thermal Structure

The question of the thermal structure of the solar nebula is crucial for planet formation for several reasons. First, the thermal structure will determine which regions become convectively unstable; convective motions could serve as a physical source of turbulent viscosity.[28] Second, the turbulent motions associated with convection could prevent dust grains and agglomerations from settling into a thin layer in the nebula midplane that would be dense enough to undergo the self-gravitational instability suggested by Goldreich and Ward[29] as a major step along the planet-formation sequence. Third, the disk temperature will determine the location and abundances of many solid phases, and in particular will affect the radius outside of which water and ammonia ices can remain stable. Fourth, and not least by any means, the thermal structure may have left its imprint in the form of evidence for thermal transients or sustained high temperatures implied by laboratory analysis of meteorites and samples of the terrestrial planets.

Viscous accretion disk models commonly rely on a balance between radiative losses from the disk surface and internal heating from viscous dissipation to produce steady-state thermal profiles (e.g., Wood and Morfill[30]). These models address relatively late phases of nebula evolution, after the compressional energy liberated by the initial collapse phase has presumably been radiated away. If we wish to study the earliest phases of nebula formation, including the initial thermal history, the nebula model must include the accretion of gas by the disk as well as the accretion of disk gas by the central protostar. The most important physical processes (e.g., compression from collapse, radiative losses) associated with the early thermal history can be studied with hydrodynamic collapse codes.

Tscharnuter[31] used his donor-cell hydrodynamics code to study the axisymmetric collapse of a $1.2 M_\odot$ cloud starting from a centrally condensed initial configuration with a central density of $\sim 3 \times 10^{-14}$ g cm^{-3} and a central temperature of 47 K. Angular momentum was transported outward during the calculation at a rate consistent with a turbulent nebula with a turbulent velocity equal to 0.3 times the speed of sound. Because of this angular momentum transport, and the implicit time differencing (which allows arbitrarily large time steps to be taken), the evolution was followed quite far in time, up to the point where the final protostellar core had formed and grown in mass to $\sim 0.06 M_\odot$. Because of the high initial density, the mass accretion rate of the final protostellar core was quite high, $\sim 10^{-2} M_\odot$ yr^{-1}. Inner disk temperatures were correspondingly high as well, falling to 1600 K only for radii greater than 5 AU. Because the disk mass is much greater than the protostellar mass, this model describes a very early phase of nebula evolution, well before the start of planetary accumulation.

Boss 1989[27] calculated three-dimensional donor-cell models of solar nebula formation, using the numerical artifice of a "sink cell" to represent the growing protostellar core. This artifice sidesteps calculating the physics of the protostellar core that was included in the Tscharnuter[31] calculation. The "sink cell" acted as a point source of gravity, growing in mass as gas accreted during the collapse. Starting from even higher densities ($\sim 10^{-13}$ to 10^{-12} g cm^{-3}) than Tscharnuter,[31] and initial temperatures of 10 K, some of these calculations produced $\sim 1M_\odot$ protostellar cores surrounded by relatively low mass (~ 0.05 to $\sim 0.2M_\odot$) disks. The disks had temperatures of ≈ 1500 K out to about 4 AU, dropping sharply for larger radii in the optically thin outer regions of the nebula. The nearly uniform, inner nebula temperature of ~ 1500 K was attributed to the thermostatic effect of the opacity, which is primarily due to iron grains at those temperatures; the iron grains vaporize for higher temperatures, dropping the opacity by a large factor and thereby increasing the cooling rate. However, the extremely high mass accretion rates ($\sim 10^{-3}$–$10^{-2}M_\odot$ yr^{-1}) in these models restricts the applicability of the models; mass accretion rates in the range $\sim 10^{-6}$–$10^{-4}M_\odot$ yr^{-1} are usually thought to be appropriate for low-mass star formation.

Bodenheimer et al.[32] calculated an axisymmetric solar nebula, starting from a power-law initial density profile ($n = 2$) with a central density $\sim 4 \times 10^{-11}$ g cm^{-3} and a uniform temperature of 20 K. A sink cell was employed to represent the central protostar, as in Boss,[27] though now with the sink cell allowed to radiate its energy into the rest of the cloud. The cloud was followed to the point where a quasi-hydrostatic disk had formed, with a mass $\approx 0.4M_\odot$, surrounding a protostellar mass of $\approx 0.6M_\odot$. The temperature profile in the disk midplane was relatively flat, with inner nebula (<5-AU) values ranging from 1300 K early in the calculation to about 800 K at the end. Again, this disk must undergo substantial evolution (i.e., mass accretion by the central protostar) before becoming a mature protoplanetary disk.

A series of axisymmetric solar nebula-formation models is in progress, using a new spatially second-order accurate hydrodynamics code.[7] These models attempt to leap forward in time to the mature protoplanetary disk phase, by using a sink cell with an initial mass of $1M_\odot$, and initial power law density ($n = 3/2$) and velocity ($n = 1/2$) profiles appropriate for the free-fall accretion of gas.[16] The disk has an initial mass of about $0.05M_\odot$, resulting in mass accretion rates onto the central protostar ranging from 10^{-4} to $10^{-3}M_\odot$ yr^{-1}. This mass accretion produces a central luminosity that heats the central cloud. The initial temperature profile ($T \propto r^{-5/4}$) yields a simple starting solution for the radiative transfer equation, and is usually normalized to 1500 K at 1 AU. The initial temperature profile relaxes to a quasi-steady profile determined by the heating and cooling processes in the nebula, with $T \approx 1400$ K inside 5 AU in a model including heating from artificial viscosity. However, it was found that the inner disk temperatures depend on this artificial viscous heating; when this heating was eliminated, the temperature at 2 AU dropped to ≈ 700 in one model. In comparison, lowering the mass accretion rate by a factor of 3 produced only slightly lower temperatures (≈ 1300 K) in the inner nebula.

The models described in this subsection show that compared to the problem of fragmentation of protostellar disks, the problem of determining the physical structure and evolution of protoplanetary disks is in an even more embryonic phase, with major challenges still remaining. Considerably more work will be required before we can make a satisfactory link with the theoretical studies of planetary accumulation described by Ward in this volume.[33]

REFERENCES

1. BODENHEIMER, P., T. RUZMAIKINA & R. D. MATHIEU. 1992. Stellar multiple systems: Constraints on the mechanism of origin. *In* Protostars & Planets III, E. H. Levy, J. I. Lunine, and M. S. Matthews, Eds. Univ. of Arizona Press, Tucson. In press.
2. BOSS, A. P. 1990. Fragmentation of isothermal and nonisothermal protostellar clouds. *In* Physical Processes in Fragmentation and Star Formation, R. Capuzzo-Dolcetta, C. Chiosi, and A. DiFazio, Eds.: 279–292. Kluwer. Dordrecht, the Netherlands.
3. MONAGHAN, J. J. 1988. A introduction to SPH. Comput. Phys. Commun. **48:** 89–96.
4. BONNELL, I., H. MARTEL, P. BASTIEN, J.-P. ARCORAGI & W. BENZ. 1991. Fragmentation of elongated cylindrical clouds. III. Formation of binary and multiple systems. Astrophys. J. **377:** 553–558.
5. SIGALOTTI, L. D. G. 1990. Gravitational collapse of rotating protostellar gas clouds not constrained by the condition of equatorial symmetry. Mon. Not. R. Astron. Soc. **246:** 243–255.
6. MYHILL, E. A. & W. M. KAULA. 1992. Numerical models of the collapse and fragmentation of centrally condensed molecular cloud cores. Astrophys. J. **386:** 578–586.
7. BOSS, A. P. & E. A. MYHILL. 1992. Protostellar hydrodynamics: constructing and testing a spatially second-order accurate method. I. Spherical Coordinates. Astrophys. J., Suppl. Ser. In press.
8. FELICE, F. D. & L. D. G. SIGALOTTI. 1991. Tidally induced fragmentation of rotating protostellar gas clouds. Mon. Not. R Astron. Soc. **249:** 248–261.
9. BASTIEN, P., J.-P. ARCORAGI, W. BENZ, I. BONNELL & H. MARTEL. 1991. Fragmentation of elongated cylindrical clouds I. Isothermal clouds. Astrophys. J. **378:** 255–265.
10. MYERS, P. C., G. A. FULLER, A. A. GOODMAN & P. J. BENSON. 1991. Dense cores in dark clouds. VI. Shapes. Astrophys. J. **376:** 561–572.
11. BOSS, A. P. 1992. Formation of binary stars. *In* The Realm of Interacting Binary Stars, J. Sahade, G. McCluskey, and Y. Kondo, Eds. Kluwer. Dordrecht, the Netherlands. In press.
12. MONAGHAN, J. J. & J. C. LATTANZIO. 1991. A simulation of the collapse and fragmentation of cooling molecular clouds. Astrophys. J. **375:** 177–189.
13. BOSS, A. P. & J. G. HABER. 1982. Axisymmetric collapse of rotating, interstellar clouds. Astrophys. J. **255:** 240–244.
14. MIYAMA, S. M., C. HAYASHI & S. NARITA. 1984. Criteria for collapse and fragmentation of rotating, isothermal clouds. Astrophys. J. **279:** 621–632.
15. LARSON, R. B. 1969. Numerical calculations of the dynamics of a collapsing proto-star. Mon. Not. R. Astron. Soc. **145:** 271–295.
16. SHU, F. H. 1977. Self-similar collapse of isothermal spheres and star formation. Astrophys. J. **214:** 488–497.
17. ZHOU, S., N. J. EVANS II, H. M. BUTNER, M. L. KUTNER, C. M. LEUNG & L. G. MUNDY. 1990. Testing star formation theories: VLA observations of H_2CO in the Bok Globule B335. Astrophys. J. **363:** 168–179.
18. BOSS, A. P. 1987. Protostellar formation in rotating interstellar clouds. VI. Nonuniform initial conditions. Astrophys. J. **319:** 149–161.
19. TOMASAKA, K., S. IKEUCHI & T. NAKAMURA. 1990. The equilibria and evolutions of magnetized, rotating, isothermal clouds. IV. Quasistatic evolution. Astrophys. J. **362:** 202–214.
20. MOUSCHOVIAS, T. CH. 1991. Magnetic braking, ambipolar diffusion, cloud cores, and star formation: Natural length scales and protostellar masses. Astrophys. J. **373:** 169–186.

21. Boss, A. P. 1991. Formation of hierarchical multiple protostellar cores. Nature **351:** 298–300.

22. ———. 1989. Protostellar formation in rotating, interstellar clouds. VIII. Inner core formation. Astrophys. J. **346:** 336–349.

23. Bodenheimer, P., M. Różyczka, H. W. Yorke & J. E. Tohline. 1988. Collapse of a rotating interstellar cloud. In Formation and Evolution of Low Mass Stars, A. K. Dupree & M. T. V. T. Lago, Eds.: 139–151. Kluwer, Dordrecht, the Netherlands.

24. Cassen, P. M., B. F. Smith, R. H. Miller & R. T. Reynolds. 1981. Numerical experiments on the stability of preplanetary disks. Icarus **48:** 377–392.

25. Adams, F. C., S. P. Ruden & F. H. Shu. 1989. Eccentric gravitational instabilities in nearly Keplerian disks. Astrophys. J. **347:** 959–975.

26. Savonije, G. J., J. C. Papaloizou & M. H. M. Heemskerk. 1992. Unstable interaction between a self-gravitating gaseous disk and its central mass. This issue.

27. Boss, A. P. 1989. Evolution of the solar nebula I. Nonaxisymmetric structure during nebula formation. Astrophys. J. **345:** 554–571.

28. Lin, D. N. C. & J. Papaloizou. 1980. On the structure and evolution of the primordial solar nebula. Mon. Not. R Astron. Soc. **191:** 37–48.

29. Goldreich, P. & W. R. Ward. 1973. The formation of planetesimals. Astrophys. J. **183:** 1051–1061.

30. Wood, J. A. & G. E. Morfill. 1988. A review of solar nebula models. In Meteorites and the Early Solar System, J. F. Kerridge and M. S. Matthews, Eds.: 329–347. Univ. of Arizona Press. Tucson.

31. Tscharnuter, W. M. 1987. A collapse model of the turbulent presolar nebula. Astron. Astrophys. **188:** 55–73.

32. Bodenheimer, P., H. W. Yorke, M. Różyczka & J. E. Tohline. 1990. The formation phase of the solar nebula. Astrophys. J. **355:** 651–660.

33. Ward, W. R. 1992. Disk–protoplanet interactions: Torques from the coorbital zone. This issue.

Disk–Protoplanet Interactions: Torques from the Coorbital Zone[a]

WILLIAM R. WARD

Jet Propulsion Laboratory
California Institute of Technology
Pasadena, California 91109

INTRODUCTION

Disk–protoplanet tidal interactions have become an important issue in modeling solar system formation. Until the early 1980s, the principal dynamical effect of a circumstellar disk (aside from providing the accreting material) was assumed to be the influence of aerodynamic drag. Although drag is an important mechanism for modifying the orbits of small planetesimals (i.e., centimeters to meters in size), its importance diminishes as planetesimals grow and their surface-to-volume ratio decreases. Accretion models generally predict that it is the end-stage of accretion, when objects are relatively large, remote, and characterized by low collision probabilities that requires the overwhelming majority of the time necessary to assemble a planetary-sized object. Hence, although important in early stages of growth, it seems unlikely that drag has more than a minor influence on overall accretion timescales.

With increasing applications of density wave theory to planetary ring problems, it has become evident that disk tidal torques may also play an important role in coupling an emerging planetary system to its precursor nebula.[1,2] Indeed, since disk torques tend to scale with the square of the protoplanet's mass, they become *more* important as objects grow and would complement drag effects. The combined influence of these two processes could provide a degree of radial mobility to accreting material over virtually the entire size range spanned by the growth process. Thus, a key question under study is whether the incorporation of density wave torques in accretion modeling can significantly shorten the predicted timescales for planetary formation. This issue has particular application to the formation of the giant planets. By virtue of their predominately hydrogen and helium composition, the formation of Jupiter and Saturn clearly predated nebula dispersal. However, the estimated lifetime for the solar nebula based on T-tauri observations is only of order 10^6–10^7 years, a factor of $O(10^2)$ shorter than estimates for the formation of the giant planet cores based on "standard" accretion models without density wave assistance.

The first attempt to quantitatively assess the importance of disk tides in the context of the solar nebula was made by Goldreich and Tremaine.[3] They calculated the torques associated with Lindblad and corotation resonances and related these torques to changes in both the perturber's semimajor axis and eccentricity. As an application, a Jovian-sized protoplanet embedded in a minimum mass model solar

[a]This research was supported by NASA under contract with the Jet Propulsion Laboratory, California Institute of Technology. This paper is based on an invited talk presented at the Seventh Annual Florida Workshop in Nonlinear Astrophysics: Astrophysical Disks.

nebula was considered. It was concluded that density wave torques could, indeed, significantly alter the protoplanet's orbit an interval that was much shorter than its expected accretion timescale. This strongly supports the notion that the omission of disk tides from accretion models is potentially a serious deficiency. Subsequent studies have further clarified the role of disk torques and suggest that the accretion of the giant planet cores may have been especially influenced by their operation.[4] Although progress has been made on many issues, other areas remain uncertain. In particular, this paper discusses possible effects of *coorbiting* corotation resonances, that is, corotation resonances that fall in the region of the disk referred to as the horseshoe orbit region. These resonances were omitted in the original treatment by Goldreich and Tremaine, but could have important consequences for orbit evolution.

COROTATION TORQUE

Consider a protoplanet of mass M orbiting a primary, $M_\odot$, in a circular orbit with angular velocity, Ω_p, and embedded in a disk of surface density $\sigma(r)$ and rotational frequency, $\Omega(r)$. The disturbing function is

$$\Phi = -\frac{GM}{|\mathbf{r} - \mathbf{r}_p|} + \frac{M}{M_\odot} \Omega^2 (\mathbf{r} \cdot \mathbf{r}_p), \tag{1a}$$

which contains both direct and indirect parts. For a circular orbit, Φ can be Fourier decomposed into a fundamental term with frequency, Ω_p, and its harmonics

$$\Phi = \sum_m \phi_m \cos m(\theta - \Omega_p t). \tag{1b}$$

The wavelength of the mth-order Fourier component is $\lambda = 2\pi r/m$, and all terms have a pattern speed, Ω_{ps}, that is equal to the orbital frequency of the perturber, Ω_p.

For each mth-order term there are generally three positions in the disk where a resonant interaction exists: a corotation resonance, where the local orbital frequency equals the pattern speed, $\Omega = \Omega_{ps}$; and inner and outer Lindblad resonances, where the local epicycle frequency equals the Doppler-shifted forcing frequency, $\kappa = \pm m(\Omega - \Omega_{ps})$. At each resonance there is a forced disturbance in the surface density of the disk. At Lindblad resonances, the disturbance is in the form of spiral density waves that for a non-self-gravitating disk, propagate away from corotation. A torque is associated with the perturber's attraction for this disturbance[5]

$$T_m^L = \frac{m\pi^2\sigma}{\mathscr{D}} \left[r\frac{d\phi_m}{dr} \pm 2m\phi_m \right]^2, \tag{2}$$

where $\mathscr{D} = rd/dr\{\kappa^2 - m^2(\Omega - \Omega_{ps})^2\} = \pm 3m\Omega$ to lowest order at inner and outer resonances, respectively. At a corotation resonance, disk material is set into libration around the pattern speed. The associated torque is

$$T_m^c = \frac{m\pi^2\phi_m^2}{2(-d\Omega/dr)} \frac{d}{dr} \left(\frac{\sigma}{B}\right), \tag{3}$$

where $B = (2r)^{-1}d(r^2\Omega)/dr$ is the disk vorticity. Both (2) and (3) are derived for low-order resonances in a thin disk with wavelengths longer than the disk scale height, $m \ll h/r$. For high order, the formulas must include a correction factor $f(\xi)$ called the torque cutoff that is a function of $\xi \equiv mh/r$. The exact form of the function depends on the resonance type, but $f(\xi)$ generally approaches zero quickly as $\xi \gg 1$. In this paper, we concentrate on (3) in the vicinity of the coorbital circle, $r = r_p$.

The Fourier amplitudes of (1b) can be written in terms of generalized Laplace coefficients, $b_s^m(\gamma, z)$:

$$\phi_m = -\frac{GM_p}{2r_p}(2 - \delta_{m,0})(b_{1/2}^m(\gamma, z) - \gamma\delta_{m,1}) \tag{4}$$

where $\mathbf{r} = r\mathbf{e}_r + z\mathbf{e}_z$, $\gamma = r/r_p$, δ is the Kronecker delta, and

$$b_s^m(\gamma, z) = \frac{2}{\pi}\int_0^\pi \frac{\cos m\theta \, d\theta}{(1 - 2\gamma\cos\theta + \gamma^2 + (z/r_p)^2)^s}. \tag{5}$$

Following Goldreich and Tremaine,[3] if $m \gg 1$ and $(1 - \gamma)^2 + (z/r_p)^2 \ll 1$, $\cos\theta$ can be replaced by $1 - \theta^2/2$ in the denominator to a good approximation and the integration limit extended to ∞. Since we are interested in the nearby coorbiting region, γ is set to unity except when it appears in the combination $(1 - \gamma)$. Integration with $s = 1/2$ then gives the Laplace coefficient in terms of a modified Bessel function, that is,

$$b_{1/2}^m(\gamma, z) \approx \frac{2}{\pi}K_0(\sqrt{m^2(1 - \gamma)^2 + (mz/r)^2}) = \frac{2}{\pi}K_0(\sqrt{\alpha^2 + t^2}), \tag{6}$$

where $\alpha = m|1 - \gamma|$ and $t = mz/r_p$. Laplace coefficients diverge at $\gamma = 1$, $z = 0$. However, if we consider a gaseous protoplanetary disk with a finite scale height $h \sim c/\Omega$, most of the disk material does *not* lie in the orbit plane of the perturber ($z = 0$). This suggests we might vertically average the equations of motion including the disturbing potential. Essentially, this assumes that a column of disk material responds as a unit to the total torque exerted on it. Since in the vicinity of a corotation resonance, the pattern speed of the perturbing terms are nearly equal to the local speed of the disk, the Doppler-shifted frequency is very low and the disk should remain in near hydrostatic equilibrium. Vertical averaging will be most valid for wavelengths $\gtrsim O(h)$.

The Fourier expansion of the vertically averaged potential, $\langle\phi\rangle$, can now be obtained by simply averaging (4), that is, $\langle\phi\rangle = \Sigma\langle\phi_m\rangle\cos m(\theta - \Omega_p t)$, where

$$\langle\phi_m\rangle = -\frac{GM_p}{2r_p}(2 - \delta_{m,0})\left(\frac{2}{\pi}\langle K_0\rangle - \gamma\delta_{m,1}\right). \tag{7}$$

For the coorbiting region, $\gamma \to 1$, $\alpha \to 0$,[6]

$$\langle K_0\rangle = \frac{1}{h\sqrt{\pi}}\int_{-\infty}^{\infty} e^{-(z/h)^2}K_0(m|z|/r_p)\,dz$$

$$= \frac{2}{\xi\sqrt{\pi}}\int_0^\infty e^{-(t/\xi)^2}K_0(t)\,dt = \frac{1}{2}\exp\left(\frac{\xi^2}{8}\right)K_0\left(\frac{\xi^2}{8}\right). \tag{8}$$

Combining (3), (7), and (8), restricting our attention to $m \geq 2$, and using the Oort constant, $A \equiv (r/2)d\Omega/dr$,

$$T_m = 4m\sigma \left(\frac{GM_p}{r_p\kappa}\right)^2 \left(\frac{\Omega}{A}\right)\left(\frac{d\ln(\sigma/B)}{d\ln r}\right)\left[\frac{1}{2}\exp\left(\frac{\xi^2}{8}\right)K_0\left(\frac{\xi^2}{8}\right)\right]^2. \tag{9}$$

The total torque is to be found by summing (9) over all orders, m. However, at large $m \gg r/h$, $\xi \gg 1$, the asymptotic form of the Bessel function is $K_0(\xi^2/8) \approx 2\sqrt{\pi}\xi^{-1}\exp - (\xi^2/8)\{1 - \xi^{-2} + (9/2)\xi^{-4} + \cdots\}$ and $T_m \propto m\xi^{-2} \propto \xi^{-1}$. Consequently, an integral of the form $T_C = \Sigma T_m dm \rightarrow (r/h)\int T_m d\xi$ will diverge logarithmically as $m, \xi \rightarrow \infty$.

TORQUE CUTOFF

Ward[7] has argued that at high order, $m \gg r\kappa/c$, additional terms should be included in the equation for density perturbations at a corotation resonance, and that this leads to a modified form for the torque:

$$T_m = \frac{m\pi^2 r\sigma}{c^2 q^2}\phi_m(\phi_m - \psi_m/q^2)\left(\frac{\Omega}{A}\right)\frac{d}{dr}\ln\left(\frac{\sigma}{B}\right), \tag{10}$$

where

$$q^2 = \frac{\kappa^2}{c^2} + \frac{m^2}{r^2}\left(1 - 2\frac{A}{B} + \frac{A^2}{\Omega B}\right) \tag{11}$$

$$\psi_m = -\frac{d^2\phi_m}{dr^2} + \frac{m^2}{r^2}\phi\left(1 - 2\frac{A}{B}\right). \tag{12}$$

The ratio of (10) to (3) defines a torque cutoff function, $f(\xi)$, for high-order resonances that must be included in the torque integral:

$$f(\xi) = \left(\frac{\phi_m - \psi_m/q^2}{\phi_m}\right)\left(\frac{\kappa}{cq}\right)^2 = \frac{1 + \xi^2(\Omega/\kappa)^2(A^2/\Omega B) + (c/\kappa)^2\ddot\phi_m/\phi_m}{[1 + \xi^2(\Omega/\kappa)^2(1 - 2A/B + A^2/\Omega B)]^2}. \tag{13}$$

The final term in the numerator of (13) contains the second derivative, $d^2\phi_m/dr^2 = -(2/\pi)(GM_p/r_p^3)d^2\langle K_0\rangle/d\gamma^2$, which must be evaluated at $\gamma = 1$, $\alpha = 0$ to complete the cutoff function.

Following Ward,[6] we write $d^n\langle K_0\rangle/d\gamma^n = \sqrt{\pi}\, m^n\xi^{-1}\mathscr{F}_n(\alpha, \xi)$, where $\mathscr{F}_n = (-1)^n d^n\mathscr{F}_0/d\alpha^n$, and

$$\mathscr{F}_0(\alpha, \xi) = \frac{2}{\pi}\int_0^\infty e^{-(t/\xi)^2}K_0(\sqrt{\alpha^2 + t^2})\, dt. \tag{14}$$

Differentiating (14) with respect to α yields

$$\mathscr{F}_1(\alpha, \xi) = \frac{2}{\pi}\int_0^\infty e^{-(t/\xi)^2}\frac{\alpha K_1(\sqrt{\alpha^2 + t^2})}{\sqrt{\alpha^2 + t^2}}\, dt \tag{15}$$

$$\mathscr{F}_2(\alpha, \xi) = \frac{2}{\pi} \int_0^\infty e^{-(t/\xi)^2} \left\{ \frac{K_1(\sqrt{\alpha^2 + t^2})}{\sqrt{\alpha^2 + t^2}} - \frac{\alpha^2 K_2(\sqrt{\alpha^2 + t^2})}{\sqrt{\alpha^2 + t^2}} \right\} dt. \tag{16}$$

Quantities $\mathscr{F}_n(0, \xi)$ can then be found by letting $\alpha \to 0$ in (14)–(16). FIGURE 1 which is taken from Ward,[6] displays the behaviors of $\mathscr{F}_n(0, \xi)$ as functions of ξ. In particular, $\mathscr{F}_1(0, \xi) \equiv 1$, while $\mathscr{F}_2(0, \xi)$ approaches unity for large ξ, but increases as $2/\xi\sqrt{\pi}$ for $\xi \ll 1$.

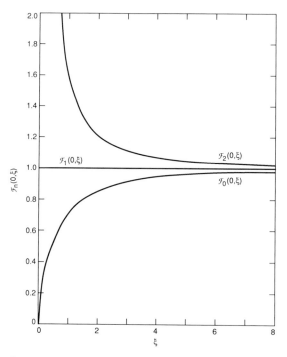

FIGURE 1. Amplitude function and its derivatives vs. ξ for the vertically averaged potential. (From Ward.[6] Reproduced by permission.)

To obtain analytic expressions for $\mathscr{F}_n(0, \xi)$, the Bessel function, K_0, is replaced with an alternative integral representation[8]

$$K_0(\sqrt{\alpha^2 + t^2}) = \int_0^\infty \frac{\cos tx}{\sqrt{x^2 + 1}} \exp -\alpha\sqrt{x^2 + 1} \, dx. \tag{17}$$

Reversing the order of integration in (14) and using the definite integral, $\int_0^\infty \exp\left[-(t/\xi)^2\right] \cos (tx) \, dx = (\sqrt{\pi}/2)\xi \exp\left[-(\xi x/2)^2\right]$, leads to an alternative version of $\mathscr{F}_0 (\alpha, \xi)$:

$$\mathscr{F}_0(\alpha, \xi) = \frac{\xi}{\sqrt{\pi}} \int_0^\infty \exp\left[-\left(\frac{\xi x}{2}\right)^2 - \alpha\sqrt{x^2 + 1}\right] \frac{dx}{\sqrt{x^2 + 1}}. \tag{18}$$

Note that setting $\alpha = 0$ and integrating yields

$$\mathscr{F}_0(0, \xi) = \frac{\xi}{\sqrt{\pi}} \int_0^\infty e^{-(\xi x/2)^2} \frac{dx}{\sqrt{x^2 + 1}} = \frac{1}{2} \frac{\xi}{\sqrt{\pi}} \exp\left(\frac{\xi^2}{8}\right) K_0\left(\frac{\xi^2}{8}\right), \tag{19}$$

which, when multiplied by $\sqrt{\pi}/\xi$, recovers (8). Successive differentiation of (18) with respect to α, prior to setting it to zero, provides integral forms for $\mathscr{F}_1(0, \xi)$ and $\mathscr{F}_2(0, \xi)$:

$$\mathscr{F}_1(0, \xi) = \frac{\xi}{\sqrt{\pi}} \int_0^\infty e^{-(\xi x/2)^2} dx \tag{20}$$

$$\mathscr{F}_2(0, \xi) = \frac{\xi}{\sqrt{\pi}} \int_0^\infty e^{-(\xi x/2)^2} \sqrt{x^2 + 1} \, dx. \tag{21}$$

Equation (20) is now easily recognized as the complete error function, that is, $\mathscr{F}_1(0, \xi) = \text{erf}(\infty) \equiv 1$. [The result also follows directly from (15) if, in the limit $\alpha \to 0$, one identifies $\alpha K_1/(\alpha^2 + t^2)^{1/2} \to \pi \delta(t)$, where $\delta(t)$ is the Dirac delta function.[6]] Finally, to find $\mathscr{F}_2(0, \xi)$, note that the integral in (21) is a special case of

$$\mathscr{I}(\beta, \xi) = \int_0^\infty e^{-(\xi x/2)^2} \sqrt{x^2 + \beta} \, dx. \tag{22}$$

Differentiating (22) with respect to β, and changing variables to $x' = x/\sqrt{\beta}$ gives

$$\frac{d\mathscr{I}}{d\beta} = \frac{1}{2} \int_0^\infty e^{-\beta(\xi x'/2)^2} \frac{dx'}{\sqrt{x'^2 + 1}} = \frac{1}{4} \exp\left(\frac{\beta \xi^2}{8}\right) K_0\left(\frac{\beta \xi^2}{8}\right), \tag{23}$$

where the integration follows directly by comparison with (19). Integration of (23) is now done via King's integral,[9] $\int e^t K_0(t) \, dt = te^t[K_1(t) + K_0(t)]$. Setting $\beta = 1$ and multiplying the result by $\xi/\sqrt{\pi}$ yields $\mathscr{F}_2(0, \xi)$;

$$\mathscr{F}_2(0, \xi) = \frac{1}{4} \frac{\xi}{\pi} \exp\left(\frac{\xi^2}{8}\right)\left[K_1\left(\frac{\xi^2}{8}\right) + K_0\left(\frac{\xi^2}{8}\right)\right]. \tag{24}$$

As $\xi \to \infty$, $K_\nu(\xi^2/8) \to (2\sqrt{\pi}/\xi) \exp -(\xi^2/8)$ and $\mathscr{F}_2(0, \xi) \to 1$; as $\xi \to 0$, $\mathscr{F}_2(0, \xi) \to (2/\sqrt{\pi})[\xi^{-1} - (\xi/4)\ln(\xi/2) + \cdots]$, which confirms the limiting behaviors found by Ward.[6]

The quantity $\langle \ddot{\phi} \rangle / \langle \phi \rangle$ can now be evaluated:

$$\langle \ddot{\phi} \rangle / \langle \phi \rangle = \left(\frac{m}{r}\right)^2 \frac{\mathscr{F}_2(0, \xi)}{\mathscr{F}_0(0, \xi)} = \frac{1}{2}\left(\frac{m}{r}\right)^2\left[1 + \frac{K_1(\xi^2/8)}{K_0(\xi^2/8)}\right] \tag{25}$$

and the complete cutoff function written as

$$f(\xi) = \frac{1 + \xi^2(\Omega/\kappa)^2[A^2/\Omega B + 1/2 + K_1(\xi^2/8)/2K_0(\xi^2/8)]}{[1 + \xi^2(\Omega/\kappa)^2(1 - 2A/B + A^2/\Omega B)]^2}. \tag{26}$$

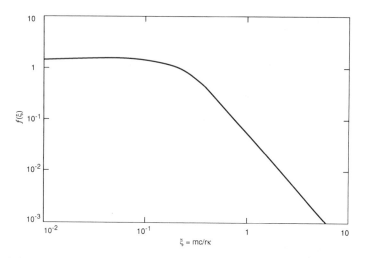

FIGURE 2. The torque cutoff function, $f(\xi)$, for coorbiting, corotation torques.

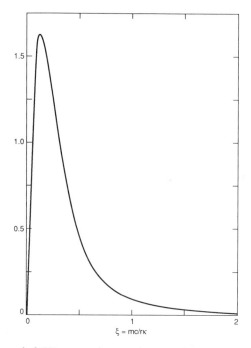

FIGURE 3. Integrand of (27); area under curve is proportional to total corotation torque.

This quantity is now to be included in the integral for the total torque

$$T_C = 4\sigma \left(\frac{GM_p}{r_p\kappa}\right)^2 \left(\frac{\Omega}{A}\right) \left(\frac{r}{h}\right)^2 \left(\frac{d\ln(\sigma/B)}{d\ln r}\right) \int_0^\infty f(\xi) \left[\frac{1}{2}\exp\left(\frac{\xi^2}{8}\right) K_0\left(\frac{\xi^2}{8}\right)\right]^2 \xi \, d\xi. \quad (27)$$

As $\xi \to 0, f(\xi) \to 1$; as $\xi \to \infty, f(\xi) \to (\Omega/\kappa)^2 [1 + A^2/\Omega B][1 + A^2/\Omega B - 2A/B]^{-2}\xi^{-2}$. The behavior at large ξ causes the integrand in (27) to fall off as ξ^{-3} and the integral converge.

If we are interested in application to the solar nebula, Oort constants appropriate for a Keplerian disk are to be used: $A = -3\Omega/4, B = \Omega/4, \kappa = \Omega$. The cutoff function becomes

$$f_K(\xi) = \frac{1 + (11/4)\xi^2 + \xi^2 K_1(\xi^2/8)/2K_0(\xi^2/8)}{[1 + (37/4)\xi^2]^2}, \quad (28)$$

which falls off as $52/(37\xi)^2 = 0.038\xi^{-2}$, as shown in FIGURE 2. The resulting torque strength as a function of ξ is plotted in FIGURE 3; numerical integration gives $\int_0^\infty f(\xi) [(1/2)\exp(\xi^2/8)K_0(\xi^2/8)]^2\xi \, d\xi = 0.673$.

SATURATION

So far our analysis has been linear. However, the overlapping resonances in the coorbital zone produce strong nonlinear effects, which are manifested in the well-known "horseshoe"-type behavior of nearly coorbiting material. This, in turn, can cause saturation weakening of the corotation torque.

Mass elements can execute librations referred to as horseshoe orbits due to the perturbation potential.[10,11] An interior test particle approaching the perturber from the rear, gains angular momentum during close encounter and, if $B > 0$, is promoted to a higher orbit. The reversal in mean motions, $\Omega - \Omega_p$, causes the particle to fall behind the perturber on a new exterior orbit. A particle initially on an exterior orbit suffers the opposite fate. If the perturber occupies a ring of such particles, gradients in the properties of the ring introduce asymmetries into the problem, and a net exchange of angular momentum can exist.[12] The ring torque exerted by independent streamlines filling a horseshoe region of half-width, w, can be shown to be[13]

$$T = 4\sigma|A|Bw^4 \left(\frac{d\ln(\sigma/B)}{d\ln r}\right). \quad (29)$$

However, (29) remains valid only until the outermost horseshoe particles reencounter the perturber in a time $P(w) \sim \pi r/|A|w$. At this point the torque drops precipitously as the angular momentum exchanged with the outer streamlines reverses sign. Since the liberation period is inversely proportional to the streamline half-width, the ring becomes progressively mixed as liberations drift out of phase. Eventually, the surface density adjusts so that σ/B becomes constant along a given streamline and the torque vanishes.[14]

For a thin particle ring, the maximum width of the horseshoe orbit region should be on the order of the Hill sphere radius, L. However, for a gaseous disk with a scale height, h, that exceeds the Hill sphere radius, the large column height of a mass element, $\delta m = \sigma r \delta \theta \delta r$, weakens the perturbation and narrows the horseshoe zone. Epicycle theory can be used, in conjunction with the vertically averaged potential, to obtain a rough estimate of w for this case; $w \approx \zeta(2\Omega/B)^{1/2}(L/h)^{1/2} L$. Substitution into (29) yields,

$$T = 4\sigma \left(\frac{GM_p}{r_p\kappa}\right)^2 \left(\frac{\Omega}{A}\right) \left(\frac{r}{h}\right)^2 \left(\frac{d \ln(\sigma/B)}{d \ln r}\right)\zeta^4, \tag{30}$$

which closely resembles (27). Thus a simplified epicycle model reproduces the main features of the corotation torque. [For consistency, the coefficient of (27) implies a value of order unity for ζ. An improved estimate of w from first principles could be found by numerical integration of the equation of motion of a fluid disk including the effects of pressure gradients.[15] However, a precise knowledge of ζ is not required for our order-of-magnitude estimate of the saturation time scale.] The saturation time for a thick disk is of order.

$$\tau_{sat} \sim \frac{\pi r}{\zeta |A|} \left(\frac{B}{2\Omega}\right)^{1/2} \left[\frac{h}{L^3}\right]^{1/2} \sim \frac{\pi}{\zeta\Omega} \left(\frac{2}{3}\right)^{1/2} \left(\frac{M_\odot}{M_p}\right)^{1/2} \left(\frac{h}{r}\right)^{1/2}, \tag{31}$$

where the final term on the right-hand side has been evaluated for a Keplerian disk. This time is only of order 10^{2-3} years for an earth mass ($M_p/M_\odot \sim 3 \times 10^{-6}$) in the solar nebula ($h/r \sim$ few $\times 10^{-2}$).

DISCUSSION AND SUMMARY

A torque is exerted on a protoplanet by the nearly coorbiting portion of the nebula. Disk material is set into libration along horseshoe orbits. The unsaturated torque is estimated by treating the protoplanet's perturbation as a series of corotation resonances and summing the associated torques. The disturbing potential is vertically averaged through the disk to avoid singularities in the Laplace coefficients appearing in its Fourier amplitudes. This procedure has validity if the Doppler-shifted forcing frequency is less than the reciprocal of the vertical transit time for sound, $c/h \sim \Omega$; and if the perturbation wave length exceeds the disk's scale height. The first condition is generally fulfilled for corotation resonances because their Doppler-shifted frequencies approach zero. As a consequence, the disk can maintain approximate hydrostatic equilibrium. The calculation includes a torque cutoff function, $f(\xi)$, that describes a suppression of the torque at high order. The resulting peak in torque strength, $f(\xi)T_m$, occurs for $\xi < 1$ [FIG. 3], so that for the most important resonances, the second condition is fulfilled as well.

The corotation torque is given by (27), which for the Keplerian disk with surface density $\sigma \propto r^{-k}$, reads

$$T_C = 3.57(\tfrac{3}{2} - k) \left(\frac{M_p}{M_\odot}\right)^2 \sigma r^2 (r\Omega)^2 (r/h)^2. \tag{32}$$

This is comparable in strength to estimates of the differential Lindblad torque.[2] The torque is zero for $k = \tfrac{3}{2}$, because no *net* angular momentum is exchanged with a horseshoe orbit streamline for this density profile; the torque on the protoplanet becomes positive (negative) for $k \lesssim \tfrac{3}{2}$.

There remains a question as to the persistence of the corotation torque. Unlike a Lindblad resonance, angular momentum is not transported from the resonance zone by wave action. Consequently, the corotation resonances can saturate. This occurs if libration removes the gradient in the specific vorticity, $d(\sigma/B)/dr$. The timescale for saturation is set by the libration time, $\tau_{sat} \sim \pi r/|A|w$. However, there are two processes that tend to prevent this. (1) Disk tidal torques may cause the protoplanet to drift across the coorbital zone in a time,[2] $\tau_w \sim \Omega^{-1}\mu^{-1}(M_\odot/\sigma r^2)(h/r)^2(w/r) \lesssim \tau_{sat}$, where $\mu \equiv M_p/M_\odot$. This would require a surface density such that $\pi\sigma r^2/M_\odot > O(h/r)$, which implies a rather substantial disk. (2) Disk turbulence can reestablish a gradient in (σ/B) in a time $\tau_\nu \sim w^2/\nu < \tau_{sat}$. This requires a viscosity $\nu/(c^2/\Omega) = \alpha \gtrsim O[\mu^{3/2}(r/h)^{7/2}]$. For $h/r \sim 0.05$, $\mu \sim 3 \times 10^{-6}$, the criterion reads $\alpha \gtrsim O(10^{-4})$, implying that a relatively mild turbulence is sufficient. Under either condition, the coorbital corotation torque should be included in the disk torques modifying the protoplanet's orbit.

ACKNOWLEDGMENTS

The author thanks the San Juan Capistrano Research Institute for their hospitality during a portion of this research project.

REFERENCES

1. PAPALOIZOU, J. & D. N. C. LIN. 1984. On the tidal interaction between protoplanets and the primordial solar nebula. I. Linear calculation of the role of angular momentum exchange. Astrophys. J. **285:** 818–834.
2. WARD, W. R. 1986. Density waves in the solar nebula: Differential Lindblad torque. Icarus **67:** 164–180.
3. GOLDREICH, P. & S. TREMAINE. 1980. Disk-satellite interactions. Astrophys. J. **241:** 425–441.
4. WARD, W. R. 1989. On the rapid formation of giant planet cores. Astrophys. J., Lett. **345:** L99–L102.
5. GOLDREICH, P. & S. TREMAINE. 1979. The excitation of density waves at the Lindblad and corotation resonances by an external potential. Astrophys. J. **233:** 857–871.
6. WARD, W. R. 1988. On disk-planet interactions and orbital eccentricities. Icarus **73:** 330–348.
7. ———. 1989b. Corotation torques in the solar nebula: The cut-off function. Astrophys. J. **336:** 526–538.
8. GRADSHTEYN, I. S. & I. M. RYZHIK. 1965. Table of Integrals, Series, and Products. Academic Press. New York.
9. ABRAMOWITZ, M. & I. A. STEGUN. 1972. Handbook of Mathematical Functions. National Bureau of Standards, U.S. Department of Commerce. Boulder, Colo.
10. DERMOTT, S. F. & C. D. MURRAY. 1981. The dynamics of tadpole and horseshoe orbits. I. Theory. Icarus **48:** 12.
11. HENON, M. & J.-M. PETIT. 1986. Series expansion for encounter-type solutions of Hill's problem. Celestial Mech. **38:** 67–100.
12. QUINN, P. J. & J. GOODMAN. 1986. Sinking satellites of spiral systems. Astrophys. J. **309:** 472–495.
13. WARD, W. R. 1991. Horseshoe orbit drag. Lunar Planet. Sci. **XXII.**
14. ———. 1991b. Horseshoe torque. In preparation.
15. MIKI, S. 1982. The gaseous flow around a protoplanet in the primordial solar nebula. Prog. Theor. Phys. **67:** 1053–1067.

Observations of Resonance Phenomena in Planetary Rings[a]

PHILIP D. NICHOLSON

Astronomy Department
Cornell University
Ithaca, New York 14853

INTRODUCTION

We review the observations and interpretations of features in planetary rings attributed to resonant interactions with external satellites, with particular attention to the numerous density and bending waves in Saturn's A and B Rings. These waves have proved to be excellent examples of the classic Lin–Shu density wave model,[1] originally proposed as an explanation for grand spiral structure in galactic disks, as well as of the analogous vertical or bending waves. In the case of waves driven in planetary rings, the source of the perturbation that gives rise to the waves is known, as is the associated pattern speed Ω_P. This is unlike the usual galactic situation, where neither the triggering perturbation nor Ω_P is generally known *a priori*. A further distinction is the extremely tightly wound nature of the waves in planetary rings, as opposed to the relatively loosely wound galactic spirals. The pitch angle of typical planetary density waves, $m\lambda/2\pi r$ is of order 10^{-4}, and some strong waves have been traced for as many as 20 complete revolutions.[2]

Via the standard density wave dispersion relation, and simple linear damping models, density and bending waves have yielded the most reliable estimates of surface mass densities and velocity dispersions in Saturn's rings, and thus have played a crucial role in the development of our current physical picture of ring structure. Typical mass densities are 30–60 g/cm^2, implying an average mass-weighted particle size of ~ 100 cm.[2,3] This is compatible with independent size estimates obtained from the low microwave emissivity and high radar reflectivity of the rings, given a dominantly water ice composition. The velocity dispersion is found to be ~ 0.25 cm/s, which in turn implies a vertical scale height H of order 20 meters.[2] The aspect ratio, H/R, of Saturn's A Ring is thus $\sim 10^{-7}$, making it truly a "thin disk!"

Recent theoretical work in this area has concentrated on the development of nonlinear wave models[4,5] and on a more realistic treatment of "viscous" wave damping arising from physical collisions between ring particles.[6] Despite the obvious nonlinearity of many of the waves, the dispersion relation derived from linear theory is generally found to provide a surprisingly good match to the observations, although in the case of the strongest resonances allowances must be made for the effect of the wave on the background surface density.[3]

[a]This work was supported by the NASA Planetary Geology and Geophysics program, under Grant NAGW-544.

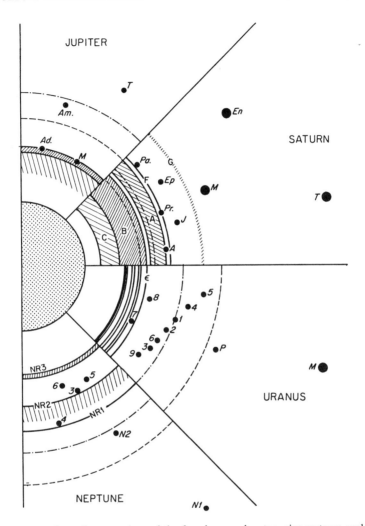

FIGURE 1. A schematic comparison of the four known planetary ring systems, scaled to a common planetary equatorial radius.[37] The *dashed line* indicates the location of the synchronous orbit, and the *dot-dashed line* the Roche limit for a particle density of 1 g cm^{-3}. Satellites are identified by their initial letters or, in the case of Uranus and Neptune, by their temporary IAU designations 1986U1, . . . , U9 and 1989N1, . . . , N6.

Other features in planetary rings that are attributed to resonant interactions with external satellites, or to the effects of small satellites embedded within the ring system itself, include the sharp outer boundaries of Saturn's A and B Rings; the confinement of the eccentric Uranian ϵ ring, as well as several other narrow, noncircular ringlets observed at Saturn and Uranus;[7,8] the existence of several narrow gaps in Saturn's rings;[9] and the curious "arcs" that characterize Neptune's ring system.[10] For most of these examples, sufficiently precise kinematic data exist

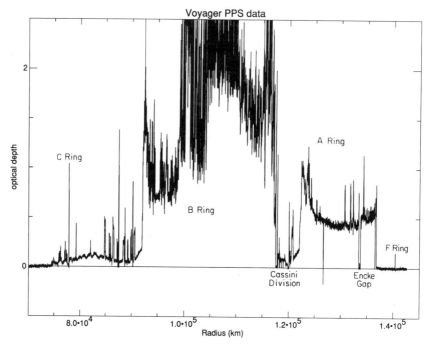

FIGURE 2. The normal optical depth profile of Saturn's rings at λ0.27 μm, derived from the Voyager PPS stellar occultation experiment and averaged to 20-km resolution.

from either stellar occultation or spacecraft imaging experiments to permit unambiguous identification of the specific resonance involved, and to permit detailed dynamical models to be developed. In the case of the Encke Gap in Saturn's A Ring, such models led to a prediction,[11] subsequently confirmed,[12] of the orbital location of the 10-km radius satellite responsible for opening and maintaining the gap.

FIGURE 1 compares, on a relative scale set by the planetary equatorial radii, the major components of each of the four known planetary ring systems, along with the orbital locations of all inner satellites, the synchronous orbit, and the Roche limit for icy objects. In FIGURE 2 we show the normal optical depth profile of Saturn's main rings at a resolution of 20 km, as measured by the Voyager Photopolarimeter (PPS) stellar occultation experiment[13] at a wavelength of 0.27 μm. The major ring components are identified, as are the 4000-km-wide Cassini Division and the 325-km-wide Encke Gap. Many, though by no means all, of the structural features evident in this figure are attributable to resonances, or to suspected embedded satellites.

DENSITY AND BENDING WAVES IN SATURN'S RINGS

In a self-gravitating, differentially rotating disk spiral density waves are driven at both the inner (ILR) and outer (OLR) Lindblad resonances with a nonaxisymmetric perturbing potential. In the context of planetary rings the perturber is a satellite, usually but not always located outside the rings.[14] At an ILR/OLR, the orbital angular velocity n and epicyclic frequency κ of a ring particle must satisfy the resonant condition

$$m(n - \Omega_P) = \pm\kappa,$$

where Ω_P is the pattern speed of a potential component with azimuthal wavenumber m. Noting that $\kappa = n - \dot{\varpi}$, where $\dot{\varpi}$ is the pericenter precession rate, we have the equivalent expression

$$(m \mp 1)n \pm \dot{\varpi} - m\Omega_P = 0.$$

For the near-Keplerian orbits of ring particles, $\dot{\varpi} \simeq \frac{3}{2}J_2[R/a]^2 n$, where J_2 measures the quadrupole component of the planet's gravitational field, R is the planet's radius, and a is the orbital semimajor axis. Typically, $\dot{\varpi} \sim (10^{-3} - 10^{-2})n$. In general, any single satellite can give rise to many different potential components of differing pattern speeds, but for low-eccentricity, low-inclination satellites the strongest components have a pattern speed equal to the satellite's mean motion, n_S. The ILR condition thus becomes

$$(m - 1)n + \dot{\varpi} - mn_S = 0,$$

and the resonance is commonly referred to in the planetary literature as an $m{:}m - 1$ ILR.

The several small- to medium-sized satellites orbiting outside Saturn's main ring system give rise to numerous ILRs, primarily in the A Ring. In FIGURE 3 the principal resonances in the outer A Ring associated with Mimas and the coorbital satellites Janus and Epimetheus are identified; note the sharp peak in optical depth visible at each of these resonances. At higher resolution, as illustrated in FIGURE 4, these peaks are resolved into individual density wavetrains. Also visible in this figure are the weaker but much more numerous waves associated with the Prometheus and Pandora ILRs. At 1-km resolution, at least 27 different wavetrains are visible in this region, with values of m as high as 35.

The density wave driven at a Lindblad resonance satisfies the Lin–Shu dispersion relation:[14,15]

$$(mn - m\Omega_P)^2 - \kappa^2 + 2\pi G\sigma|k| - c^2 k^2 = 0,$$

where σ is the ring surface mass density, c is the "thermal" speed (the rms non-Keplerian velocity), and $k(a)$ is the radial wavenumber. As we approach the resonance $|k| \to 0$, and only here does the radial "shape" of the wave couple effectively with the smoothly varying satellite potential. The waves observed in planetary rings are of the "long" variety, and the $c^2 k^2$ term may safely be neglected. Because $\kappa < n$, propagating solutions (i.e., real k) exist only exterior to an ILR, or interior to an OLR, for all $m \geq 1$. The radial group velocity of the long waves, $v_G = s\pi G\sigma/m(n - \Omega_P)$, where $s = +1$ for trailing waves and $s = -1$ for leading waves.[15] As $n > \Omega_P$ at an ILR, only trailing waves can propagate away from the resonant radius, a_L. (Trailing waves could also propagate inwards from an OLR, but no examples of such waves have yet been identified in planetary rings.) Because of the

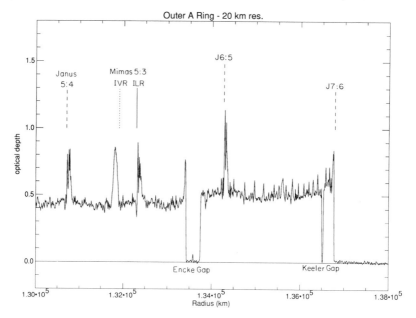

FIGURE 3. PPS optical depth profile for Saturn's outer A Ring, identifying the locations of the principal Lindblad (ILR) and vertical (IVR) resonances due to the satellites Mimas and Janus/Epimetheus, as well as the narrow Encke and Keeler Gaps. Resolution is 20 km.

small pitch angles that characterize waves in planetary rings, the Wentzel–Kramer–Brillouin (WKB) approximation underlying the Lin–Shu dispersion relation is actually much more likely to be valid here than it is in the case of the relatively open spiral waves found in galactic disks.

Close to the resonance, the radial wavelength satisfies the approximate relation

$$\lambda(a) \simeq \frac{4\pi^2 G \sigma a_L}{3(m-1)n_L^2(a-a_L)} \simeq 306 \frac{\sigma_{100}(a_L/R)^4}{(m-1)(a-a_L)} \text{ km,}$$

where σ_{100} is the surface density in units of 100 g cm^{-2} and $a - a_L$ is expressed in kilometers. Simple linear damping models[15] lead to an exponential damping length for the waves of

$$l_d \simeq \frac{\pi G \sigma}{n_L}\left(\frac{a_L^2}{(m-1)^2 \nu n_L^2}\right)^{1/3},$$

where ν is the effective kinematic viscosity. Fits of these expressions to the observed density waves in Saturn's rings yield estimates of the local surface density and viscosity, the latter being determined by the rms radial velocity dispersion c and the ring optical depth τ:[16]

$$\nu \simeq \frac{0.5c^2\tau}{n(1+\tau^2)}.$$

FIGURE 5 is a compilation by the author of published surface density determinations in the A Ring, which indicate a mean value of ~ 40 g cm^{-2}, as well as a slow decrease in σ with increasing radius. The average viscosity derived from application of the linear damping model to several density waves is ~ 100 cm^2 s^{-1}, corresponding to $c \simeq 0.25$ cm s^{-1} and a ring scale height, $H = c/n \simeq 20$ m.[2] It is of interest to note that the resulting value of the Toomre stability parameter, $Q = cn/\pi G\sigma \simeq 4$ in the A Ring. This marginal stability may account for the pronounced visibility of waves in this region.

Because of the tightly wrapped nature of density waves in rings, their true spiral nature is not immediately apparent, either in images or in individual occultation profiles. By comparing the profiles of waves due to the same satellite, but of differing m values, and therefore different phases, it is nevertheless possible to demonstrate the progressive change in waveform with wave phase through a complete azimuthal wavelength, $2\pi/m$. Such a comparison of wave profiles due to the satellite Prometheus is shown in FIGURE 6, where theoretical (linear) waveforms are shown superimposed on the observed profiles and arranged in order of increasing phase, $\phi = m(\lambda_S - \lambda)$,

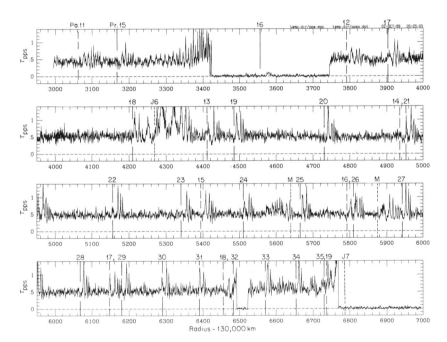

FIGURE 4. PPS optical depth profile of the outer 4000 km of the A Ring, at 1-km resolution, showing individual density and bending wavetrains. Resonance locations are indicated by *vertical lines,* and coded by the corresponding values of the azimuthal wavenumber, m. Note in particular the Mimas 8:5 ILR/IVR waves at 135,900 km and 135,600 km, denoted "M," and the strong Janus 6:5 density wave at 134,300 km ("J6"). The Janus 7:6 ILR ("J7") effectively terminates the ring at its outer edge. The high-frequency wavelike structure immediately interior to the Encke Gap is the gravitational "wake" produced by the moonlet that orbits within the gap.[11] All other wavetrains are density waves driven at ILRs with Prometheus (*solid lines*) or Pandora (*long dashed lines*). (Figure created by Maren Cooke.)

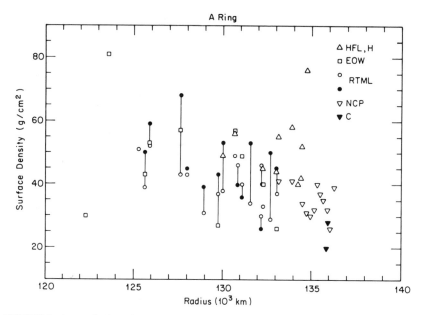

FIGURE 5. A compilation of surface mass density estimates for Saturn's A Ring derived from dispersion model fits to individual density and bending wavetrains. Data from various sources. *Vertical lines* connect multiple analyses of the same wave.

where λ and λ_S are the longitudes of observation and the satellite at the time of observation, respectively.[17] The agreement between the predicted and observed waveforms in both wavelength and phase is quite striking, and provides a nice confirmation of the spiral-wave nature of the optical depth oscillations, as well as of the validity of the underlying theory. Nonlinear models provide much improved fits to the actual shape of the optical depth peaks.[4,5]

In addition to the many density waves, a few vertical or bending waves are also observed in Saturn's rings. These waves, also originally invoked in the galactic dynamics context[18] to explain warps in disks, involve out-of-plane motions of the ring particles and are driven at "vertical resonances" with satellites on inclined orbits. The only inner Saturnian satellite with a substantial inclination is Mimas ($i = 1.5°$), and all but one of the observed bending waves[19] are due to this satellite. Inner (IVR) and outer (OVR) vertical resonances occur where the vertical oscillation frequency $\mu = n - \dot{\Omega}$ satisfies

$$m(n - \Omega_P) = \pm\mu,$$

or for an IVR

$$(m - 1)n + \dot{\Omega} - m\Omega_P = 0,$$

where $\dot{\Omega} \simeq -\dot{\varpi}$ is the nodal regression rate. Since $\kappa < n < \mu$, an IVR always falls slightly interior to the ILR corresponding to the same m and pattern speed. Bending waves satisfy a variant of the density wave dispersion relation:[15,18]

$$(mn - m\Omega_P)^2 - \mu^2 - 2\pi G\sigma|k| = 0,$$

from which it may be seen that, in contrast to density waves, bending waves must propagate *inwards* from the resonant radius, a_V, at least for $m > 1$ (see below). The wavelengths are otherwise the same as those of the corresponding density wavetrain. At the Mimas 5:3 resonance, shown at higher resolution in FIGURE 7, both an inward-propagating bending wave and an outward-propagating density wave are

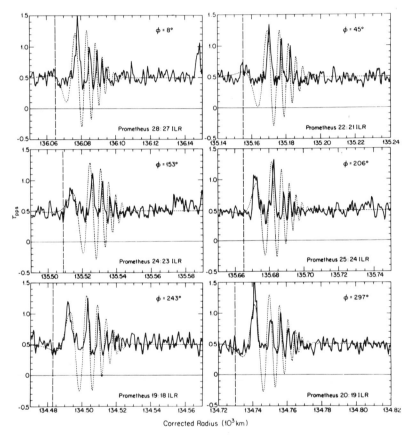

FIGURE 6. Optical depth profiles for six density waves due to Prometheus in Saturn's outer A Ring, arranged in order of increasing wave phase, $\phi = m(\lambda_S - \lambda)$.[17] In each panel, the *solid curve* is the Voyager PPS data at 1-km resolution, while the *dashed curve* is a simple linear model (after reference 15) for the wave calculated with a surface density $\sigma = 35$ g cm^{-2} and a damping length of ~ 4 wavelengths. The *vertical dashed line* indicates the resonant radius, a_L. Neither the phase of the model nor the radial position has been adjusted to fit the observations; residual systematic errors in the absolute radius scale of the PPS data are no greater than ~ 1.5 km. Note the progressive outward motion of the individual wave crests with increasing phase (i.e., decreasing longitude), due to the trailing nature of the waves.

visible in the Voyager PPS occultation data. The visibility of the bending wave is due to the variation in the local incidence angle of light from the star on the warped ring, which in turn affects the *apparent* optical depth of the ring. Analysis of Voyager images indicates that the vertical amplitude of this wave is ~ 700 meters,[20] in good agreement with the amplitude predicted by linear theory and ~ 30 times greater than the local thickness of the ring. The phase of this wave is also found to match that predicted by linear theory.

A final, somewhat pathological example of a resonantly forced wave is shown in FIGURE 8. This wave, seen clearly only in the very shallow incidence angle Voyager radio occultation data, has been identified[21] as an $m = 1$ bending wave associated with the $-1{:}0$ IVR with the large satellite Titan:

$$n - \Omega_P = \mu = n - \dot{\Omega}.$$

In this case, $\Omega_P = n_T - \kappa_T - \mu_T$, and we have $\dot{\Omega} = \Omega_P \simeq -n_T$. It is a one-armed leading spiral wave with a retrograde pattern speed, unique among all known waves, but nevertheless consistent with standard wave theory. Unlike the usual case for $m > 1$, this particular bending wave propagates outwards from the IVR, a fact that delayed its correct interpretation until recently. This wave provides one of the few estimates[21] of surface density and viscosity in the C Ring: $\sigma \simeq 0.4\,\mathrm{g\,cm^{-2}}$ and $\nu = 0.24$

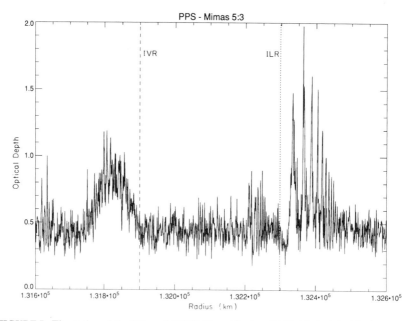

FIGURE 7. The region of the Mimas 5:3 ILR (*dotted line*) and IVR (*dashed line*) in Saturn's A Ring, as seen in the Voyager PPS occultation data. The density wave propagating outward from the ILR and the bending wave propagating inward from the IVR are clearly visible, and show the predicted decline in wavelength with distance from the resonance. The weaker wavetrain at $\sim 132{,}250$ km is due to overlapping density waves driven at the Prometheus 13:12 ILR and the Pandora 10:9 ILR. Resolution is 1 km.

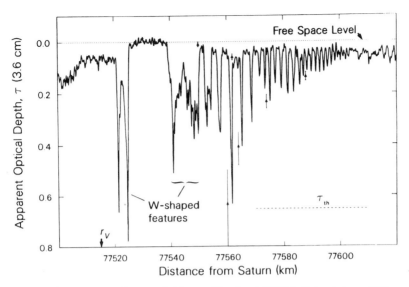

FIGURE 8. The "nodal bending wave" driven at Titan's $-1{:}0$ IVR in Saturn's inner C Ring, as seen in the Voyager radio occultation data at 200-m resolution.[21] The large apparent variations in optical depth are interpreted as being due to the oscillations in ring surface slope associated with the wave, combined with the very low incidence angle (6°) of the radio beam. The "W-shaped features" are thought to represent regions of multiple penetration of the ring by the beam. (From Rosen and Lissauer.[21] Reproduced by permission.)

$cm^2 s^{-1}$, both much lower than in the A Ring. The corresponding mass-weighted mean particle size and ring scale height are ~ 10 cm and 2.5 m, respectively. The stability parameter, $Q \simeq 250$, which is much greater than the value characterizing the A Ring.

Apart from their importance as probes of the surface density and velocity dispersion in the rings, density waves are believed to play a major role in the long-term evolution of Saturn's rings.[22] The waves excited at ILRs carry away a negative flux of angular momentum, which is eventually shared with the ring particles when the waves damp.[23] The result is a slow but inexorable transfer of angular momentum from the rings to the perturbing satellites, driving the satellites outward and leading to the eventual inward collapse of the rings. For the A Ring, the timescale for decay into the B Ring is $\sim 10^8$ yr, much less than the age of the solar system. Several of the inner satellites, notably Prometheus, cannot have occupied their present orbits for more than $\sim 10^7$ yr. This is only one of several cogent arguments that suggest that the present Saturnian ring system is of relatively recent origin.[24]

RESONANTLY CONTROLLED RING EDGES

In addition to driving waves, Lindblad resonances also act in some cases to define the edges of rings. As may be seen in FIGURES 3 and 4, the outer boundary of

Saturn's A Ring coincides closely with the 7:6 ($m = 7$) ILR with the satellite Janus. An even more striking example is the outer edge of the B Ring, shown in FIGURE 9, which is clearly controlled by the 2:1 ($m = 2$) resonance with Mimas, the strongest ILR within Saturn's rings.[14] A close examination[25] of this abrupt boundary, which also forms the inner edge of the Cassini Division, reveals a double-lobed radial distortion with an amplitude of ~ 75 km, which rotates with a pattern speed $\Omega_P = n_{Mimas}$ (see FIG. 10). Models of the resonant interaction[26] require that, at such a boundary, the resonant torque acts to transfer to the satellite the entire outward viscous flux of angular momentum being carried through the ring, thus preventing the spreading of the ring beyond the resonance. This transfer is effected, in part, by a reduction in the viscous transport due to modifications to the Keplerian angular velocity gradient induced by the resonant perturbations of ring particle streamlines.

On a less grand scale, both edges of the Uranian ϵ ring have been shown to coincide with generalized Lindblad resonances with its two "shepherd" satellites.[27] The inner edge is defined by the 24:25 outer eccentric resonance (OER) with Cordelia (U7 in FIG. 1), while the outer edge is similarly confined by the 14:13 inner eccentric resonance (IER) with Ophelia (U8). In this case, the 58-km mean width of the ϵ ring is apparently set by the spacing of these two resonances, though in the past

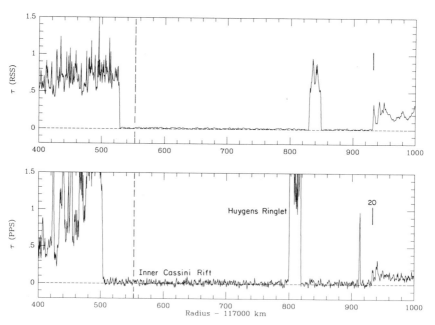

FIGURE 9. Optical depth profiles of the inner Cassini Division obtained from the Voyager radio (RSS) and stellar (PPS) occultation experiments, showing the strongly perturbed outer edge of the B Ring at $\sim 117,500$ km and the noncircular Huygens ringlet at 117,810 km.[17] The *dashed line* indicates the location of the Mimas 2:1 ILR, which is responsible for the B Ring edge's variations. Resolution is 1 km.

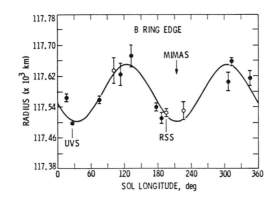

FIGURE 10. Measurements of the location of the outer edge of Saturn's B Ring from Voyager images and occultation (UVS, RSS) data, rotated to a common epoch and plotted over the best-fitting model of an $m = 2$ distortion due to the Mimas 2:1 ILR.[25] The location of Mimas at epoch is indicated, and aligns almost perfectly with a radial minimum in the distortion, as predicted by theory. (From the Ph.D. thesis of Carolyn Porco. Reproduced by permission.)

other nearby resonances may have played this role, as the ring–satellite resonant torques are steadily pushing the satellites away from the ring.

NEPTUNE'S RINGS AND ARCS

Neptune's recently discovered ring system consists of three narrow rings (named the Adams, Leverrier, and Galle rings, after the "codiscoverers" of Neptune), the outer of which (Adams) contains at least four localized enhancements in optical depth, or "arcs," 5°–10° in length. The mean motion of the arcs closely matches that of a 42:43 corotation resonance (CR) with the nearby satellite Galatea (N4 in Fig. 1):

$$m_C n = m_C \Omega_P = (m_C - 1)n_G + \dot{\Omega}_G,$$

where $m_C = 43$, and the arcs are suspected to occupy several of the $2m_C$ possible stable corotation sites equally spaced around the resonant orbit. Support for this model is provided by analysis of high-resolution Voyager images,[28] which reveal that the arcs are perturbed radially by the neighboring 42:43 Galatea OLR,

$$(m_L + 1)n - \dot{\varpi} - m_L n_G = 0,$$

($m_L = 42$), with a radial amplitude of 30 km, an azimuthal wavelength of $2\pi/m_L = 8.6°$, and the expected orientation relative to the satellite.

Although resonances are rather closely spaced this close to the satellite, with successive CRs separated by only ~23 km, the observed difference between the arcs' semimajor axis (inferred from their mean motion[29]) and the 42:43 CR is only 0.11 ± 0.13 km, making the identification almost certain. The ILR falls 1.65 km interior to the CR. Theoretical work[30] indicates that the OLR can act to "shepherd," or radially confine, material librating about the corotation sites. Problems remain, however, in accounting for the observed 15-km width of the arcs, which greatly exceeds the maximum libration width of the corotation resonance.[28]

OTHER RESONANCE-RELATED FEATURES

In addition to the features discussed earlier, for which the evidence of resonance control is well-documented, there are numerous other features in the ring systems of Jupiter, Saturn, and Uranus that are at least suspected to be due to resonant action of some form. The boundary between the main Jovian ring and the inner, vertically extented halo (see FIG. 1) coincides with the 3:2 Lorentz resonance[31] with Jupiter's magnetic field. A Lorentz resonance is analogous to a Lindblad resonance, but the periodic perturbations are due to electromagnetic forces on micron-sized charged particles orbiting in a strong, rotating and asymmetric or tilted magnetic field. The stronger 2:1 Lorentz resonance may effectively truncate the inner edge of the halo, but this boundary is poorly defined in the present data.

In Saturn's C Ring, which is more distant from the external satellites than are the A and B Rings, few strong ILRs exist, and very few density or bending waves have been unambiguously identified.[32] The C Ring is instead characterized by a puzzling series of higher optical depth regions, dubbed "plateaux," interspersed in a low optical depth undulating background. FIGURE 11 shows the optical depth profile of the C Ring, derived from the Voyager radio occultation experiment at $\lambda 3.6$ cm.[33] While most of the plateau edges do not match known satellite resonances, there is a significant correlation between the five strongest resonances in this region and three of the five narrow gaps in the C Ring, as indicated in the figure. The inner edge of the 20-km-wide gap at 90,200 km is aligned with the Mimas 3:1 ILR, while the outer edge of the ~10-km-wide gap at 88,700 km matches the Mimas 3:1 IVR.[17] In both cases the agreement is within 2 to 3 km, although in neither case has it been possible to establish the existence of resonantly forced radial distortions similar to that seen at the B Ring edge.[34] However, the expected amplitude of the distortions is only a few kilometers, comparable to the resolution of much of the available data. Probably coincidentally, the ringlets or plateaux associated with the gaps just mentioned also straddle the Pandora and Prometheus 2:1 ILRs, which are only slightly weaker than the Mimas resonances.

Finally, the narrow Colombo Gap at 77,800 km approximately coincides with the Titan 1:0 ILR, where $\dot{\varpi} = n_T$. The ringlet within the gap has an eccentricity that is clearly forced by this strong $m = 1$ resonance, with an amplitude of 40 km and a measured precession rate that matches Titan's mean motion.[35] The apocenter of the ellipse is aligned within 15° of the direction to Titan.

The striking difference[3] in the manifestation of strong resonances (both ILRs and IVRs) between the A and B Rings on the one hand (density/bending waves, and few gaps) and the C Ring and Cassini Division on the other (few waves, but many gaps and narrow isolated ringlets) is of unknown origin. Although the most obvious difference lies in the mean optical depth (0.4–2.5 vs 0.05–0.5), which controls the mean interparticle collision frequency $n\tau$, there also appear to be differences in mean particle size (see earlier) and perhaps in composition.[36] Perhaps of more fundamental importance is the much greater stability of the C Ring to near-axisymmetric wavelike perturbations, as indicated by the Toomre stability parameter Q.

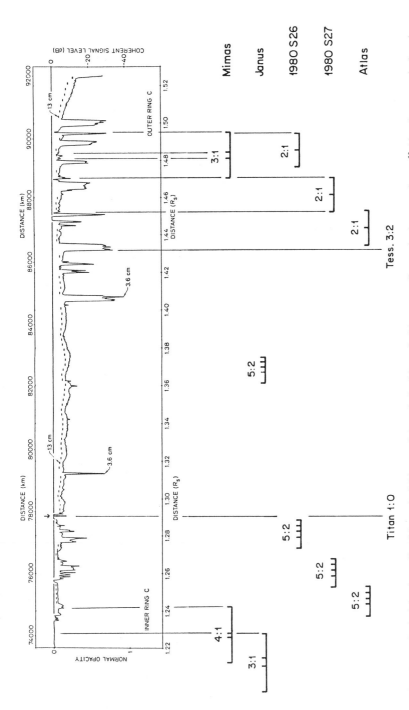

FIGURE 11. Optical depth profile of Saturn's C Ring at λ3.6 cm derived from the Voyager radio occultation experiment.[33] Also shown are the locations of the principal families of satellite resonances in this region, due to Titan, Mimas, Janus, Pandora (1980S26), Prometheus (1980S27), and tiny Atlas. The outer member of each family is the ILR, the inner is the IVR, and the remainder are corotation resonances. The location of the 3:2 tesseral resonance with Saturn, due to hypothetical asymmetries in the planet's gravity field, is also indicated, though it is unlikely to be dynamically important.

DISCUSSION

With the advent of spacecraft obervations, planetary rings have provided both an unexpectedly complex picture of real disk systems, and an ideal venue for testing new and preexisting theoretical descriptions of the dynamical state of such systems. Although smaller by some twelve orders of magnitude than galactic disks, planetary rings are sculpted by the same fundamental processes of gravity and collisions that determine the structure of spiral galaxies and of accretion disks around compact stellar objects, which form the principal subject of this conference. The applicability of galactic density wave theory to the numerous satellite-driven wavetrains observed in Saturn's rings is the most striking illustration of this underlying similarity, but the fundamental importance of viscous angular momentum transport to the structure of accretion disks is almost certainly mirrored in the long-term evolution of planetary ring systems.

It may in turn be asked whether the surprising variety of satellite–ring interactions observed in the Jovian, Saturnian, Uranian, and Neptunian systems—including narrow gaps, sharply defined ring edges, isolated noncircular ringlets, and even "arcs"—may well have counterparts in other astrophysical disks that are currently far below our limits of resolution. It is sobering to recall that, as recently as fifteen years ago, before the discovery of the narrow Uranian and Jovian rings and the Voyager encounters with Saturn, our blurry picture of Saturn's rings was of a broad, almost featureless flat disk, with a single gap (the Cassini Division) at the location of the 2:1 resonance with Mimas.

ACKNOWLEDGMENTS

The optical depth profiles for Saturn's rings used in many of the figures were generated by the author from data originally acquired by the Voyager PPS and RSS teams, and generously made available by the science teams through NASA's Planetary Data System (PDS) Ring Node. I would particularly like to acknowledge the assistance of Lonne Lane and Karen Simmons of the PPS team, Len Tyler and Paul Rosen of the RSS Team, and Mark Showalter at the PDS Node. FIGURE 4 was created by Maren Cooke, while FIGURE 8 is from reference 21, courtesy of Paul Rosen, and FIGURE 10 is from the Ph.D. thesis of Carolyn Porco, with her permission. Ignacio Mosqueira kindly reviewed the manuscript and suggested several improvements.

REFERENCES

1. LIN, C. C. & F. H. SHU. 1964. Astrophys. J. **140:** 646–655.
2. ESPOSITO, L. W., M. O'CALLAGHAN & R. A. WEST. 1983. Icarus **56:** 439–452.
3. HOLBERG, J. B., W. T. FORRESTER & J. J. LISSAUER. 1982. Nature **297:** 115–120.
4. SHU, F. H., C. YUAN & J. J. LISSAUER. 1985. Astrophys. J. **291:** 356–376.
5. BORDERIES, N., P. GOLDREICH & S. TREMAINE. 1986. Icarus **68:** 522–533.
6. SHU, F. H., L. DONES, J. J. LISSAUER, C. YUAN & J. N. CUZZI. 1985. Astrophys. J. **299:** 542–573.
7. PORCO, C. C. 1990. Adv. Space Res. **10**(1): 221–229.

8. FRENCH, R. G., P. D. NICHOLSON, C. C. PORCO & E. A. MAROUF. 1991. *In* Uranus, J. T. Bergstralh, E. D. Miner, and M. S. Matthews, Eds. Univ. of Arizona Press. Tucson.
9. LISSAUER, J. J., F. H. SHU & J. N. CUZZI. 1981. Nature **292:** 707–711.
10. LISSAUER, J. J. & P. D. NICHOLSON. 1990. Adv. Space Res. **10**(1): 231–237.
11. SHOWALTER, M. R., J. N. CUZZI, E. A. MAROUF & L. W. ESPOSITO. 1986. Icarus **66:** 297–323.
12. SHOWALTER, M. R. 1991. Nature **351:** 709–713.
13. ESPOSITO, L. W., *et al.* 1983. J. Geophys. Res. **88:** 8643–8649.
14. GOLDREICH, P. & S. TREMAINE. 1978, Icarus **34:** 240–253.
15. SHU, F. H. 1984. *In* Planetary Rings, R. Greenberg and A. Brahic, Eds. Univ. of Arizona Press. Tucson.
16. GOLDREICH, P. & S. TREMAINE. 1978. Icarus **34:** 227–239.
17. NICHOLSON, P. D., M. L. COOKE & E. PELTON. 1990. Astron. J. **100:** 1339–1362.
18. HUNTER, C. & A. TOOMRE. 1969. Astrophys. J. **155:** 747–776.
19. LISSAUER, J. J. 1985. Icarus **62:** 433–447.
20. SHU, F. H., J. N. CUZZI & J. J. LISSAUER. 1983. Icarus **53:** 185–206.
21. ROSEN, P. A. & J. J. LISSAUER. 1988. Science **241:** 690–694.
22. BORDERIES, N., P. GOLDREICH & S. TREMAINE. 1984. *In* Planetary Rings, R. Greenberg and A. Brahic, Eds. Univ. of Arizona Press. Tucson.
23. GOLDREICH, P. & P. D. NICHOLSON. 1991. Astrophys. J. **342:** 1075–1078.
24. ESPOSITO, L. W. 1986. Icarus **67:** 345–367.
25. PORCO, C., G. E. DANIELSON, P. GOLDREICH, J. B. HOLBERG & A. L. LANE. 1984. Icarus **60:** 17–28.
26. BORDERIES, N., P. GOLDREICH & S. TREMAINE. 1982. Nature **299:** 209–211.
27. PORCO, C. C. & P. GOLDREICH. 1987. Astron. J. **93:** 724–729.
28. PORCO, C. C. 1991. Science **253:** 995–1001.
29. NICHOLSON, P. D., M. L. COOKE, K. MATTHEWS, J. ELIAS & G. GILMORE. 1990. Icarus **87:** 1–39.
30. GOLDREICH, P., S. TREMAINE & N. BORDERIES. 1986. Astron. J. **92:** 195–198.
31. SCHAFFER, L. E. & J. A. BURNS. 1987. J. Geophys. Res. **92:** 2264–2280.
32. ROSEN, P. A., G. L. TYLER, E. A. MAROUF & J. J. LISSAUER. 1991. Icarus **93:** 25–44.
33. TYLER, G. L., E. A. MAROUF, R. A. SIMPSON, H. A. ZEBKER & V. R. ESHLEMAN. 1983. Icarus **54:** 160–188.
34. PORCO, C. C. & P. D. NICHOLSON. 1987. Icarus **72:** 437–467.
35. PORCO, C., P. D. NICHOLSON, N. BORDERIES, G. E. DANIELSON, P. GOLDREICH, J. B. HOLBERG & A. L. LANE. 1984. Icarus **60:** 1–16.
36. CUZZI, J. N., *et al.* 1984. *In* Planetary Rings. R. Greenberg and A. Brahic, Eds. Univ. of Arizona Press. Tucson.
37. NICHOLSON, P. D. & L. DONES. 1991. *In* U.S. National Report to the IUGG 1987-1990. Rev. Geophys., Suppl.: 313–327.

Index of Contributors

Underline the right answers.

All the summer through poor Thumbelina lived alone in the forest. She plaited herself a bed of green stalks and hung it up under a large dark leaf so that no rain might fall on her. She gathered honey from the flowers and every morning drank the dew which lay on the leaves. In this way she spent the summer and autumn, but then winter came – the long cold winter. The birds which had sung so sweetly for her flew away on their long journeys. The trees and flowers withered, the large dark leaf which she had lived under shrivelled up and became nothing but a yellow, withered stem, and she felt frightfully cold, for her clothes were now all torn and she herself was so tiny and frail.

From *Thumbelina* by Hans Christian Andersen

1 Her bed was made of: wood, grass, stalks, leaves
2 Her bed was: hanging up, on the grass, on the ground
3 "Plaited" means: placed, knitted, picked, wove
4 Thumbelina ate: bread, honey, grass, stalks
5 She drank: rain, lemon, honey, dew
6 Why do you think she was called "Thumbelina"? She was very small, she was cold, her clothes were torn
7 "Shrivelled up" means: very wet, withered, cold, frozen
8 Thumbelina lived in: a house, a wood, a tent, a park

FIRST
ASSESSMENT PAPERS IN
ENGLISH

JM BOND

Nelson

Thomas Nelson and Sons Ltd
Nelson House Mayfield Road
Walton-on-Thames Surrey
KT12 5PL UK

Distributed in Australia by

Thomas Nelson Australia
102 Dodds Street
South Melbourne Victoria 3205
Australia

© **J M Bond 1973, 1987, 1993**
First published by Thomas Nelson and Sons Ltd 1973
Revised edition 1987
Reprinted 1987,1988
This fully revised edition 1993
Reprinted 1995

I(T)P Thomas Nelson is an International
       Thomson Publishing Company

I(T)P is used under licence

Pupil's book   ISBN 0-17-424521-1
                NPN 9 8 7
Answer book   ISBN 0-17-424522-X
                NPN 9 8 7 6 5

By the same author
First, Second, Third, Fourth and Further Fourth Year
Assessment Papers in Mathematics

First, Second, Third, Fourth and Further Fourth Year
Assessment Papers in English

First, Second, Third, Fourth and Further Fourth Year
Assessment Papers in Reasoning

Printed in Croatia.

Daddy fell into the Pond (Paper 6) is produced by
kind permission of John Murray (Publishers) Ltd.

Chips (Paper 9) from *Come along* by Stanley
Cook is reproduced by kind permission of the
poet.

The publishers have made every attempt to trace
copyright holders of reprinted material and
apologise for any omissions.

One word in each line rhymes with the word on the left.
Underline it.

9	**shoe**	slow	shut	do	show	go
10	**tail**	find	sand	tile	sale	foal
11	**stay**	stand	my	hate	me	hay

12 We say one **woman** but two ....

13 We say one **box** but two ....

14 We say one **leaf** but three ....

15 We say one **man** but four ....

16 We say one **foot** but two ....

17–22 Write each mixed up word correctly in the space.
"That **hsoue** .... is for sale," said Mum.
"I **khint** .... we will have a look at it." They opened the
geta .... and went up the **hapt** .... There were
wot .... **tseer** .... in the garden.

23–27 Write each wrongly spelled word correctly in the space.
The girl had three or **for** .... books in her desk. She did
not **no** .... which **won** .... to read. Her teacher
said, "**Their** .... is one you **wood** .... like
on the shelf."

28–30 Which of the following are sentences? Underline them.

The cat's milk   The dog barked The flower is red

The grass is green   The red house   No food!

Underline the right answers.

Kim and her mother were in a pet shop. Kim saw a black and white sheepdog puppy.

"Look, Mum," she said. "He is lovely. Can we buy him? I promise to feed him, and take him for a walk every day."

"He is house-trained, and fond of children. He only costs £10," said the shopkeeper.

"No," said Kim's mother. "He is very nice, but I think he will be too big for our little flat."

1   The puppy was (black, white, black and white, grey)

2–3   Kim promised to (feed him, brush him, take him for walks)

4   "Fond of children" means that the dog (bit children, was afraid of children, liked children)

5–7 Why did the shopkeeper think they should buy the dog? (He was clean, he was gentle, he was small, he was cheap, he had brown eyes)

8 The puppy cost (£11, ten pounds, five pounds)

9 Why did Kim's mum say no? (The puppy was fierce, she did not have enough money, he would grow too big)

10 How do you think Kim felt then? (Happy, afraid, sad)

Put the right number in each space.

11	A bicycle	( )	(1)	has brushes
12	An elephant	( )	(2)	has a class
13	A camel	( )	(3)	has wheels
14	A bird	( )	(4)	has a hump
15	A teacher	( )	(5)	has a roof
16	A painter	( )	(6)	has a nest
17	A house	( )	(7)	has a trunk

Choose one of the words below to fit each space.

fire   clock   bee   bird

18 A .... buzzes.   **19** A .... ticks.

20 A .... flies.   **21** A .... smokes.

Write out these sentences, putting capital letters in the right places.

22–25 anne and her friend carol went to london last thursday.

....

26–30 they went to london zoo and oxford street.

....

51 Low Road
17th October

Dear Zoe,
I am writing to tell you that I have a baby sister, and her name is Philippa. She was born last Sunday, and she came home today. She has fair hair and blue eyes. My sister and I are very excited. I do hope you will be able to come and see her soon.
Love, Charlotte

Underline the right answers.

1   Charlotte has (0, 1, 2, 3) sisters.

2   How many sisters has Zoe? (0, 1, 2, 3, I don't know)

3   Philippa was born in the month of
(October, December, 1982, 1983)

4   (Charlotte, Philippa, Zoe) has fair hair and blue eyes.

5–6   (Charlotte, Philippa, Zoe) live at 51 Low Road.

7–9   Put a line under the smaller one of each pair.
kitten/cat   sea/pond   day/hour

Put one letter in front of the "ees" and one letter after them to make words with the following meanings:

10   A plant grows from this   .... ee ....
11   To give food to   .... ee ....
12   Seven days make a   .... ee ....
13   To have a quick look   .... ee ....
14   To cry   .... ee ....
15   An animal   .... ee ....

16–21 Amanda is having a party on Wednesday, 21st July. Her mother bought her some printed invitation cards to send to her friends. The party starts at 4 p.m. and ends at 8 p.m. Fill in the card she sent to Kevin.

Dear ....
    I hope you will be able to come to my party on
.... from .... to ....
       Love from   ....

The events listed below have become jumbled. Look at them carefully, and then write the numbers to show the order in which they should come.

22	They get dressed.	....
23	They cycle to the swimming pool.	....
24	They cycle home.	....
25	They get undressed.	....
26	They jump in the water.	....
27	They dry themselves.	....
28	They swim about.	....
29	They put on their swim suits.	....
30	They get out of the pool.	....

9

Underline the right answers.

Find a washbasin, and wash the cut with hot water and cotton wool. Make sure that all the dirt comes out. Next, put some T.C.P. on the cut. This will stop the pain, and kill the germs. If you are going out to play, you should put a plaster over the cut, so that you won't hurt it again. As soon as you can, leave the plaster off. That will help the cut to heal.

1   What does this passage tell you? (About germs, what to do if you cut your knee, what happens in a hospital)

2   What is the first thing you should do? (Wash the cut, find a plaster, go out to play, go to the doctor)

3–4   Why should you put T.C.P. on the cut? (To make it look nice, to stop the pain, to make the plaster stick, to kill germs)

5   "Heal" means (to get better, to get worse, to get wet, to get dry)

6   When should you leave the plaster off? (Monday, when you go out to play, as soon as you can)

7–11   You can make longer words by putting these words together in pairs.

rail	pet
car	cup
cup	way
green	board
butter	house

....

Complete these sentences by underlining the correct endings.

12 The boys were playing cricket. Peter hit a ball through the classroom window, and broke it. First, Mr Wells, the caretaker, would have to:

throw another ball   put new glass in the window

sweep up the broken glass   stop them playing cricket

13 Anne brought some lovely roses to school. Mrs. Wright, her teacher, told her to put them in a vase full of water. Anne spilt the water all over her desk so she:

threw away the flowers   wiped up the water with a cloth

moved her desk   swept the floor

14–18 Change the word in capital letters to show that these things have already happened.

Today I SEE my friends   Yesterday I .... my friends

Today I WRITE a story   Yesterday I .... a story

Today I SING a song   Yesterday I .... a song

Today I PLAY the computer game   Yesterday I .... the computer game

Today I PAINT a picture   Yesterday I .... a picture

19–30 Put these words under the right heading.

ash, axe, deer, bread, elm, hammer, salad, fox, spade, jam, pony, willow

ANIMALS	FOODS	TOOLS	TREES
....	....	....	....
....	....	....	....
....	....	....	....

Underline the right answers.

Now he was running up a hill. He was so tired he felt he could not go on, but he did. He couldn't feel his legs at all, and his chest felt as though it was on fire. His mouth was dry as he gasped for air. But worse than all these things was the terrible fear. Would it catch him? He didn't dare look behind him. Then he felt its claws on his shoulder.

1   Who was chasing him? (Another boy, his mother, a monster)

2   What was the worst feeling? (Fear, a dry mouth, painful legs)

3   Why was the boy feeling ill? (He had a cold, he had a bad leg, he had been running for a long time)

4   Why was he running? (He was late for school, he was trying to catch his dog, he was escaping from a monster)

5   His chest felts as though it was on fire because (it was burning, he was out of breath, he was a dragon)

6   Where did the monster touch him? (On the legs, on the chest, on the face, on the shoulder)

Write down the opposites of these words:

7   black   8   up ....

9   short   10   in ....

11–14   Underline any word which should begin with a capital letter.

john and his dog went to brighton for the day last sunday. The weather was warm although it was late october.

15–20 Put the right number in each space.

The baby is asleep	( )	(1) but Jason is paddling
Mark is running	( )	(2) but the sun is out
Rover has four legs	( )	(3) but Sarah is cycling
Alan is swimming	( )	(4) but Emma is reading
The snow is falling	( )	(5) but the gate is open
The door is shut	( )	(6) but the boy has only two

Choose one of the words below to complete each line.

clown   dentist   nurse   miner   postman

21 I dig coal out of the ground. I am a ....

22 I bring you letters and parcels. I am a ....

23 I look after your teeth. I am a ....

24 I make you laugh at the circus. I am a ....

25 I look after you in hospital. I am a ....

Write the opposite of each word.

26 big ....   **27** old ....   **28** early ....

29 quick ....   **30** wet ....

Paper 6

Underline the right answers.

Everyone grumbled. The sky was grey.
We had nothing to do and nothing to say.
We were nearing the end of a dismal day.
And there seemed to be nothing beyond,
THEN   DADDY FELL INTO THE POND!
And everyone's face grew merry and bright,
And Timothy danced for sheer delight.
"Give me the camera, quick, oh quick!
He's crawling out of the duckweed!" Click!
Then the gardener suddenly slapped his knee,
And doubled up, shaking silently,
The ducks all quacked as if they were daft,
And it sounded as if the old drake laughed.
Oh, there wasn't a thing that didn't respond
WHEN DADDY FELL INTO THE POND!

Daddy fell into the Pond by Alfred Noyes

1–2 At first they were all: happy, bored, busy, cross

3   The weather was: wet, sunny, cloudy

4   Who took a picture of Dad? the gardener, Timothy, Mum, we all did

5   "Click" was the sound of: the camera, Dad getting out of the pond, people laughing, the ducks

6   Why did the gardener shake? He was upset, he laughed so much, he was crawling in the duckweed

7   What is a drake? a male duck, a swan, a gardener

8   Where was the duckweed? in the garden, in the pond, where the ducks lived

14

Complete the sentences by underlining the correct endings.

9 Tom cannot go on the bus because:

   he is wearing a cap
   the bus is green
   he has no money.

10 Anne is making a cake because:

   she has a new dress
   it is her sister's birthday
   she wants to play a game.

11 Ahmed is running because:

   he doesn't like reading
   he is late for school
   he has new shoes.

12 Conran is having a drink because:

   he is thirsty
   he can't read
   he is greedy.

Make a word ending in ing from the word at the beginning of each line.

13 help   I am .... to wash up.
14 play   She was .... with her toys.
15 fly   The plane was .... overhead.
16 wear   Tara was .... her best dress.
17 kick   Tom was .... the ball.
18 read   The children were .... their books.

Put these words in the order in which you would find them in a dictionary.

   rat   dog   cat   bear   pig   horse

19 (1) ....   20 (2) ....   21 (3) ....
22 (4) ....   23 (5) ....   24 (6) ....

Underline the right word in the brackets.
25–26 The sailor did (knot, not) know how to tie the (knot, not).
27–28 She (blew, blue) up the (blew, blue) balloon.
29–30 The nurse (sore, saw) that she had a (sore, saw) finger.

Paper 7

Underline the right answers.

Find two small bowls. They must be clean and dry. Crack the egg carefully on the side of a bowl and gently break the shell in two over the bowl. Let the white run into the bowl as you tip the yolk from one half of the shell to the other, taking care not to break it. When all the white has left the shell, tip the yolk gently into the other bowl.

1 An egg is in two parts, the white and the (yoke, yolk, yellow)

2 The (cracks, bowls, shells) must be clean and dry.

3 To "separate" eggs means to (take the white from the yolk, put them in order, stand them on their sides)

4 Why do you think we separate eggs?
(So that we can whisk up the whites, so that we can throw the whites away, because they look nicer)

5 What is the best way to crack an egg? (Drop it on the floor, break it on the side of a bowl, bang it with a spoon)

6 Why must you tip the yolk from one half of the shell to the other? (To whisk the yolk, to let all the white run out, to see how strong the shells are)

Karen was ill. Who do you think said these things about her? Use these words to fill in the spaces.

the doctor   the teacher   her mother   her friend

7 "I'll fetch you some milk and a biscuit, and then I'll read you a story from your new book," said ....

8 "She will have to stay in bed for a day or two. Bring her to see me again next Friday," said ....

9 "I'm sorry she can't come to my party, but I'll take her a piece of my birthday cake," said ....

10 "It is a pity she is not at school. I was going to give her a part in the class play," said ....

11–16 Put a line under any word which should begin with a capital letter.
"london, leeds and manchester are all british cities," miss green said.

Write **is** or **are** in each space.

17–18 My brothers .... going to the party but
my sister .... staying at home.

19–20 Where .... the book? .... the comics on the shelf?

21–22 John .... happy, but Michael .... sad.

23–24 The boy .... there. .... the men there too?

25 Houses are usually made of (straw, bricks, cardboard)

26 Windows are usually made of (paper, curtains, glass)

27 Chairs are usually made of (wood, wool, stool)

28–30 Put a line under the "happy" words.
tears   laughter   sadness   misery   joy
sorrow   delight   pain

Paper 8

Underline the right answers.

Have you ever visited a farm? This is a picture of Growberry Farm, where Mr. and Mrs. Growberry live. They have twelve cows which give milk and six pigs. The pigs will be killed to make bacon and ham. There is a large flock of sheep, from which Mr. and Mrs Growberry get wool. As well as the animals, they grow corn, cabbages, apples and pears. In the picture you can see the sheepdog Jasper sitting near the hens. Perhaps he is guarding the eggs!

1 Mr. and Mrs. Growberry are (farmers, dogs, shepherds)

2 (1, 2, 3, 4, 5, 6) kinds of animal are named.

3 (2, 4, 6, 8, 10, 12) kinds of food are named.

4 What will happen to the pigs? (They will eat the apples, they will be killed to make bacon and ham, they will go into the field)

5 Jasper is (a sheep, a dog, a boy)

18

6–7 Which fruits are named? (Oranges, apples, cabbages, corn, pears)

8 (A flock, a herd, a farm, wool) is the name for a group of sheep.

Put each word in the right space.

replied   whispered   shouted   asked

9 When they scored a goal the children   ....

10 Mum ...., "Have you got your coat?"

11 "Where is the key?" "Here," .... Ben.

12 The children .... because Grandad was asleep.

Write the plural of these words.

13	loaf	....	**14** sheep	....
15	child	....	**16** brush	....
17	woman	....	**18** glass	....

Choose one of these words to fill each space.

cream   bright   sharp   woollen   sailing   rough   rainy

19 .... light   **20** .... pencil

21 .... day   **22** .... scarf

23 .... sea   **24** .... cake

25 .... boat

Write the opposite of the word in the heavy type in each space.

26 Yesterday the clock was **fast**, but today it is   ....

27 Michael is **fat**, but his brother is   ....

28 The **back** is red, but the .... is blue.

29 George is **tall**, but his sister is   ....

30 Tim's hands were **dirty**, but Tom's were   ....

Out of the paper bag
Comes the hot breath of the chips
And I shall blow on them
To stop them burning my lips.

Before I leave the counter
The woman shakes
Raindrops of vinegar on them
And salty snowflakes.

Outside the frosty pavements
Are slippery as a slide
But the chips and I
Are warm inside

Stanley Cook

Underline the right answers.

1   There were (sweets, flakes, chips) in the bag.

2–3 The woman put (snow, salt, sauce, vinegar) on them.

4   The weather was (hot, wet, frosty, snowy)

5   The salt was like (snow, frost, vinegar)

6   The chips were hot so I cooled them by (leaving them for a
    while, blowing on them, putting them in the fridge)

7   What was slippery? (The paper bag, the pavements,
    the snowflakes)

20

Fill in the spaces with words linked to the words on the left.

8   play   The kitten is .... with the string.

9   help   Joanna is .... Mum to cook the tea.

10   stick   Kevin is .... in stamps.

11   cook   Dad is .... us beans on toast.

12   blow   The boy is .... on the hot chips.

13   wait   Tracy is .... for the record shop to open.

14   bark   The dog was .... all night.

Put these sentences in order by writing a number at the end of each line.

15   The children take off their hats and coats.   ....

16   The children are each given a present before
they go home.   ....

17   Lisa writes the invitations to her party.   ....

18   The children play party games.   ....

19   The children go home.   ....

20   The children arrive at the party.   ....

Put a question mark (?) where there should be one.

21   I like beefburgers   Will you have some cake

22   Where is it   I am seven years old

23   May I have some   Open the door

24   It is too big   Has the cat been fed

Put each word in the right space.

     travel   stretch   remove   remain   permit   create

25   .... = make   26   .... = lengthen

27   .... = stay   28   .... = move about

29   .... = allow   30   .... = take away

Paper 10

Underline the right answers.

There was once a boy called Robin, who lived in a cottage with his father. His father was often cross, and was not kind to his son. Though Robin was a good boy he was simple and not very clever at doing things. He worked as hard as he could doing odd jobs about the house and garden, but his father always scolded him when anything went wrong, and Robin was not happy.

1   Which word means "not kind"?
     (Cross, unkind, clever)

2–3   Robin was (clever, good, cruel, simple, happy)

4   "Odd jobs" are (small jobs, hard jobs, easy jobs)

5   "Robin was simple" means (that he was easy,
     that he was not very clever, that he was hard)

6   To be cross means (to be hard, to be bad-tempered,
     to be unkind)

7   To scold means (to find fault with, to be pleased with,
     to leave alone)

8 Robin lived with (his father, his son, alone, I do not know)

Two words on each line have a similar meaning. Underline them.

9-10 large   small   little

11-12 quick   stop   fast

13-14 sea   ocean   beach

In the following passage every tenth word has been left out. Can you fill them in?

15 Once upon a time there lived a woodcutter who .... two

16 children named Hansel and Gretel. They lived in ....

17 middle of a big forest. Their father warned them ....

18 to go too far away or they would get ....

Use a word from the list below to complete each sentence.

marched   crept   crawled   climbed

19 The soldier .... on parade.

20 The baby .... to the door.

21 The thief .... downstairs.

22 The man .... up the steeple.

Here are some sentences about dogs, and some about elephants. At the end of a line describing a dog write D, and at the end of one describing an elephant write E.

23 He lives in the jungle. ....

24 He can bark. ....

25 He is often a family pet. ....

26 He has a trunk. ....

27 He often guards our houses. ....

28 He is one of the biggest animals. ....

29 He is very, very strong. ....

30 He is a wild animal. ....

Underline the right answers.

"Tell us a story!" said the March Hare.

"Yes, please do!" pleaded Alice.

"And be quick about it," added the Hatter, "or you'll be asleep again before it's done."

"Once upon a time there were three little sisters," the Dormouse began in a great hurry; "and their names were Elsie, Lacie, and Tillie; and they lived at the bottom of a well —"

"What did they live on?" said Alice, who always took a great interest in questions of eating and drinking.

"They lived on treacle," said the Dormouse, after thinking a minute or two.

"They couldn't have done that, you know," Alice gently remarked. "They'd have been ill."

"So they were," said the Dormouse; "*very* ill."

From *Alice's Adventures in Wonderland* by Lewis Carroll

1	Who was telling the story?	Alice, the Hatter, the Dormouse
2	The sisters live in a:	hole, well, house, tree
3	What is usually in a well?	water, treacle, stones, animals
4	Who slept a lot?	Alice, the Hatter, the Dormouse
5	Who was very ill?	Alice, the sisters, the Dormouse
6–7	Who asked for a story?	Alice, the Hatter, March Hare
8	"lived on" means:	built a house, all they had to eat, kept on doing

Change the word in heavy type to show that these things have already happened.

9 Today I **give** her a book.
   Yesterday I .... her a book.

10 Today I **sit** in the garden.
   Yesterday I .... in the garden.

11 Today I **run** to school.
   Yesterday I .... to school.

12 Today I **eat** my tea.
   Yesterday I .... my tea.

13 Today I **wait** for Keith.
   Yesterday I .... for Keith.

14–21 Put in the full stops and capital letters.
mum said she would take paul and amanda to london to
buy some roller skates they set off from walton at nine o'clock

....

....

....

Underline the word on each line which rhymes with the word on
the left.

22	sew	flew	few	blue	low
23	go	bough	though	cow	how
24	stain	lane	win	pine	find
25	bone	come	home	tonne	loan
26	road	read	roam	code	wood
27	two	tow	do	so	low

Underline any word which should have a capital letter.

28–30 "would you like to swim in the river or would you rather go
to frankby?" asked carl.

Paper 12

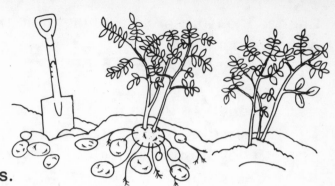

Underline the right answers.

We often think of the potato as being a root. This is not so;
it is a stem growing underground. In the spring tiny brown leaves
begin to grow from it. I am sure you will have seen the "eyes" of
a potato, but do you know what they are? Each eye is a group of
buds with a leaf just below them. When the shoots grow above
the ground they turn a pale green. At first the shoot gets its food
and water from the potato, but soon it grows roots which collect
food and water from the soil.

1 The "eyes" of a potato (help it to see, are a group of buds,
   are a group of stems)

2 Underground potato leaves are (green, black, brown)

3 Pale green is (a dark green, a light green, grey)

4 A potato is a (root, stem, shoot)

5 At first the shoot gets its food from (the eye, the ground,
   the potato)

6 "Often" means (many times, a few times, always, never)

Put commas in the right places.

7–8 I like apples grapes peaches and pears.

9–10 The girl who was lazy left her work.

11–12 "I want sausages eggs and chips " said the
       greedy boy.

You can often add **un** at the beginning of a word, to make it mean the opposite. See if you can fill in these spaces.

13 Shaun is not **happy**. He is ....
14 The wicked witch was not **kind**. She was ....
15 The spaceman was not **afraid**. He was ....
16 The teacher is not **fair**. She is ....
17 Those books are not **tidy**. They are ....
18 The fish are not **cooked** yet. They are ....

Complete the poem with these words.
        carpet   band   October   everything   name

19–23   .... gave a party
         The leaves in hundreds came
         The chestnuts, oaks and maples,
         And leaves of every ....

         The sunshine spread a ....
         And .... was grand
         Miss Weather led the dancing
         Professor Wind the ....

Write the opposite of the word in heavy type in the space at the end of each line.
24 The book is **found**, but the pencil is still ....
25 Some went **up** but the others went ....
26 The jug was **full**, but the cup was ....

Complete the words.
27–30   Here is a clock.   Here is some soap.
         I can hear it ti ....   I use it with wat...........
         It tells the ti ....   to wa .... my hands.

Paper 13

Underline the right answers.

"Mum! Mum! I don't feel very well. I don't think I'd better go to school today."

"What's the matter? Have you got a pain?"

"Yes, in my tummy. It really hurts. I think I'd better just stay in bed and rest. I'll read my new comics."

"Well – all right. But first I'll give you some of that brown medicine. I'll fetch it from the bathroom."

"No! Mum, come back! It's all right, I mean I feel much better now. I'll get dressed and go to school."

1   There are (1, 2, 3, 4, 5, 6) people in the passage.

2–3   Who are they? (A father, a mother, a teacher, a child, a granny)

4   Where was the medicine? (On the table, in the bathroom, in the kitchen, in the chemist's)

5   Why did the child say he didn't want to go to school? (He was tired, he didn't like his teacher, he had a pain, it was cold)

6   Why did he get better so quickly? (He drank the medicine, the pain went away, he wasn't really ill)

7   What happened in the end? (He stayed in bed, he read comics, he went to school, he went to the doctor)

Underline the "doing" words in these sentences.

8   Matthew is going to the football match.

9   Jamie hates football.

10   Mum and Dad took the children on holiday.

11   Sarah grew some herbs in a pot.

12   Wash behind your ears, Tim!

13   We feed the kittens at six o'clock.

14   The cat drinks the milk.

Each of these words has two meanings. Can you match the word to the meanings? Put two numbers in each space.

15–16   duck   17–18   record   ....

19–20   stick   ....

    (1)   a bird which swims

    (2)   a twig

    (3)   a black plastic disc which plays music

    (4)   to glue

    (5)   to dip your head quickly

    (6)   to measure

Use the words below to fill the spaces.

    scribble   sparrow   repair   slipper   search   price

21   A .... is a kind of shoe.

22   To .... is to write carelessly.

23   The .... is the cost of something.

24   To .... is to look for something.

25   A .... is a small bird.

26   To .... is to mend.

Write the opposite of each word.

27   dirty   28   in   ....

29   work   30   top   ....

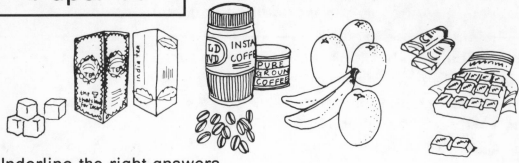

Underline the right answers.

Have you ever thought how many different parts of the world supply us with food? Tea, as I expect you know, comes from India and Sri Lanka. The coffee we enjoy comes from Brazil in South America, and the sugar which some people like to put into tea and coffee probably comes from the West Indies. Chocolate is made from beans of the cacao tree which grows in parts of Africa. Oranges come from Spain, and bananas come from northern Australia.

1. Which of the foods comes from South America? (Tea, coffee, chocolate)

2. The West Indies grow (apples, beet, sugar)

3. Chocolate is made from (chocolate peas, chocolate drops, chocolate beans)

4. What do we use to sweeten cakes and drinks? (Sugar, chocolate, tea)

5. Which fruit comes from Spain? (Apples, oranges, bananas)

6. Which fruit comes from Australia? (Apples, oranges, bananas)

7. Sri Lanka grows (chocolate, tea, coffee)

8. The cacao tree grows chiefly in (Africa, Sri Lanka, Spain)

Make a word ending in **ing** from the word at the beginning of the line. You may need to drop the final **e** or double the last letter. Write the new word in the space.

9 cut   Michael is .... his birthday cake.

10 write   David is .... a letter to his friend.

11 run   Caroline is .... up the garden path.

12 ride   Susan is .... a donkey on the beach.

13 put   Tony is .... on his swimming trunks.

Put the following words into the order in which you would find them in a dictionary.

cake   apple   orange   bread   fish

14 (1) ....   15 (2) ....   16 (3) ....

17 (4) ....   18 (5) ....

In each space write the opposite of the word in heavy type.

19 Mum says I must stay **in**. I want to go ....

20 First I turned on the **hot** tap and then I turned on the .... one.

21 Andrea was **first**, but Sally was ....

Underline the two words in each line which have similar meanings.

22–23 large   small   big

24–25 hard   easy   simple

26–27 weep   shout   sob

28–30 Put a line under any word which should start with a capital letter.

cat   cupboard   butcher   baker

tame   tim   green   france   india

Paper 15

Underline the right answers.

Long, long ago there was only one fire in the northland. An old man and his son took turns in caring for it, and kept it burning day and night. Their great enemy was the bear. He wanted them to die so that he could have the northland to himself. One day the old man became ill, and the boy had to look after the fire and care for his sick father. At last he became so tired that he fell fast asleep. The bear crept to the fire and beat it out with his great paws, and then went off chuckling. A little robin flew down. She found a tiny spark and she fanned it with her wings. After a while her breast was burned but she kept on fanning the fire till a fine blaze started. She had saved the northland! Ever since that day robins have had red breasts.

1 (His son, the robin, the bear) was the old man's enemy.

2 (The old man, the son, the robin) became ill.

3 "Chuckling" means (muttering, laughing, crying)

4 Paws are an animal's (legs, wings, feet)

5 The boy fell asleep because he was (lazy, tired, ill)

6 The robin's breast turned red because
   (it was scorched, it was bleeding, the boy painted it)

Look at the pictures and then complete the words.

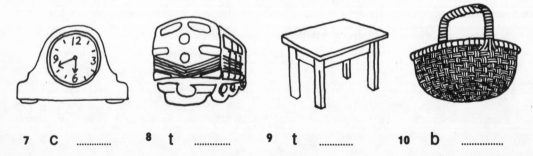

7 c ....   8 t ....   9 t ....   10 b ....

Put an exclamation mark (!) where you think there should be one.

11–15
Be quiet
Help
I want to watch a video
Sit down at once

What is your name
Look what I've found
Hurry up
Is it big

Put the number of the right answer in the space.

16 How many legs has a cat? ....
17 How many wheels has a car? ....
18 How many arms has a boy? ....
19 How many days has a week? ....
20 How many wheels has a bicycle? ....
21 How many hours has a day? ....

(1) He has two arms.
(3) It has seven days.
(5) It has four legs.

(2) It has twenty-four hours.
(4) It has four wheels.
(6) It has two wheels.

Join each pair of sentences with **and** or **but**.

22 It was a frosty morning .... I felt very cold.
23 I went to the party .... Gary stayed at home.
24 I have a new dress .... my coat is an old one.
25 The sea is warm .... I must go for a swim.
26 I like apples .... they give me a pain.
27 The new puppy was very sweet .... Helen loved him.

Can you think of a better word than **nice** in these sentences?

28 We had a **nice** holiday. (peaceful, tiring, happy)
29 Danny is a **nice** boy. (friendly, noisy, quiet)
30 This pie tastes **nice**. (tough, strong, delicious)

Paper 16

Underline the right answers.

Birds build their nests in many kinds of places and use material such as mud, moss, twigs, dry leaves and grass. Some are skilful builders, while others make quite a rough and ready nest. A few birds make no nest at all, but lay their eggs on the seashore or on a ledge of rock. Birds use their beaks and feet as tools when they build.

Birds do not live in nests as we live in houses. The nests are made to hold eggs and nestlings, and in most cases are not used after the young birds have flown.

1–2   When building nests birds use their (hands, feet, wings, beaks)

3   Nests are used (as houses, to hold eggs and baby birds, as ledges)

4   A nestling is (a small nest, a large nest, a small bird, a large bird)

5   "Rough and ready" means (it was made by rough birds, not made well)

6–10   For their nests birds use (sand, mud, moss, flowers, leaves, twigs, bricks, grass, tiles)

11–12   Birds who do not make nests lay eggs in (nestlings, cracks in rocks, nests, on the beach)

Underline the correct word in the brackets.

13   A (wren, nest, owl, crow, duck) is not a bird.

14   (Red, pink, green, sky, blue) is not a colour.

15 (Water, milk, beer, glass, coffee) is not a drink.

16 (Cod, salmon, loaf, sole) is not a fish.

17 A (carrot, peach, potato, cabbage) is not a vegetable.

Write **yes** or **no** in each space.

18 The girl is sitting on a cushion.   ....

19 The man is bringing in the food.   ....

20 Mum is holding up three tickets.   ....

21 The children are in the garden.   ....

22 Mum is wearing an apron.   ....

23 Mum has dropped the newspapers.   ....

24 I can see two chairs.   ....

25 Dad is coming out of the kitchen.   ....

26 They are going to have a meal.   ....

The sentences below are not in the right order. Read them
carefully and then put numbers to show the order in which they
should come.

27 He hurt his knee.   ....

28 Michael went out to play.   ....

29 Mum put a plaster on it.   ....

30 He fell over.   ....

Underline the right answers.

Steve and his mum and dad were talking about going on holiday. Steve wanted to go on an adventure holiday, but his mum said he was too young. Steve's mum wanted to go abroad but they couldn't really afford that. His dad wanted to go somewhere where he could do a lot of fishing, but no one else was keen on that. They couldn't agree on anything.

"Oh, well," said Steve's mum in the end, "we'll go to Blackpool then."

"Oh no," cried Steve. "We always go there."

1   What is the passage about? (Holidays, Steve's dad, Blackpool)

2   Why couldn't Steve go on an adventure holiday? (It cost too much, he was too young, it was too far)

3   What was Steve's dad's hobby? (Talking, swimming, fishing, driving)

4   Why couldn't they go abroad? (It cost too much, nobody wanted to go abroad, they liked Blackpool better)

5–6   Who didn't like fishing? (Steve, his mum, his dad)

7   Why didn't Steve want to go to Blackpool? (It was too far, they always went there, he didn't like the sea)

Here are six sentences. Three of them describe milk and three of them describe bread. Read them carefully, and then at the end of each line write M for the ones which describe milk, and B for those which describe bread.

8   It comes from a cow. ....
9   We buy it from the baker. ....
10   We can make it into toast. ....
11   We can drink it from a cup. ....
12   We often put butter and jam on it. ....
13   We buy it from the dairy. ....

The sentences below are not in the right order. Read them carefully and then put numbers to show the order in which they should come.

14   He came back from school. ....
15   He went to bed ....
16   John got up. ....
17   He went to school. ....
18   He had his breakfast. ....

Put these words into the order of the dictionary.

dog   cat   ape   dinosaur   badger   rat

19   20   21   ....
22   23   24   ....

Underline the word which goes with each meaning.

25   A baby goat (foal, calf, kid)
26   Knives, forks and spoons (cookery, furniture, cutlery)
27   To jump into deep water (dive, jive, leap)
28   A place where books are kept. (surgery, library, school)
29   A seat on the back of a horse (bridle, stirrup, saddle)
30   An aircraft without an engine (jumbo, glider, Concorde)

Paper 18

> **LOST!**
>
> SOMEWHERE NEAR BRAMLEY PARK,
> A SMALL BLACK DOG CALLED MAC.
> THE FINDER WILL GET A
> REWARD OF £10
>
> PLEASE PHONE THE OWNER:
>
> J. BROWN, 17 TELEGRAPH ROAD,
> MORETON. TEL: MORETON 1234

1–5   Here are some sentences about this story. Five of them are true, but the others are not. Underline the true sentences.

The dog was lost on Telegraph Road.
It is a small black dog.
The owner's name is Bramley.
The dog's name is Mac.
The owner's home is in Moreton.
The dog was stolen.
The dog has been found.
The finder will get a reward of £10.
The dog ran away from home.
The owner has a telephone.

Two words on each line have similar meanings. Underline them.
6–7   go   stop   halt
8–9   pick   choose   present

Fill in the gaps.
10–18   This year we are .... to Spain for our .... We shall go by .... from Gatwick Airport. I .... looking forward to staying .... a big hotel, but .... am not sure about .... the strange food. The .... will be very hot .... we shall get brown.

38

Complete each sentence by putting the right number in each space.

19 Anita wears a striped dress ....
20 Mr. Long is very tall ....
21 The river is wide ....
22 Mr. Dunton wears a dark suit ....
23 Simon has a bowl of cornflakes ....
24 Fiona has curly hair ....

(1) but the stream is narrow.
(2) but John has a light suit.
(3) but Sally has a slice of toast.
(4) but Deborah has straight hair.
(5) but James is very short.
(6) but Sara has a plain dress.

Below are some words which you might use to describe someone's hair, eyes or skin. Put them in the right column.

25–30 bright, freckled, short, kind, curly, sunburnt

HAIR   EYES   SKIN

....
....

Underline the right answers.

Thousands of years ago a Chinese Emperor was sitting by his camp fire, boiling some water in a cauldron. The fire was made from twigs broken off the flowering trees growing all around. As the water boiled, some leaves fell from the trees into the cauldron, and the mixture smelled so delicious that the Emperor decided to taste it. No one knows if this story is true but we do know that the Chinese people have been drinking tea for thousands of years.

1   The fire was made of (coal, logs, twigs, pieces of wood)

2   A cauldron is (a large pan, a vegetable, a flowering tree)

3   The Emperor had put (leaves, water, milk) in the cauldron.

4   What kind of leaves fell into the water? (tea leaves, flowers, twigs)

5   Is this story true? (yes, no, I do not know)

6   The flowering trees were (rose bushes, tea bushes, weeds)

Write the plural of these words.

7   orange ....   8 man ....   9 cow ....

10   mouse ....   11 roof ....

Choose one of the words below to fill each space.

purrs   crows   sings   pops   chimes

12   The choir   13   The clock ....

14   The cork   15   The cock ....

16   The cat ....

Write the name of each thing in the space below the picture. Take care to spell it correctly. The first letter has been put in to help you.

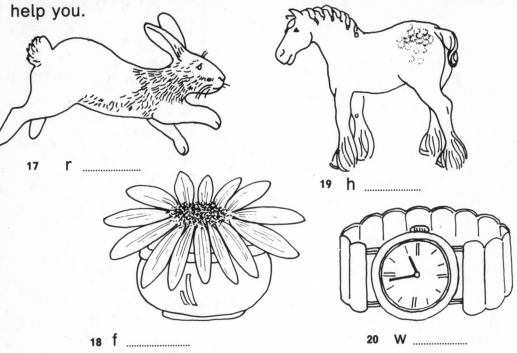

17 r ....

19 h ....

18 f ....

20 w ....

The sentences below are not in the right order. Put numbers in the spaces to show the order in which they should come.

21 They grew into plants. ....
22 He watched the fruits form. ....
23 Peter sowed some seeds. ....
24 He watched them flower. ....
25 He watched the seedlings come through the soil. ....

Look at the pairs of words below. If they are alike in meaning, write A, but if they are opposite, write O.

26 bad   good   ....
27 pretty   lovely   ....
28 wild   rough   ....
29 hot   cold   ....
30 big   large   ....

41

27 Kings Road,
Welby
Tuesday 3rd April

Dear Katie,
It is my birthday on Saturday and Mummy says I may ask my friends to come to tea at 3 o'clock and stay until 8 o'clock.
I do hope you can come.
Love from
Debbie

Underline the right answers.

1   Who lives at 27 Kings Road, Welby? (Katie, Debbie)

2   Who wrote the letter? (Katie, Debbie, Mummy)

3   Who was the letter sent to? (Katie, Debbie, Mummy)

4   Whose birthday is on Saturday? (Katie's, Debbie's, Mummy's)

5   What is the date of her birthday? (3rd April, 13th April, 7th April)

6   How many hours will the party last? (4 hours, 5 hours, 6 hours)

7   What meal will they have at the party? (tea, lunch, supper)

Put the following words in the order in which you would find them in a dictionary.

elm   pine   beech   yew   oak

8   9   10   ....

11   12   ....

13–15 Three words are spelled wrongly. Draw a line under them, and then write them correctly below.

Please put the knives in the drawer, the plaits on the shelfs and the saucepans and kettel in the cupboard.

....

Put the correct number in each space.

16 What time does John start school? .... (1) He has two.

17 What does Elaine have for supper? .... (2) It is December.

18 How many hands has John? .... (3) He is seven.

19 Which is the last month of the year? .... (4) He starts at nine o'clock.

20 How old is Nick? .... (5) She has sausages.

The sentences below have been divided and now the second halves are not in the right order. Write the number of the correct second part in the space.

21 A book .... (1) can fly.

22 A fish .... (2) boils water.

23 A plane .... (3) can swim.

24 A wardrobe .... (4) can be blown.

25 A kettle .... (5) has leaves.

26 A tree .... (6) can be read.

27 A trumpet .... (7) holds clothes.

Take away the first letter of each word. Underline any of the groups of letters which are left that still make words.

28–30 steel beach post gold water brays

Paper 21

Underline the right answers.

Some day I'm going to have a store
With a tinkly bell hung over the door,
With real glass cases and counters wide
And drawers all spilly with things inside.
There'll be a little of everything;
Bolts of calico; balls of string;
Jars of peppermint; tins of tea;
Pots and kettles and crockery;
Seeds in packets; scissors bright;
Bags of sugar, brown and white;
Biscuits and cheese for picnic lunches,
Bananas and rubber boots in bunches.
I'll fix the window – and dust each shelf,
I'll take the money in all myself.
It will be my store and I will say:
"What can I do for you today?"

Rachel Field

1 Do you think I am (a shopkeeper, a child, a grown-up)?

2 Why do I want a bell over the door? (to tell people to shut the door, so I know when someone comes in, to look pretty)

3–4 What will I sell to eat at picnics? (biscuits, cheese, sugar, peppermint)

5 Crockery is (saucepans, cups and saucers, part of a garden)

6 The tea would be kept in (glass cases, drawers, tins, packets, jars)

7 What is sold in packets? (sugar, peppermint, seeds)

8 In my shop (I would like to do everything myself,
I would like some help)

9–18 Put in the capital letters and full stops.
i am in class one of hill school my friends are tracy and
sharon

....

....

Complete each sentence by putting the
right number in each space.

19 One basket is round, but ....
20 A pram has four wheels, but ....
21 The vase has two handles, but ....
22 A bird has two legs, but ....
23 Mum drives the car, and ....
24 A fish swims, but ....

(1) a camel has four legs.
(2) Dad sits beside her.
(3) the other one is oblong.
(4) a bird flies.
(5) a bicycle has two.
(6) the cup has one.

Underline two words on each line which have opposite meanings.

25–26 first   stop   last
27–28 good   bad   work
29–30 left   centre   right

Underline the right answers.

The Green Cross Code

First find a safe place to cross, then stop.
Stand on the pavement near the kerb.
Look all around for traffic and listen.
If traffic is coming, let it pass. Look all around again.
When there is no traffic, walk straight across the road.
Keep looking and listening while you cross.

1   While you are crossing the road you should (look straight ahead, keep looking and listening, shut your eyes)

2   The place where the pavement meets the road is called the (code, traffic, kerb)

3   Cars, buses, vans and bicycles are called (code, traffic, kerb)

4   What should you do first? (cross the road, close your eyes, find a safe place to cross)

5   When can you cross the road? (when it is full of traffic, when there is no traffic, when you hear a noise)

6   Why do we have the Green Cross Code?
     (to stop us from being run over, because it sounds nice, because it tells us all about cars)

7–9   Take away the first letter of each word. Underline any of the groups of letters which are left that still make words.
      bleat   tiger   trout   down   wink   sheep

10–19   Sort out the jumbled words.

Do you have a **tac** .... ? They are very friendly
malinas .... , and have interesting **sway** ....
They are very good at looking **ferta** .... themselves
too. Make **erus** .... your cat has two **wolbs** .... of
food every day, and **rewat** .... or **klim** .... Put a
act .... flap in your door so your cat can **og** .... out.

Fill each space with one of these words.

bowling   writing   polishing   knitting   sweeping   shopping

20   Tom is .... the table.
21   Dad is .... in the store.
22   Mum is .... a jumper.
23   Sally is .... a letter.
24   Karen is .... a ball.
25   David is .... up the crumbs.

Write the opposite of each word.

26   light   27   old   28   open ....

29   easy   30   fat ....

47

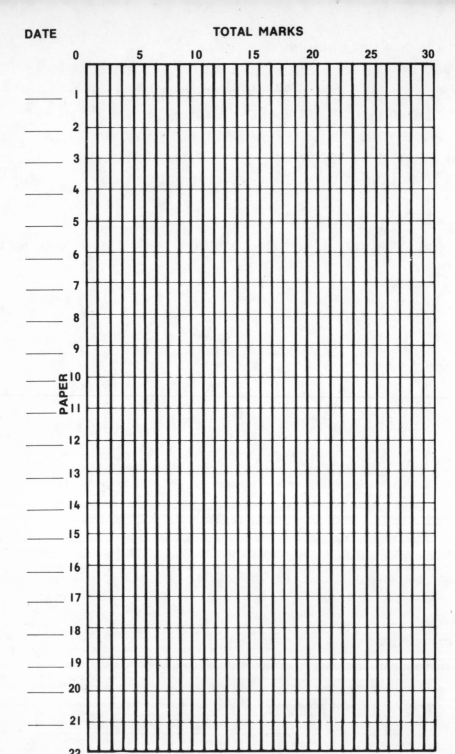

DATE

TOTAL MARKS

PAPER